THE MACDONALD ENCYCLOPEDIA OF MEDICINAL PLANTS

THE MACDONALD ENCYCLOPEDIA OF MEDICINAL PLANTS

Roberto Chiej

Macdonald

A Macdonald BOOK

English translation by Sylvia Mulcahy

First published in Great Britain in 1984
by Macdonald & Co (Publishers) Ltd
London & Sydney

A member of BPCC plc

British Library Cataloguing in Publication Data

Chiej, Roberto
The Macdonald encyclopedia of medicinal plants.
1. Medicinal plants – Europe
I. Title II. Piante medicinali. *English*
581.6'34'094 QK99.E85

ISBN 0-356-10541-5 hb
ISBN 0-356-10542-3 pb

Printed and bound in Italy
by Officine Grafiche A. Mondadori Editore, Verona

Macdonald & Co (Publishers) Ltd
Maxwell House
74 Worship Street
London EC2A 2EN

CONTENTS

KEY TO SYMBOLS

Plant habit

Erect herbaceous plant

Creeping herbaceous plant

Evergreen shrub

Evergreen tree

Deciduous tree

Other plants

Habitat

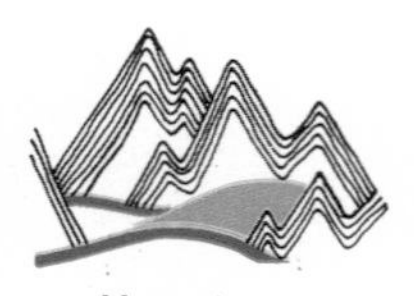

Mountain

Lowland

Coast

Marsh

Toxicity of the plant

Edible plant

Suspect plant

Poisonous plant

Plant usage

Essential oil

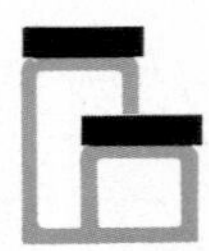

Culinary use

Industrial use

NOTE

The symbols in this book represent only the most important or the most common features of each plant. Many plants can be highly variable in habit, size, and habitat, depending on local climatic conditions and terrain. For instance, alpine species in central Europe may be found growing at sea level in the far north. A plant's edibility, or its toxicity, may also vary from place to place. Each symbol, therefore, should be regarded only as a rough guide to a plant's typical characters, to be combined with a careful reading of the descriptive text.

Warning
Many of the plants in this book are poisonous and can be damaging or even fatal if consumed. **Never** use a plant that is or may be poisonous, and never use one whose identity is in doubt. Remember also that many rare plants are legally protected – which is indicated wherever possible in the text – and that it is an offence to disturb them.

INTRODUCTION

It can be argued that during the last few decades, there has been a progressive decline in the relationship between man and his surroundings. We live in a society orientated to the production of consumer goods that are designed to make our lives as easy as possible but which, all too often, become quickly obsolete. The cost, even if economically acceptable, is, from the ecological viewpoint, enormously damaging.

The most important area affected by this trend is that of food production. Few of the things we eat today are naturally produced. Fruit and vegetables, for example, are extensively treated with weed-killers, insecticides and chemical fertilizers and are harvested long before their maturation so that they can be programmed to ripen artificially during those periods which are economically most profitable.

Nowadays, many foods produced industrially are artificially coloured to make them appear more attractive in the shops. These foods are often sold in plastic containers which, although hygienically acceptable, can become toxic when they come into immediate contact with certain substances, especially acid, present in their contents. Furthermore, many foods are treated with chemical additives that guarantee their preservation over a long period.

These are just some of the impositions thrust upon us by modern technology to ensure the best results as far as availability, preservation and convenience are concerned.

Detergents and disposable packaging are two items that are particularly convenient to the consumer, yet the former, which poison

*Opposite, the rhododendron in its typical habitat, a plant often used in mountain regions to obtain oil of marmot, a highly-esteemed antirheumatic remedy. Below, the field poppy (*Papaver rhoeas*) which so often adds its brilliant colour to golden cornfields. It is used in folk-medicine as an expectorant.*

the water discharged from our homes and industrial plants, and the latter, because they are indestructible forms of litter, are progressively ruining our natural surroundings.

Many other factors contribute to this process. The building industry uses various kinds of powdered rock, which involves the mechanical digging of huge quarries in many mountainous areas of the world. This, together with intensive stock-rearing in such regions, pollutes the springs that supply water to the towns and cities in the valleys. Because of the proliferation of cars constantly emitting fumes, and the establishment of new industries filling the air with noxious gases, the air in these cities may also be polluted.

Each item in this long but obviously incomplete list represents the price that modern society has had to pay, in ecological terms, for the way it has developed. There is clearly no escaping the cost of the 'convenience' products which are now an accepted part of modern life.

Some of these evils may be explained by the tremendous rise in food requirements throughout the world, which is due both to the enormous increase in population and to large-scale urbanization. The unprofitability of agriculture and related activities resulting from the economic development which began in the nineteenth century and which accelerated after the First World War, has greatly increased the number of people who are dependent on the retail trade for their supplies of foodstuffs. As a result of these growing needs, goods available to the public have been adapted and modified both in terms of quality and quantity – two factors which, invariably, are diametrically opposed. The solution is often reached at the expense of the genuine article.

One of the main consequences of this artificially forced lifestyle is the increasing number of younger people who are falling victim to fatal illnesses which were at one time found almost exclusively in the elderly. The health problems that plague modern society are well-known in the medical world, but the rapid strides being made in current pharmacology are barely able to keep pace with them, and even the vast range of drugs available is often far from satisfactory. Underlying the praises heaped upon such products for their efficacy, is a more cautious note of warning. This propaganda, voiced in a low key, invites the consumer to turn to more natural alternative medicines, many of which were once widely used, but have long since been abandoned in favour of 'progress'.

As a result of this new trend, a large number of people who are perhaps sceptical or apprehensive about 'conventional' drugs have now turned to alternative treatments, and in particular treatments that make use of medicinal plants. They are quite willing to place their trust in the competence of herbalists, amateurs or professionals, who often have no formal medical background whatsoever. In their attempt to achieve good health by 'natural' means, they are tempted by expensive little packets of attractively wrapped and cleverly advertised herbs claiming to cure every type of complaint.

There is no official guarantee as to the purity of these products and certainly none as regards their effectiveness. The possibility always remains that the uncontrolled administration of unsuitable and toxic herbs may produce effects which are as harmful as the indiscriminate use of synthetic products. Furthermore, phytotherapeutic treatment (i.e. treatment by means of vegetable drugs) is often ineffective when it involves the use of dried plants such as those sold in health shops. Since the majority of these dried plants are imported and will inevitably have been gathered some time previously, the active principles contained in them will almost certainly be considerably reduced and, in many cases, will be non-existent. The failure of a treatment involving the use of medicinal or 'officinal' herbs (as they are sometimes called) is often due to the age of the plants; as with traditional medicines, their active properties expire after a given period. The main difference, however, is that natural products that have lost their active qualities are not harmful to the system.

In Britain the modern tendency in herbal medicine is to use tinctures and pills which require no preparation by the patients, are quickly and easily swallowed, and can be combined in a number of different ways. The patient who wishes to be treated naturally by the use of medicinal plants must be of a particular disposition because the treatment itself sets out certain conditions. Since plants act slowly on an illness, treatment takes time; therefore both patience and careful preparation of the plant are essential. The patient must be prepared to drink infusions and decoctions, often in considerable doses at inconvenient times, which are not always pleasant to take. In a society where time is invaluable, such remedies are in complete contrast to pharmaceutical preparations, which are specially designed to be easy and convenient to take, as well as fast to act.

An additional problem is created by the fact that many people living

A fine example of Brassica napus *under cultivation, particularly efficacious in the treatment of any form of arthropathy.*

outside big cities may not have access to herbalists or health food stores; it is therefore difficult for them to purchase the herbs they need, and even when the 'natural' ingredients are available, they are often expensive.

These are just some of the problems presented by herbal treatment but there is also, of course, a positive side to be considered. One of the main advantages is undoubtedly the opportunity to use a wide range of essential elements, provided by a living organism of plant origin, for the human organism. This natural affinity allows total assimilation of all those elements, developed by the growth organs of the plant, that are indispensable to human life. This is borne out by some doctors who prefer to recommend the inclusion of large amounts of cereals, vegetables or fruit in the daily diet rather than prescribe pharmaceutical products, especially in the treatment of deficiency ailments in the young.

Another advantage of plant remedies is that they are harmless, provided they are selected carefully and taken under medical guidance. This type of treatment never has to be brought to a sudden halt because of any adverse effect on the patient, although in some cases it may have to be concluded because it is too mild or is taking too long.

It must be emphasized that not all illnesses are suitable for herbal treatment. Obviously, it cannot be the answer for patients in need of more radical attention such as surgical operations and bone-setting, or for those whose life depends on quick-acting treatment.

People were making use of plants, having discovered their beneficial and curative effects, long before scientific explanations were advanced.

Pimpinella anisum *seeds from which an essential oil is extracted, widely used in pharmaceutical products and spirituous liquors, such as anisette and sambuca.*

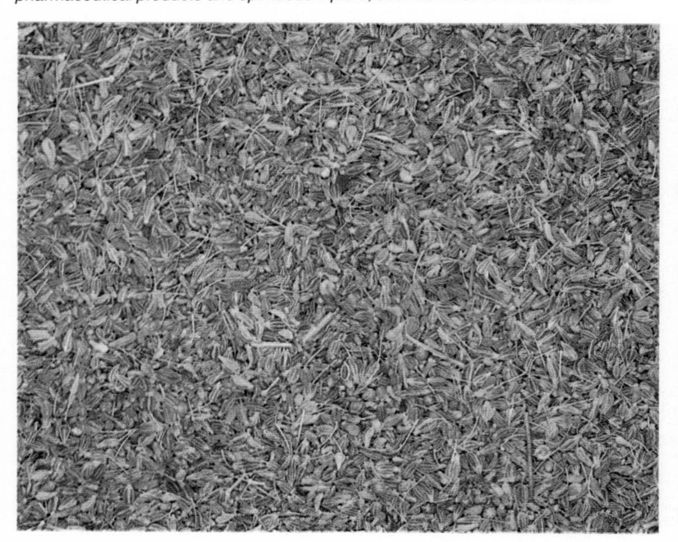

They soon came to separate edible species from poisonous ones and gradually learned how to select the most useful parts of such plants. This wealth of acquired knowledge was passed on verbally and, as so often happens when information depends on word of mouth, facts became distorted and all kinds of imaginary powers were attributed to certain plants. Although a certain mystique still surrounds herbs and their medicinal usage today, progress in scientific research has greatly clarified the subject. Officinal plants now have accepted botanical names, whilst attempts have been made to analyze them chemically and distinguish at least some of the many components and active principles.

Such analyses have recently led to the production of similar compounds by synthetic means. These are not only more convenient to take but are also easier to store. On the face of it, the two types of product would seem to be analogous. Experiments have shown, however, that from a curative point of view substances extracted from medicinal plants and the equivalent substances produced synthetically behave differently. There is variation in the absorption capacity, and the natural product has a milder effect on the system than the man-made one. Other tests have shown that synthetic drugs afford a faster rate of recovery, but that plant substances have a much more positive and lasting effect.

These, however, are not the only reasons for the present return to treatment with 'simples', as medicinal herbs were once known. Some of the interest springs, firstly, from the fact that many people are already

A method of extracting the resin from conifers by making herringbone cuts in the trunk. It was from this primary product that turpentine used to be obtained.

familiar with herbs. Who, for instance, has not heard of camomile, mint or basil? Secondly, fragrant herbalist shops are themselves an attraction, exuding an atmosphere of charm and confidence.

The study of modern herbalism (phytotherapy) is rapidly evolving throughout the world. New commercial organizations are emerging to study hitherto unknown medicinal plants, adding to the information about those already classified and selecting new seeds from cultures, in order to obtain qualitative and quantitative optimal yields, and to elaborate new, scientifically tested recipes for the more effective treatment of specific illnesses. This is not a campaign against synthetic drugs, for that would be a serious mistake – some complaints respond well to herbal remedies while others react better to synthetic ones. The sole objective, of both types of medicine, is to restore the patient to good health. It is desirable, therefore, that research in both fields should continue without conflict.

It should be remembered that the curative parts of a plant are not simply its woody stem or its leaves, but the chemical compounds it produces and uses for its own growth and development. Every living thing has an enormous number of such compounds which, in most cases, cannot as yet be chemically reproduced.

A plant is an immediate source of medicine which can be extracted, titrated and preserved. A great many natural drugs, which cannot be synthetically duplicated, may, therefore, be selected for possible use.

In view of the large number of active principles produced by plants, we can only wonder at the incredibly vast reservoir nature has to offer, in which unlimited reserves of medicinal ingredients are still largely untapped. What is more, these ingredients are not presented to us in the form of pills and potions but as flowers, fruit, leaves and seeds.

Since each compound acts in a specific way on the organism, it is not hard to imagine just how much the plant world has to offer humanity. As systematic research delves ever deeper into the secrets of the innumerable existing plant species, more and more ailments will, in time, become treatable and even curable. Modern methods of preparation will soon enable specific ingredients to be extracted from a plant, leaving others untouched, which means that the same plants can be used to treat several different illnesses. An example of this diversity of usage is the Icelandic lichen which, in domestic use, provides either a bitter substance or an expectorant, depending on the way it is prepared.

Phytotherapy is once again being recognized for the healing qualities it can offer mankind, though this time on a much wider scale and supported by all the facilities of modern science. The links with past superstitions are not entirely broken, however, for although some old legends cannot be upheld against the evidence of microscopes and electronic calculators, research scientists never cease to be amazed, even perplexed, when an active principle, which has already been defined and classified, behaves in a way that is at variance with the experimentally tested results. Such behaviour certainly explains the bewilderment of ancient scholars who could only hold supernatural powers responsible for the active properties of such plants.

We now know that these unexpected results are due to the synergetic action of the various components of a plant and not merely to the active principle on which interest is usually focused.

Icelandic lichen, which also grows in more southerly latitudes, is widely used as a pectoral and nourishing food. Usnic acid, the basis of many modern disinfectants, is obtained from a closely-related lichen.

The phenomenon of synergism is extensively used in modern therapies at all levels. Briefly, it involves the association of two or more drugs whose interaction may produce the following results:

- by equal action (synergism by addition), each of the various drugs performs the same function on the substrata of the organism;
- by different action (synergism by potentiation), the various drugs exert collateral action on different substrata of the organism;
- by antagonistic action (synergism by degradation), the drugs which individually have their own action, when combined, produce a result which is different from the predicted one.

It is obvious that exhaustive research into plants containing such a large number of active principles must offer a vast range of possibilities. Unfortunately, large-scale experimental treatment cannot be considered for hospital patients. It would take too long and would also be uneconomic, as in most countries patients are kept in hospital for as short a period as possible. Apart from a few particular cases, experiments have generally been carried out in exceptional circumstances, such as during the war, or in places where the supply of synthetic drugs was precarious or non-existent.

Another useful contribution to the better understanding of phytotherapeutic treatments is being provided by countries which, though they have a low level of technology, are the largest exporters of officinal plants. It is, therefore, in these countries that phytotherapy is most widely used, even in hospitals, although unfortunately their research facilities are limited. Information concerning the results achieved is,

Granules of pollen, obtained by means of modern apicultural methods, are widely used to give energy and as a basis for anti-allergic preparations.

nevertheless, highly important, as the data is then studied and examined in depth in more developed countries where research teams are better equipped to carry out the necessary work.

The history of herbalism

To trace the history of herbalism we must go back to the history of pharmacology, for until the last century medicinal plants were still being processed for general use.

The discovery of the curative properties in plants must have sprung from some human instinct. Primitive man used plants for both food and medicine. He would have learnt, after perhaps many unfortunate experiences, that some plants contained certain properties, and was able to identify them by the results they induced. He would also have observed which plants animals utilized when they were sick. After seeing an injured deer rubbing itself against the geum, he might have discovered, for instance, that this plant would heal his own wounds; and realized that dog tooth grass would act as an emetic, as it did with the cat. Many remarkable examples of animals intuitively knowing how to treat themselves with appropriate plants are quoted by numerous writers. Cicero, for example, mentions the hartwort being used by young does to ease parturition, while Plutarch refers to bears using the wild arum (lords-and-ladies). Cases of accidental poisoning must have been common occurrences before the benign, curative herbs had been distinguished from the poisonous ones. The German botanist Molisch

A cluster of Coffea arabica *berries which contain that all too familiar constituent, coffee, with its nervine properties. It is also used in homoeopathic medicine.*

made an interesting observation concerning six plants containing caffeine – namely coffee, cola, maté, tea, cocoa and guaranà; among innumerable plant species man was able to pick out these six with great precision, even though they lack particular features which enable them to be easily distinguished for their medical properties.

The earliest botanical knowledge, as applied to medicine, was thus based on instinct; but in due course, as prehistory gave way to antiquity, man began to make rational deductions from his observations and to use these deductions creatively in order to improve the quality of life. An example of this is ancient Egyptian medicine, as recorded in the *Ebers Papyrus* (G.M. Ebers, German Egyptologist and novelist, 1837-98) which illustrates the great advances that had been made in the understanding of suitable drugs and pharmaceutical preparations. The medicinal value of *Ricinus communis*, from which castor oil is made, and of peppermint and flax (used for linseed oil as well as for linen) were already known. Embalmers, too, made use of resins such as sweet flag or sweet rush (*Acorus calamus)*) – also used for dyspepsia – benzoin and a number of fragrant essences that have still to be identified.

We know, too, from cuneiform tablets, that the Babylonians knew as much about the medicinal uses of plants as the Egyptians. There is also mention in the Bible of how hyssop and cedar were used by the Hebrews to treat various disorders.

The Greek physician Hippocrates (460-357 B.C.), generally regarded as the founder of medicine, exerted a great influence on the Roman world and on much of the mediaeval world as well. He is still

Spores of Dryopteris filix-mas*, of the Polypodiaceae family, seen through a microscope (magnified 180 times). Its rhizome provides the most efficacious taenifuge (a preparation to combat tapeworms) that is known, in the form of an ethereal extract.*

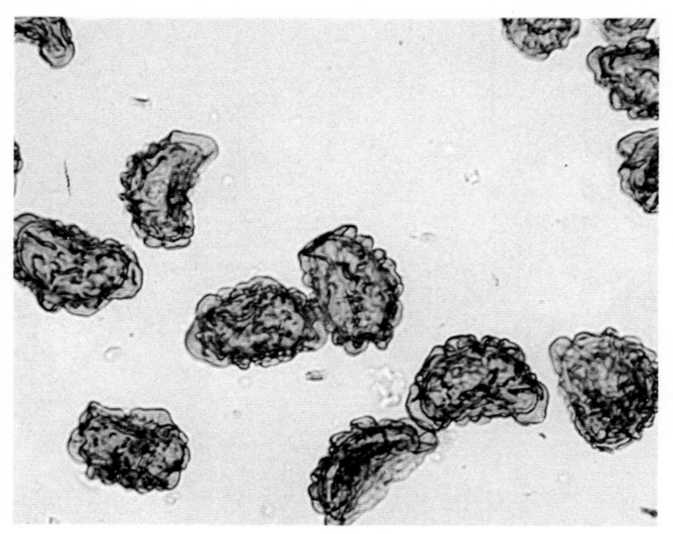

remembered for his expressive writings, but his descriptions, his dosage methods and his diets also contributed to his great reputation.

With the rise of Greek civilization came the first systematically compiled treatise on pharmaceutical botany. This was the work of Theophrastus (circa 370-285 B.C.) entitled *De Historia Plantarum* (History of Plants). Although a remarkable attempt to give scientific order to an important subject, it reveals the narrow boundaries within which the author was forced to work, due to the limited knowledge that then existed. Nevertheless, among a great many interesting items, there are references, for the first time, to ferns being used as an anthelmintic (a substance used to counteract parasitic worms) and to the difference between the long and the round pepper. This is, incidentally, not an easy book to read because all the plant names differ totally from those in current usage, making identification extremely difficult.

The work of Pedanius Dioscorides, however, is much more important medicinally. This consists of five volumes in which all the medical knowledge available at the time is expounded. Here there is a tentative attempt to classify medicinal plants, not in alphabetical order, but according to their affinities. The descriptions are precise, expressed simply and without superstitious connotations, and the preparations are very accurate. Having travelled a great deal as an army physician, Dioscorides had the opportunity to study and record the uses of exotic plants. His writings were, in fact, regarded as the standard work in the pharmacological field until almost the end of the sixteenth century,

Pages from a sixteenth-century herbal by the Sienese physician and botanist Pietro Andrea Mattioli, Sopra i Discorsi di Dioscoride *(On the Discourses of Dioscorides) a systematic account of the 60* A.D. *treatise on the natural history of plants, illustrated by wood cuttings.*

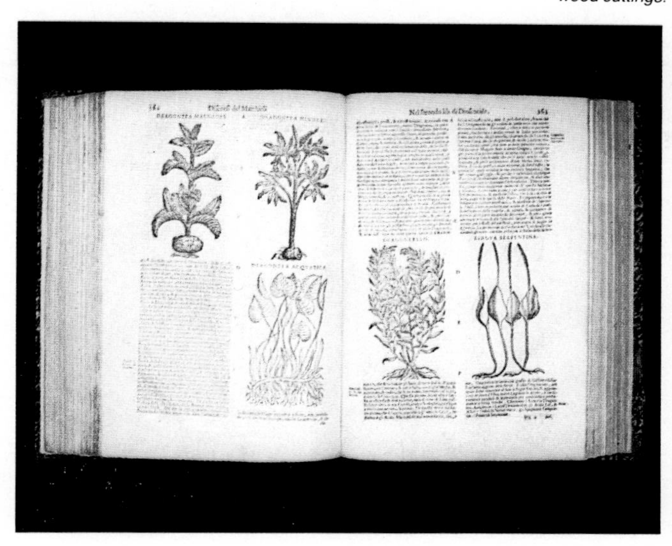

which is proof of how extensive his knowledge of the subject was.

The importance given to the Dioscoridean text spurred many other writers on to produce critical works or enlarge on his themes. These books were often of a purely philological nature but, of all of them, the most complete and practical was undoubtedly *I Discorsi* (Discourses), written in the sixteenth century by a Sienese doctor, P.A. Mattioli. His work was to replace that of Dioscorides as the accepted work. Mattioli criticized and analyzed the assertions of his predecessor, re-cataloguing the plants, resolving uncertainties and attributing precise names to each individual herb. He introduced into his text such new plants as the sunflower and included a number of 'exotic' plants such as the horse-chestnut.

Other Roman writers included Scribonius Largus, Pliny the Elder (23-79 A.D.) and Oribasius. Largus is remembered today because several words which he introduced, such as anodyne and epispastic, are still current in pharmaceutical terminology, even though he naturally dealt only with medicinal botany. Oribasius, on the other hand, dealt with the recognition of drug falsification. It was Pliny, however, who made the most important contribution with his numerous volumes of *Historia Naturalis* (Natural History), in which he described the scientific thought and knowledge of his time. His work, which was a compilation of facts collected from 400 authors, is still essential reading for students keen to learn about pharmacology in the ancient world.

Claudius Galen (131-201 A.D.), certainly a better known physician than Dioscorides, was a great authority on medicinal flora. He

catalogued the medicines according to a 'heat' scale, in increasing degrees, thus making it possible with this parameter to select the appropriate drug for every illness.

With the fall of the Roman Empire, and the subsequent barbarian invasions, progress in scientific knowledge was generally interrupted except in monasteries, which contributed enormously to keeping alive economic, cultural and religious activity during this period.

It was at this time that the School of Salerno, with its *Regimen sanitatis*, became the centre of the fusion of Graeco-Roman and Arab cultures. It is believed that the discovery of herbs such as asafoetida, senna and mace, to mention only a few of the most important, was made by this school.

Further developments took place during the period when maritime republics such as Venice were trading with the Eastern Mediterranean. More was becoming known about the properties of medicinal plants, and, at the same time, new drugs were being discovered. Venice was to become a clearing house in medicinal plants for the whole of the Western world, and a considerable number of botanical books, especially those dealing with healing plants, were printed there. It was a time when not having some pepper in one's home to offer a guest was considered a sign of dire poverty.

The pre-eminent and prestigious position of Venice declined with the discovery of America, when the centre of the medicinal drug trade shifted to Spain. New medicinal and edible plants such as tobacco, potatoes, maize, lignum vitae (*Guaiacum*) and sarsaparilla (*Smilax*)

were introduced from the New World. While exerting an enormous influence on sixteenth-century botany, these newly discovered plants in due course also led to confusion: there was too much information available which was not properly recorded and annotated. Eventually, this situation triggered off a critical and constructive revision of the whole topic. Attention was once more turned to the ancient texts so that their meaning could be clarified. The main purpose of such strides was to eliminate points of variance in texts, which were created by the use of fanciful names – often invented – by different authors describing the same plants. The resulting work was, therefore, primarily a commentary on the terms used rather than a scientific study.

Outstanding among the large ranks of the humanists was Ermolao Barbo, who sought to give uniformity to the wide variety of terms and names used in the old writings, and to establish parallel areas with the ancient texts, thus permitting a more comprehensible view of the whole subject. In his work *Castigationes Plinianae* (Revision of the Works of Pliny), he corrected a number of points and clarified a system of nomenclature that was no longer understood, while at the same time correcting other errors and repetitions. Although he brought nothing that was scientifically new to the text, he shed a great deal of light on a subject that, with the passing of time, had become unintelligible.

This criticism of nomenclature was accompanied by criticism of the current fashion for foreign plants. Imported exotic plants were no longer passively accepted as panaceas and credence was not automatically given to claims of miraculous remedies. Instead, attempts were made to

Page 22, an old pharmacy in Santa Maria Novella in Florence. Various examples of Florentine flasks can be seen in the showcases at the end of the room. In the foreground there is a bronze pestle and mortar with a porphyry grinder which was used to pulverize the drugs.

Page 23, the dispensary of the old pharmacy in Trisulti Abbey, Frosinone, central Italy. The wooden containers were ideal for storing the simples.

find local plants with similar properties, in the conviction that there was still a great deal to be discovered. A new discipline in research into medicinal herbs was thus introduced (confirmed by the founding of various university chairs, most notably those of Bologna and Padua in Italy).

At the same time herbaria (systematically arranged collections of dried plants) were established and botanical gardens created where, at last, 'simples' could be grown and studied on the spot. In due course, botanical gardens were established in almost all Italian universities and also began to appear elsewhere in Europe. In Britain perhaps the largest and best known gardens were founded in Edinburgh (1670) and near London at Kew (1759).

With the invention of printing in the fifteenth century, a great number of herbals were published. The sixteenth, seventeenth and eighteenth centuries subsequently produced a wealth of information on the subject which, for the first time, became accessible to the public at large.

Another important development at this time was xylography (wood-engraving). Now plants could be recorded illustratively by means of prints. In Britain probably the best known herbal of this period, *The Herball or General Historie of Plantes*, was published in 1597 by the English botanist and surgeon, John Gerard, who also became superintendent of Lord Burghley's gardens. Gerard's herbal was richly illustrated with examples of plants he had found growing in his London garden.

Also remembered for his botanical work, *Theatrum Botanicum* (1640), was John Parkinson, a contemporary of Gerard, who had a famous garden at Longacre in London.

One name that stands out in the history of English herbalism is that of Nicholas Culpeper, who, in 1649, published a particularly fascinating herbal. Since Culpeper linked herbs with astrology, many of the medicinal claims he made about the different plants tended to be fanciful, in contrast to the two works by Gerard and Parkinson. Nevertheless, his book enjoyed great popularity and today Culpeper is almost a household name.

By the sixteenth century a fundamental turning point had been reached in the history of medicinal herbs. With the advent of the Swiss-German physician and herbalist, Paracelsus (1439-1541), the whole scene changed. His introduction of new methods and concepts saw the beginning of chemical research which was to lead to the development of synthetic products.

Without going deeply into the mystic-scientific philosophy of Paracelsus, it is clear that it was centred on what is now defined as the 'active principle' of a plant. Paracelsus was not concerned with the 'whole', as produced by the constituent parts of the herb, but with its 'quintessence,' its closely guarded, mysterious secret – the part that was purest and noblest. The drug was thus no longer a single entity but a combination of substances which could be selected and extracted as required, to be used separately or together.

Such an idea was not new. Distillation was already understood, as was dry extraction, but nobody – except for Paracelsus – seemed much concerned with such methods. The consequence of their adoption was that the herbalist was transformed into a pharmacist, his business no

An example of pages from a pharmacopoeia in Latin; it contained several recipes, including one for making Hungary water, a tincture favoured by Queen Elizabeth of Hungary (1235) and still used today as the basis of many perfumes.

longer to blend herbs but to extract substances and form new compounds. Extracts, tinctures and similar preparations thus began to emerge. In exasperation, one group of herbalists following on after Paracelsus finally abandoned the use of plants altogether. Instead, they initiated that form of medical chemistry known as iatrochemistry.

About this time the first effective progress was being made in the use of alternative techniques to water distillation and the dry method, with the introduction of alcohol and acetic acid solvents. Lemery, physician to Louis XIV of France, and Scheele, a Swedish research worker, both produced important results in the chemical field, and the former was really responsible for rendering previous methods obsolete. His interesting discoveries all helped to substantiate his theories contained in his most important book, *A Treatise of All Sorts of Foods, Both Animal and Vegetable*. Scheele, on the other hand, was the first to isolate a number of active principles such as oxalic acid, citric acid, gallic acid and malic acid. The first alkaloids and glycosides, however, were isolated as the result of work done by Friedrich Wilhelm Sertürner, who succeeded in obtaining morphine and who recognized its alkalinity. In his wake came other researchers such as Robiquet, Pellétier, Gomez, Reimann, Hesse and Niemann who added to the general fund of knowledge by discovering quinine, nicotine, codeine and cocaine.

Another major advance was made some time later when the synthesis of active principles was achieved. This was the prelude to chemistry as we know it today. The work of Paracelsus was, therefore, fundamental to the history of herbalism, for it was he who brought about the schism that still separates the work of the herbalist from that of the modern pharmacologist.

Fortunately the trend in biochemistry today is towards a more positive approach to phytotherapy. This type of treatment, far from abandoned, is enjoying a revival, with the use of the whole plant proving to be more efficacious than the use of individual compounds. The view is widely held, however, that when the other components are blended in with the main active principle they do, in fact, play an active part through catalytic action, either stimulating or inhibiting it. The reason for using the whole plant is that it is impossible to reproduce synthetically all its elaborate compounds, as well as the fact, unproved but suggested by experiments, that its gentle curative action may be due to the low concentrations of compounds in it, thus reinforcing the concept of homoeopathic medicine.

The processing of medicinal plants

In order to make use of its latent medicinal qualities, a plant must be treated and modified in such a way that its specific curative substances can be extracted. Such transformations form part of what is known as the 'galenic' branch of pharmacy. The active principles contained in every medicinal plant consist of a number of compounds which, individually or in groups, can have a specific action on the organs of our bodies. Different methods have, therefore, been devised to extract these substances, either singly or collectively, depending on the result required. Some forms of extraction, being particularly complex, are beyond the skills of laymen and are exclusively the province of the pharmaceutical chemist or similar specialists. Others, of a more simple nature, can be carried out by anyone. There are four basic, simple preparation techniques: decoction, maceration, infusion and juice extraction. Although these are very straightforward methods, they are just as effective as the more elaborate systems involving considerably more complicated processes. These four methods will be discussed separately, with instructions as to the exact procedures for extracting the active principles and the circumstances in which each should be adopted.

Decoction is the method normally used for those medicinal herbs whose active principles are difficult to extract because they are contained in woody parts of the plant, or which require prolonged heating in order to pass into solution. The procedures dealt with here only involve water extraction, as more complex forms requiring various solvents are too technical for a book of this nature.

Extraction by decoction involves boiling the whole plant or a part of it in water for a given time and then allowing it to macerate for a further period before filtering. A slight variation of this method is to soak the plant beforehand in cold water for a specific time, depending on the drugs required, in order to soften the leathery part and thus make extraction easier at the decoction stage. This method is reserved for certain plants such as those with a high mucilaginous content.

Decoction is, understandably, quite a drastic method of extraction and one which is capable of modifying some of the plant compounds. It is important to ensure that the main active principle to be extracted is not

Examples of herbal iconography from the eighteenth-century volume by Nicolas Lémery, the French research chemist (Rouen 1645 Paris–1715).

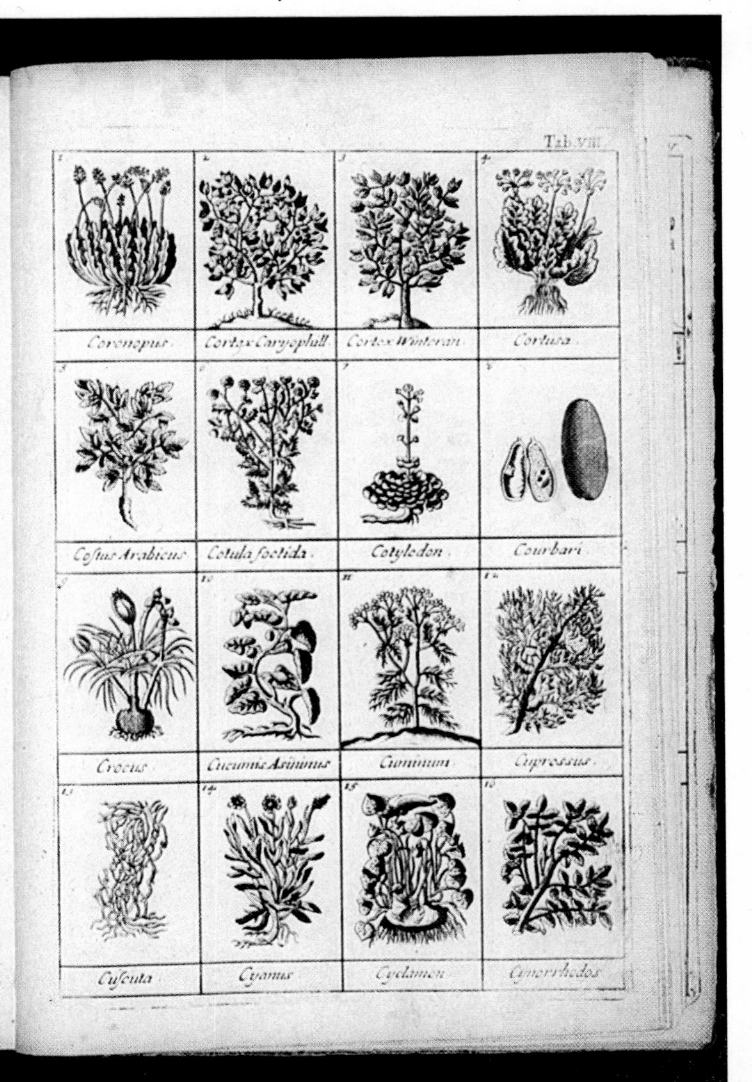

*Top, the rhizome of the common couch or twitch grass (*Elymus repens*), finely chopped to make an infusion for use as a diuretic.*
*Bottom, slivers of alder buckthorn (*Frangula alnus*) bark, an excellent anthraquinonic purgative.*

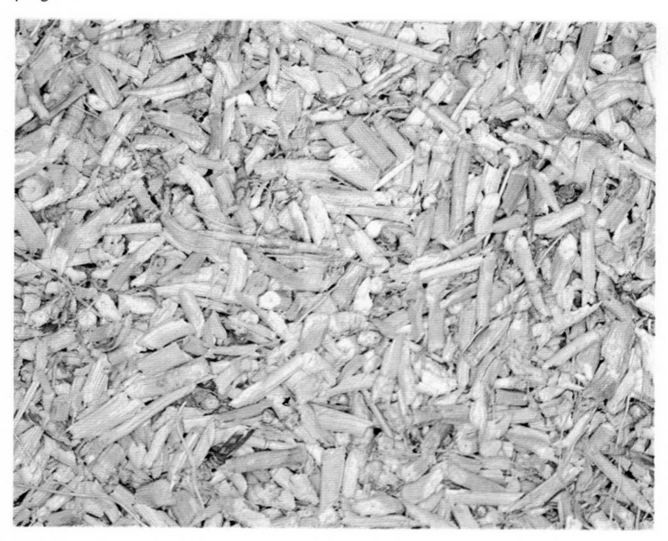

*Top, dried petals of the corn or field poppy (*Papaver rhoeas*), an excellent remedy for bronchitis in children, either used alone or with other pectoral plant remedies. Bottom, cornflower (*Centaurea cyanus*) petals, used phytotherapeutically in treating eye diseases.*

Manna, the thickened sap of the common laburnum; it is a mild purgative with a sweet, honey-like flavour and very suitable for children. This small tree thrives best in the Mediterranean climate.

affected by other harmful compounds induced by the heat. The boiling process during which water is added, nearly always destroys the volatile active principles, that is to say, those with a low boiling point. This means, therefore, that the resulting decoction will never possess all the original principles of the drug.

The filtering operation is equally important, as it serves to strain off not only the leathery residues of the plant but also the mucilage or deposits of amphorous substances that are carried in solution during the boiling.

The liquid obtained is, therefore, always left to clear before the next stage when it is filtered through paper or finely woven linen.

The second method of extraction, infusion, is much more suitable for obtaining the active principles when the parts of the plant being used are soft and fragile, such as leaves, bud or flowers. It is preferable, except in certain cases, to use herbs that have been slightly dried, as the reduction of water content will concentrate the principal constituents. Unlike decoction, this method allows retention of many of the volatile principles which would otherwise be lost, but does not permit extraction of those requiring a continuously high temperature. An expert, with extensive knowledge of medicinal plants and their medical compounds, can decide which of these two methods is more suitable for obtaining the active principles required.

Infusion entails pouring boiling water over that part of the plant known to contain the required drug. The container should be made of pottery or glass to avoid the formation of tannate of iron which, due to the presence of tannin in almost all plants, would occur if metal were used.

As soon as the water has been poured over the plants, the container should be covered, thereby allowing the steam, rich in volatile compounds, to condense. After a given time, which varies for each plant used, the liquid is filtered before being used.

The third simple method, known as maceration, is used for medicinal plants whose active principles are soluble in cold water. All that has to be done is to immerse the herb in cold water for several hours during which time all the principles that do not need heat to release them (i.e. that are not thermolabile) will be released into the solution. The yield of mucilage from certain plants, such as the mallow *(Malva)* and marsh mallow *(Althaea officinalis)*, is in fact greater when extraction is carried out by means of cold maceration rather than by infusion.

The fourth straightforward method is the extraction of juices. In this case the plants which contain the required medicinal ingredients must be fresh and have a high water content. The juice, which can be extracted by various methods, contains the mineral salts and vitamins of the plant, together with all the other substances that can be obtained through pressure. Again, the juice will not contain all the active principles of the plant but, on the other hand, cold extraction does not modify the structure of those compounds which, as we have seen, can be altered by heat. In the home, juices can be produced by first parboiling the fresh plants very briefly and then applying pressure with an appropriate utensil such as a small press. Because of the additional heat used for parboiling, however, this method will modify some of the constituents.

Better still, of course, is the modern electric blender which extracts almost the entire juice content of the plant.

In all the four methods described here, there is a time limit, hence they are considered short-term procedures. In fact, the decoction, the infusion, the maceration and the juice all contain biological compounds that immediately undergo processes of oxidization and fermentation that denaturalize the medicinal substance, often making the liquid taste repugnant and, therefore, unusable. To avoid this, it is possible to add preservatives but this, of course, would be quite contrary to the whole concept of non-adulteration, which is the aim of the methods described here. Additions of sugar and alcohol admittedly also enable juices to be kept for a slightly longer period and, if vacuum-bottled with sugars, their properties and the freshness of their components will remain unaltered; unfortunately, this kind of preservation is almost impossible in the average household because the apparatus required is often expensive.

The problem of conserving medicinal principles, once extracted, is of the utmost importance. The pharmaceutical industry has, therefore, done much work in this field, producing further preservation techniques so that active principles can be used at any time and in any dosage. The difficulty of tracking down exotic or rare drugs, combined with the relatively short harvesting period of healing herbs, have necessitated the development and regulation of highly advanced methods of extraction and preservation.

Such preparations are known as extracts and are divided into semi-solid, dry and fluid types; another means of classifying them is by their vehicle of evaporation: water, water and alcohol, or ether. Strictly speaking, an extract is the concentration of all the substances and salts diluted in the juice obtained from it. This concentration is achieved by the use of two fundamental processes: the first is based on freezing and the other on evaporation. The latter, more generally used, consists of putting the juice into an evaporating dish from which the water content is evaporated at a low heat. Obviously, depending on the length of the evaporation process, different concentrations of the juice will be obtained. Concentrations will thus range from those still possessing a high water content to concentrates in which water is no longer present. The extract obtained is termed soft or dry depending on its water content. Soft extracts have a semi-solid honey-like consistency, while dry ones are often composed of solid masses that can be reduced to powder. A classic example of a dry extract is that of aloes which has the appearance of black, solid lumps, almost vitrified, but which are friable and easily pulverized; an even better known instance is liquorice, which can be reduced to a powder or to liquorice sticks.

The water content of a juice is not, however, always the vehicle of evaporation used in obtaining an extract. Instead, to facilitate concentration through evaporation, a solution of water and alcohol is often used. Alternatively, ether may be used and then recovered through distillation. The addition of these substances to the water enables compounds to dissolve which are hardly soluble at all in water alone, but which become very soluble in a combination of the two liquids.

Extracts in which ether is used are described as ethereal and those in which alcohol is used as hydroalcoholic. Certainly the most important type of extract is the fluid extract which has only relatively recently been formulated and accepted in pharmaceutical practice. In comparison with the type of extract previously described it has one property which makes it extremely useful: one gramme of fluid extract is equivalent to one gramme of the original plant material. In other words, all the active principles contained in a precise quantity of plant matter to be treated are present in the same quantity of fluid extract obtained. The fluid extract makes it possible to have any drug available at any given time (it does not deteriorate quickly and is not modified, except very slowly, by external agents); it is of a purity and accuracy of titration that would be impossible to achieve in drugs fresh from the plant.

These extracts can be used either by themseves or as the basic ingredient of various medicinal compounds, both of which are guaranteed as a homogeneous product. Although the method of preparation varies according to the drug, it can be summarized as follows: 1,000 parts of the finely chopped dried plant are left to macerate for several hours in alcohol of the appropriate strength. This alcohol is then strained off and discarded. A similar amount of fresh alcohol is then poured over the same plant matter and a part of it strained off a day later. This alcohol, the weight of which is in direct relation to the type of herb used, is held in reserve. New alcohol is added until the dried plant material is exhausted of all the soluble extracts. The next stage is to distil this second liquid, recovering the alcohol and allowing the rest to evaporate until an extract is obtained which, when mixed with the part held in reserve, will be of exactly the same weight as the original herb material. Some experts maintain that the solvent action of the alcohol can be improved by the addition of certain substances such as inorganic

An old-fashioned copper distilling apparatus at the Fragonard Perfumeries Museum in Grasse (Côte d'Azur). Its parts are easily identifiable as the boiler (right), connecting tube and condenser (left).

or organic acids, salts and ammonia. The various pharmacopoeias certainly use one or other of these additives. The fluid extract will remain unaltered for a long time if kept in dark glass bottles which are firmly stoppered.

The above explanation demonstrates the superiority of this method of extraction over the other methods described, and accounts for its almost unreserved use throughout the world.

When, for particular purposes, it is necessary to extract only the alcohol-soluble substances such as alkaloids, bitter principles, organic acids and colouring substances, another specific method of preparation is used. This is generally known as an alcoholic tincture or, more correctly, spirit solution. Apart from the reason already given, these tinctures are produced because their high alcohol content makes them easy to preserve. A spirit solution can be prepared either by maceration, in which a measured amount of the medicinal plant is immersed in alcohol of a suitable strength for a predetermined length of time and subsequently filtered, or by digestion, passing it through a still. This apparatus is equipped with a cooling flask which causes the alcohol that has been condensed in it to fall back into the receiver flask in which the drugs to be digested have been placed. Because tinctures are very sensitive to light they are always kept in bottles made of dark glass. The alcohol in which the plants have been macerated develops varying degrees of strength, depending on the drug being used and the ease with which it releases its essential constituents, but it is usually not less than 60% vol. Although these are alcoholic preparations they cannot,

Opposite, typical hand-painted glass storage jars preserved in the pharmacy of Trisulti Abbey, Frosinone, central Italy.

unlike fluid extracts, be preserved indefinitely. They react quickly to light and air which cause flocculation and acetic fermentation.

The method of maceration described above is hardly ever used nowadays in the pharmaceutical industry. Instead, tinctures are prepared by diluting a certain amount of fluid extract of the requisite drug with alcohol of a predetermined strength. When, as is sometimes done, a sugar solution is added to spirit solutions, the resulting preparation is known as an *elixir* or *ratafia*. These preparations are, in fact, genuine liqueurs and have been almost abolished in pharmaceutical practice. Nevertheless, they are occasionally recorded in recipes included in family cookery books, cherry ratafia probably being one of the better known.

If the vehicle of maceration were to be a mixture of alcohol and ether, an '*ethereal tincture*' or, more scientifically, an *ethereal spirit solution* would be obtained. Many varieties of such preparations could once be found in all the pharmacopoeias, but are now little used. The best known is ethereal tincture of valerian.

Looking at the field of galenical preparations (those deriving from plant or natural origins) as a whole, there is one particular preparation which, although no longer in use pharmaceutically, has been reassessed by modern phytotherapy, both because of its successful results and its ease of preparation. It can even be made at home. This is medicinal wine. As long ago as the thirteenth century, Arnold of Villanova wrote his *Incipit Tractatus de Vinis*, the earliest published book on wines, which dealt particularly with 'methods of making preparations with a wine basis'. Such wines are made by simply macerating plant drugs in wine, preferably white, with a high alcohol content, such as a fortified wine. The alcohol content is sufficient to obtain an extraction of the soluble compounds if the medicinal plants are allowed to macerate in the wine for the length of time appropriate to each type. Unfortunately, medicated wines are subject to acetic fermentation (that is, they go vinegary) and form a sediment just like any other wine. It is, therefore, important to prepare only small quantities and to keep the wine completely airtight and away from the light.

The next section of galenic products to be examined are the *alcoholates* or *spirits*, produced by the distillation of spirit solutions. The difference between spirits and spirit solutions is that the former, through distillation, contain only the volatile principles of the drug and not the fixed principles, as do the latter. For the distillation, 70-80% vol. alcohols are generally used, after appropriate maceration. Only a certain part of the distillate is retained, so as not to change its characteristics with substances of low volatility which remain in the flask, following the concentration of the watery part. Some of the best known spirit solutions still used today are aqua vitae of lemon balm and Hungary water, or spirit of rosemary, the former being used as a digestive antispasmodic and the latter as a perfume component. Spirits have excellent preservation qualities due to their high alcohol content.

Instead of using alcohol as a preservative for garden herbs, sugar can be used in a concentrated form. By adopting this alternative, sugary solutions can be made which contain medicinal substances; they are known as *syrups*. Syrups also serve to disguise the unpleasant taste of many medicines.

Some examples of condensers: 1. a Liebig condenser; 2. a bulb-type water-cooled condenser often used with the Soxhlet apparatus to obtain tinctures; 3. a serpentine condenser for liquids of high volatility; 4. a water-controlled vacuum pump based on the principle of the Venturi tube.

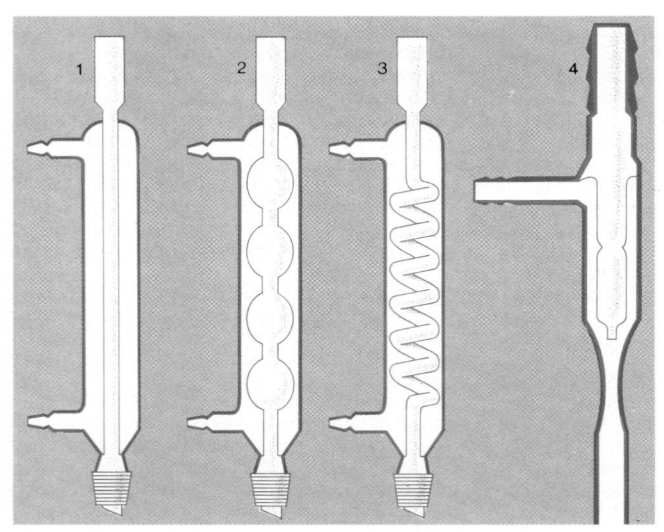

Ordinary syrup is made by dissolving a certain quantity of sugar in water, at a low heat; the mixture needs to be stirred frequently and allowed to evaporate sufficiently to obtain the concentration necessary to achieve the characteristic density of syrup. The curative substances are then dissolved in it and it is these that determine the particular qualities of each type of syrup. If the resulting liquid is cloudy, it can be clarified. Syrups should be stored in hermetically sealed bottles and kept in a cool dry place, preferably away from the light. Despite such precautions, syrup is prone to alteration, especially when the additives are organic. In such cases, the syrup will have to be re-boiled in order to increase its density and, therefore, its preservation potential. Instead of sugar, honey can be substituted using the same procedure. Such preparations are called *mellites* or honeyed syrups. For instance, 'melrosette' or 'honey of roses', which is still made for children, belongs to this category.

Nowadays there is a growing demand for plants and vegetables that have not been contaminated with insecticides or fungicides, to be used in as natural form as possible. The interest in macrobiotics has even brought back a number of preparations which, due to their short shelf-life, had become neglected. These confections are known as *electuaries* or *conserves* and are in the form of paste made by mixing the pulp of fruits, which have special nutritive or medicinal properties, with certain powders, honey or syrups. Some of these are sold commercially but, because of the high percentage of organic substances in them, preservatives have to be added. The macrobiotic

Distillation over direct heat with a serpentine condenser to prolong the time taken for the vapour to pass through, thus aiding condensation (see p. 44).

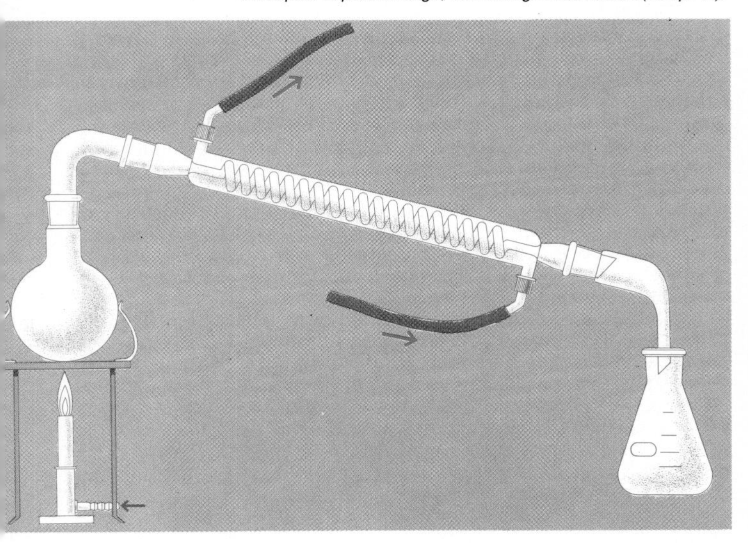

diet makes use of several types of electuaries in this double role of supplementary food and medicine.

When medicinal substances are dissolved in oil rather than the usual solvents, the preparation is known as an *oil solution* or *medicated oil*. Such preparations can be made either by dissolving one part of an oily fluid extract of a particular plant in a given quantity of refined olive oil or, alternatively, by boiling the plant itself in the oil and then filtering the mixture. These preparations are especially effective for ailments such as rheumatism, in which an oily preparation is required to facilitate localized massages.

Closely related to the medicated oils are the ointments, also known as *salves* or *unguents*, the base of which is usually a semi-solid, fatty or greasy substance such as lard or wool-fat (lanolin). They may be prepared simply by mixing powdered vegetal drugs into the fat, or the fat may be melted with medicinal substances and then allowed to solidify. These ointments are all intended for external use.

At one time simple ointments such as these were very well known and widely used, but nowadays they have been largely replaced by commercial products containing chemical additives. The creams and liniments found on the market today tend to have quite different bases. Sometimes, however, we are reminded of remedies which must have been familiar to our ancestors, when we see an old apothecary jar bearing a name such as unguent of poplar or unguent of lily root. In Britain there is, increasingly, a tendency towards these simple creams containing no chemical additives.

Opposite, a perfume distilling apparatus in operation at the Fragonard Perfumeries in Grasse. In the foreground can be seen the Liebig condensers (see p. 44) and the distillation flasks containing the substances to be distilled.

In this survey of preparations, *distillation* has deliberately been left until last because of its fundamental importance in obtaining those ubiquitous ingredients of so many medicines and cosmetics known as essential oils or essences. These are not only used for their aromatic qualities, and as the main ingredients in perfumery, but also as the main medicinal ingredients in modern aromatherapy. The rest of this section, therefore, is devoted to a fairly detailed description of the various processes necessary for the production of these oils.

Essences are complex substances which are often fragrant and, although not oily, when placed on paper will produce a translucent effect. It is now possible to reproduce a great many essential oils chemically, and although this might suggest that distillation is an outdated method, that is not the case.

The essences derived from plants do not merely consist of one or more compounds which it is possible to reproduce, but of a whole combination of substances which are often undefined. It is not difficult to differentiate between the natural and the synthetic essences, because the natural perfume is altogether more delicate. There are also cases where chemistry has to make use of natural raw materials in order to reproduce some of the compounds synthetically. An example of this is oil of turpentine, a natural product of distillation, which provides the *pinene* from which *terpineol* is synthetically produced.

The reasons why plants manufacture essential oils are still being investigated. A few of the many theories formulated have some credibility, but what is certain, in any event, is that essences are beneficial to the economy of a plant, enabling it to manufacture other products. Some authorities maintain they are either waste materials which have not yet been eliminated or that they are a means of protection against excessive sunshine. It is, in fact, true to say that nearly all alpine plants are scented and the perfume that surrounds them serves as a filter through which the solar rays must penetrate.

Essences are quite easily altered, and the least change in temperature or humidity is enough to allow the enzymes present to become activated. Another factor to be borne in mind when gathering herbs is the effect of light on the amount of essential oil contained in plants at different times of day. Experienced collectors, knowing just when the healing properties of each type of plant are at their peak, can decide exactly when to harvest it in order to derive the most benefit. Thus in some plants, the amount of essence will be reduced by light, whereas in others it will be concentrated. The composition of the soil may also affect the size of the yield.

Having made these points, it has to be said that the most satisfactory extraction is obtained when there is the least possible alteration to the characteristics of the essence itself. This type of extraction, which is described as 'cold', entails no change in the composition of the oil because no heat is involved. Unfortunately this method can only be applied to certain plants, mainly citrus, that possess a great many oil-producing glands. With the cold method the components present in the oils undergo only the slightest alteration, thus making it possible to produce essences of great purity which can even be used internally. The two main methods of cold extraction are *expression* and the *Écuelle process*. The former is carried out by putting the skins of the fruit into

special containers where they are pressed, thus causing their glands to rupture and allowing the essence to be collected together with water and other substances. Essences extracted in this way are, inevitably, cloudy, although their fragrance and substance remain unaltered and they clarify when subsequently decanted. This method is mainly used now for home-made essences. Industry has adopted the Écuelle process. This involves the use of machines in which the fruit is revolved in metal cups or drums lined with spikes which delicately rupture the oil-bearing glands to release their essences. As this is a fast process and the fruits are not identical in size or shape, there is considerable wastage of essence; this is, however, compensated for by the speed of the operation.

Essential oils are soluble in solvents that are described as 'fixed' if they do not evaporate at a normal temperature, and as 'volatile' if the reverse is the case. Fixed solvents consist of solid or liquid odourless fats such as lard, tallow or refined olive oil. These solvents enable essence to be extracted by means of a method known as *hot enfleurage*. The essence-producing plants are placed in copper containers and left to macerate in fat which is brought up to a temperature of about 104°F. (40°C.), with more plants being added until the fat is saturated. The fat is then separated from the essence to give a good yield.

Extraction with volatile solvents, while presenting much greater difficulties in obtaining the essential oil, has the advantage of making it possible to extract essences from plants that have only very low

Steam distillation. By distilling at a temperature lower than that of boiling water, it is possible to obtain essences without much change in character (see p. 44).

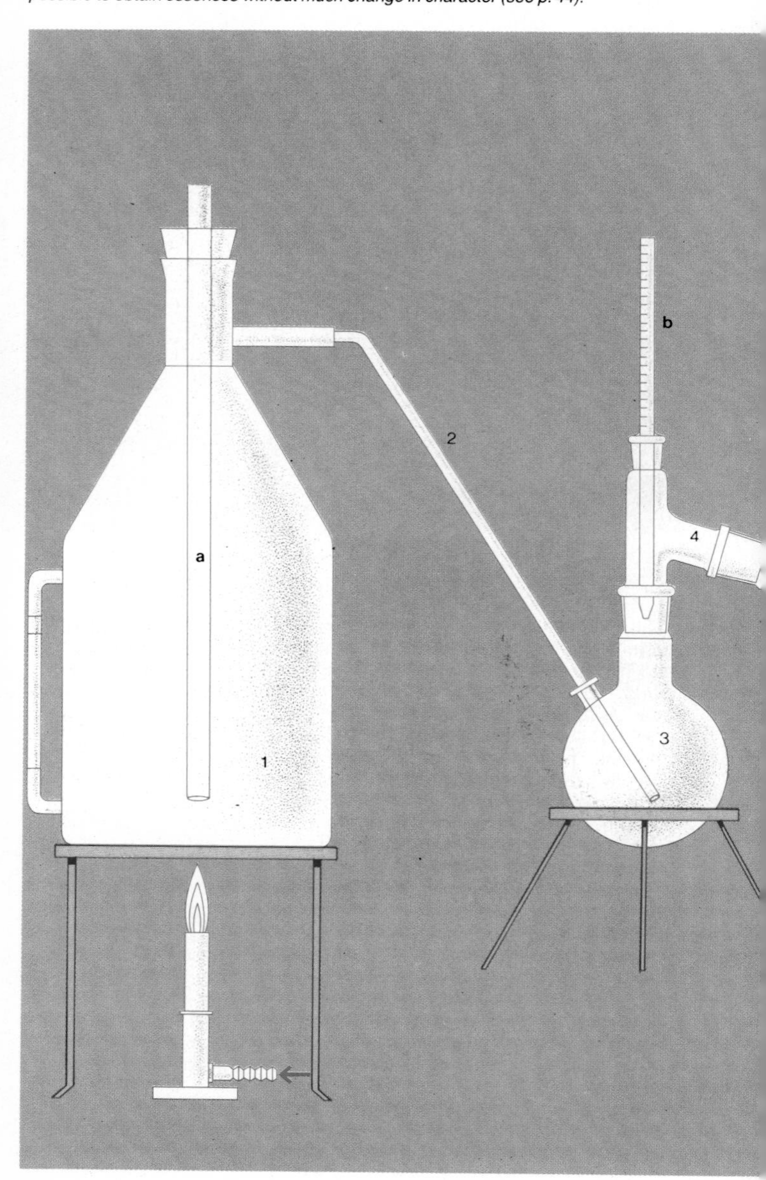

The water contained in the boiler (1) is brought to the boil by means of a Bunsen flame. The steam passes through the tube (2) into the flask (3). If the pressure inside the boiler becomes excessive, the water is pushed up the central tube (a) until the pressure is equal to the external pressure; the tube (a) thus acts as a safety-valve.
The distillation flask (3) must be pre-heated in order not to create unwanted internal condensation and differences in temperature: inside it are the substances to be distilled. As the steam breaks down the oleiferous glands in these, the mixture of water and essence in the form of vapour moves towards the connecting piece (4) between the distillation flask and condenser (5). The thermometer (b) allows the operator to judge the temperatures of distillation of the various compounds.
The vapour is finally condensed in the condenser and the resulting distillate falls through, via the connecting piece (6), into the 'Florentine flask' (7) where the substances decant to form two layers, due to the difference in their specific weights. Separation of distilled water and essence will occur automatically when the level reaches the top of the lateral overflow (8).

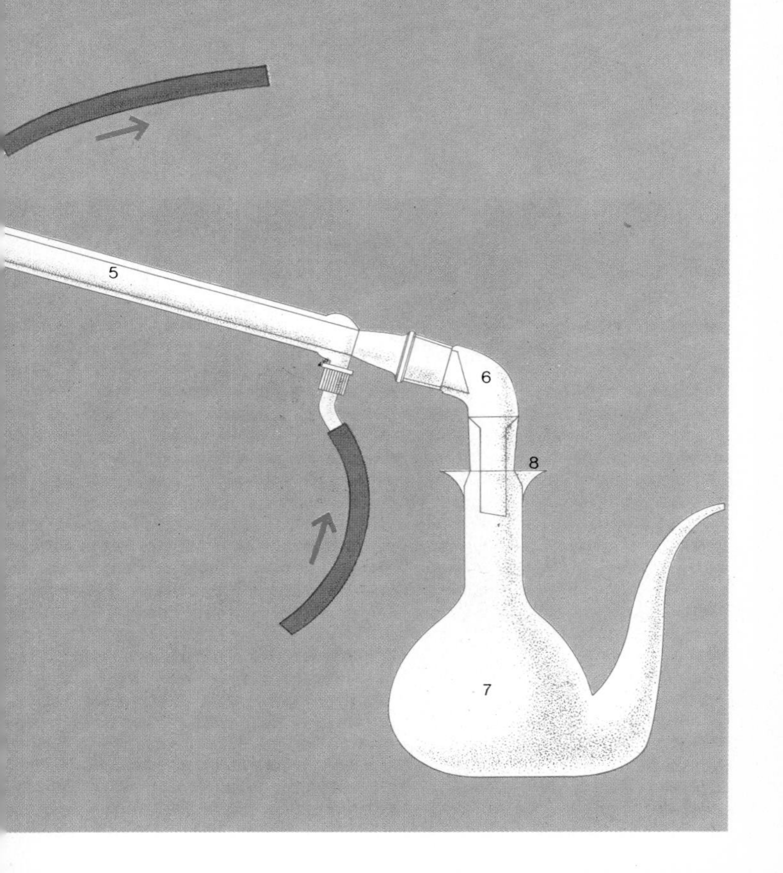

Examples of laboratory distillation glassware: 1. separatory funnel; 2. 90° connecting tube between distilling flask and condenser; 3. connecting piece for condenser exit; 4. Florentine flask; 5. volumetric flask; 6. connecting piece between distillation flask and condenser with attachment for thermometer; 7. connecting piece between condenser and volumetric flask with attachment for vacuum pump used in distillation under reduced pressure; 8. distillation flask with connection for valve to use in distillation under reduced pressure; 9. Pauly apparatus (known as the 'spider') used in fractional distillation, showing the receiver with which three fractions can be collected; 10. percolator.

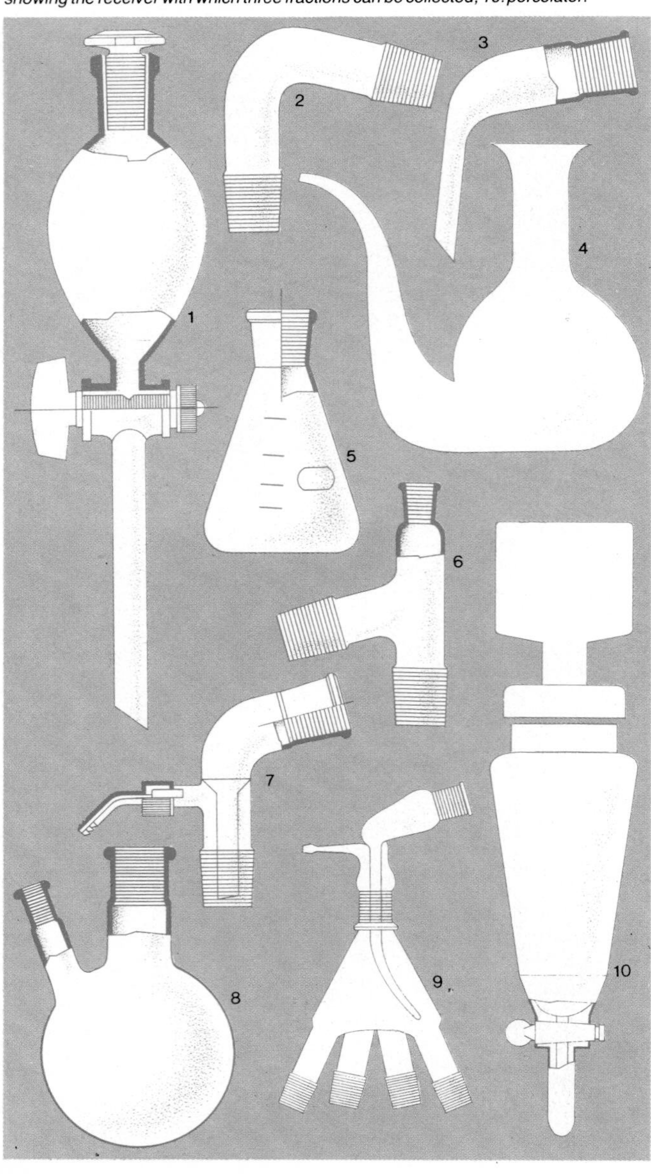

percentages of the fragrant principle. The volatile solvents normally used are benzene and petroleum ether, which carry both the essence in solution and other products, making it necessary to carry out further, rather laborious tasks in order to obtain a pure product. The first phase of extraction by this method is the soaking of the flowers in an apparatus known as a 'digester'. The solution obtained from this is distilled, during which process the solvent is recovered. The essence that is separated from this is known as 'concrete essence' because of the traces of extraneous material contained in it. In order to purify the concrete essence, it is treated with pure alcohol which takes up the essence, leaving many undissolved impurities. The alcohol is then brought to a low temperature which enables the remaining impurities to become concentrated. At this stage, the alcohol can be called an *extract*. To complete the process, the extract is distilled to give the resulting essence a high degree of purity.

A further method, which many people regard as the best, since it alters neither the perfume nor the characteristics of the oils, is that of *cold enfleurage*. This procedure is based on the special quality possessed by some substances to condense essential oils on their surface area. These substances are purified waxes which are spread over flat glass surfaces; the plants are placed on top and enclosed in special containers. After a day or two, the plants are removed and replaced by fresh ones; the process is then repeated over several months or until the wax has reached saturation point. The wax is then removed from the glass and the essence recovered by following the same procedure as for volatile solvents.

The problems involved in obtaining the products of essence-producing plants are such that the methods described are only adopted for particular purposes.

Normally, even though the process may change the composition of the essences due to the heat employed, *distillation* is used. This can be divided into three categories: simple distillation over direct heat, steam distillation and vacuum distillation. In distillation, heat both ruptures the oleiferous glands and, unfortunately, slightly modifies the essence. We shall only deal with the type of distillation in which water is the transporting vehicle. The distilled liquid will be a mixture of condensed water and essential oil which will separate naturally because of their different specific gravities. The plants to be distilled must be used while still fresh and should have been gathered when most fragrant. In order to avoid fermentation, they should never be piled on top of one another.

The apparatus used for distilling is known as an alembic, from the Arab word *al-anbiq*, a vase. This is divided into three parts: boiler, distilling column and condenser. Vaporization of the water and volatization (rapid evaporation) of the essential oils are achieved in the distilling flask. The vapours then rise up the column and come down through the condenser, whence, having recondensed rapidly, the liquid falls into a receiver.

The boiler is usually made of copper or stainless steel, but may be of glass if laboratory apparatus is being used. It is generally cylindrical in shape and its base, to which the heat is applied, is never in direct contact with the plants, as these are kept slightly raised on wire mesh racks. Part of the space between the base and the first rack contains water which produces the necessary steam. The column, which is firmly set in the neck of the boiler, leads to the condenser and allows for the expansion of the steam and for its initial cooling. If the boiler is metal, the column is clamped to it to form an airtight join, but if it is glass, either the foot of the column is shaped to fit the neck of the heater flask, or it is passed through a close-fitting stopper or cork. The condenser consists of a spiral tube which is completely immersed in a vessel containing cold running water.

When the steam from the column comes into contact with the cold walls of the condenser, it condenses and, by force of gravity, runs down into a receiver, known as a 'Florentine flask', where the essence automatically separates from the water. If this type of flask is not used, separation has to be effected by means of a separatory funnel. Under normal conditions, boiling point is reached when the tension of the water equals the atmospheric pressure and to achieve this, the heat source is placed directly under the boiler; in this case distillation is brought about by direct heat.

In the laboratory the boiler is replaced by a glass distillation flask, and the heat is also applied from below; to avoid breakages an asbestos, wire mesh or gauze mat is interposed so that the heat is not applied directly to the glass. In order to obtain uniform heating, the flask may be placed in a bed of sand or in a water-bath. In this way the heat will be diffused evenly over the lower surface of the flask.

The two main types of condenser used in a laboratory for liquids with a low boiling point are the Liebig and the serpentine (see page 36). If the steam, rather than being produced in the same container as the herbs, as described above, is produced in a separate boiler, this prevents the essence-containing plants from being 'cooked', which might adversely affect the result.

This method, known as 'steam distillation', makes it possible to distil those liquids which have a higher boiling point than water at temperatures lower than the boiling point of water. This method also makes it possible to obtain essences that are not excessively altered and is, therefore, preferable to the previously described system because of the greater purity of the resulting product.

Distillation can also be carried out at a pressure lower than that of the atmosphere. This is done by vacuum pumps and is known as 'distillation under reduced pressure' or 'vacuum distillation'. By decreasing the atmospheric pressure, the boiling point is also lowered, so enabling distillation to take place at a lower temperature to obtain a product that is even less modified than that produced by steam distillation.

Once the essences have been obtained, they are not always used in their complete state but are often broken down into their various components. This is done by *fractional distillation*, based on the already discussed principle of boiling which occurs as a result of the equality between the atmospheric pressure and the sum of the vapour tensions of the components. The distillation temperature will initially be lower than that of the most volatile component and will then gradually rise. By carefully controlling the temperatures, the fractions of the essences can thus be collected. As the various components separate, they are retained individually by changing the receiving vessel when the

An example of a deterpenator used to obtain essences that are known as 'absolute', that is, completely without terpenes; these are hydrocarbon substances used in various industrial sectors.

appropriate temperatures are reached. To carry out such work in a laboratory, a special container is used which is known as a Pauly apparatus or, more commonly a 'spider'. However, on an industrial scale such a method would be totally unsuitable because it is lengthy, laborious and, what is worse, discontinuous. For practical reasons, therefore, the 'dephlegmator' or 'fractionating column' is used. The most usual type is the Egrot dephlegmator, in which the essence vapours are cooled by a flow of water. This causes only the less volatile constituents to condense, thus effectively separating them from the more highly volatile ones.

A secondary product of distillation is the distilled water which is still used a great deal in perfumery. It is, of course, merely water in which a very small amount of essence has remained and which gives it a fragrance and character of its own.

Distilled waters do not keep well and are prone to alteration as they are subject to fungi and moulds. The only precaution possible is to store them away from the light in dark glass bottles. Their fragrance can be made more subtle by diluting a little of the essence itself in the water but this will deprive the water of its active volatile and other unknown principles that are typical of distillation.

Distilled waters are widely used today in phytotherapeutic technology because they are readily available in large quantites. Although they contain only a low level of active principles, their medicinal effect is consistent with the concept of homoeopathic medicine.

Fractional distillation. This system is used to subdivide the essences in the various components. It is based on the principle of boiling that takes place as a result of the equalization between the atmospheric pressure and that of the combined tensions of the vapours of the various components (see p. 44).

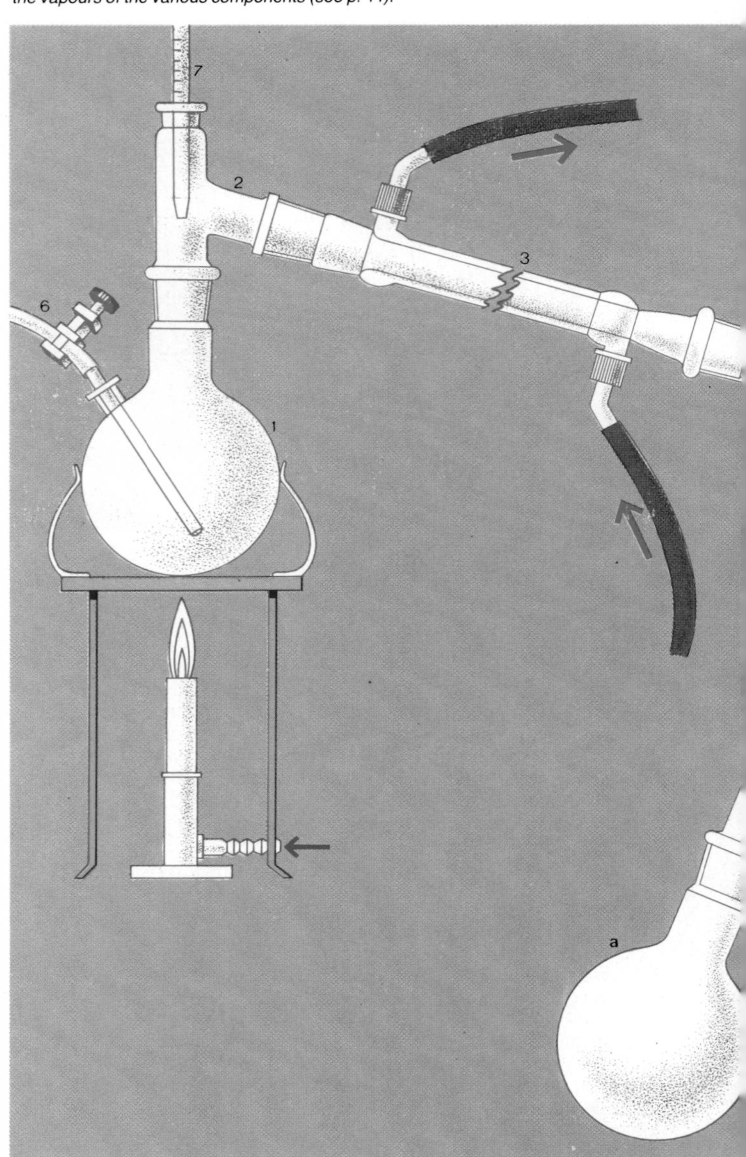

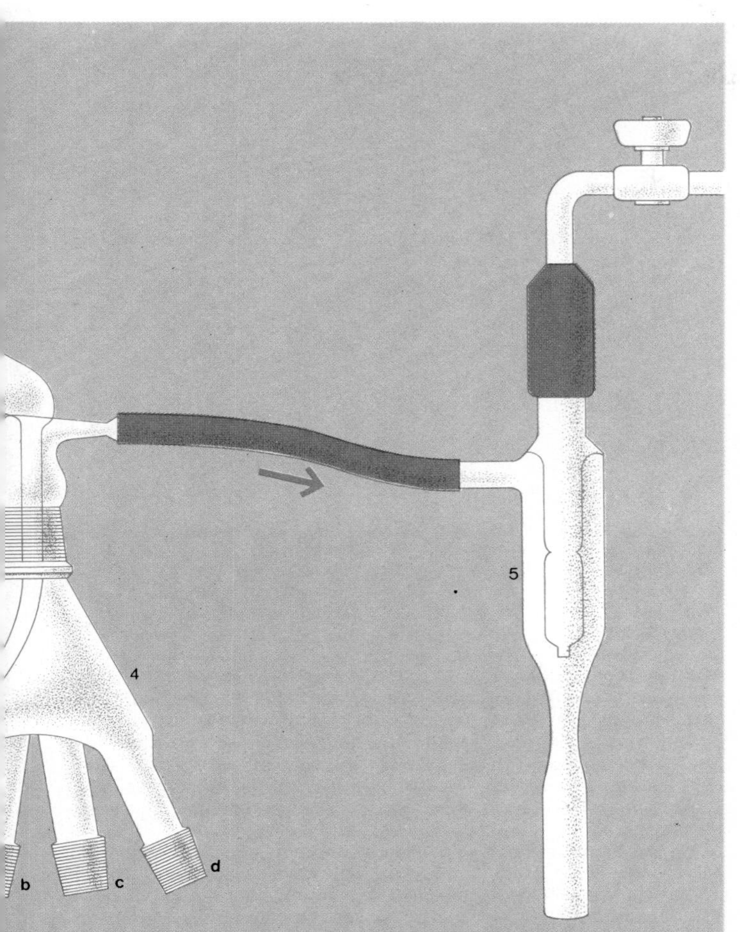

The substance to be distilled in the distillation flask (1) is heated by means of a Bunsen flame. Rich vapours of essential oil are formed which begin to cool down in the ground joint (2) and then to condense in the condenser (3). The Pauly apparatus (4) enables the various fractions of distillation to be directed to the collecting flasks (a-b-c-d). In this type of distillation, all the apparatus is completely watertight. Boiling is facilitated by reducing the temperature at which this takes place; this is done by lowering the internal pressure by means of a water pump (5) that incorporates the principle of the Venturi tube – a device used to measure the flow rate of water in conduits that are closed and under pressure. As the reduced internal pressure could cause the apparatus to implode, air is constantly fed into the distillation flask, controlled by a spring clip (6). The thermometer (7) enables the operator to know when distillation of the various fractions of the essence has begun.

Cells of Allium sativum *(garlic), containing crystals, seen through a microscope. Besides its culinary uses, the essence forms the basis for various pharmaceutical rubefacient (counter-irritant) preparations.*

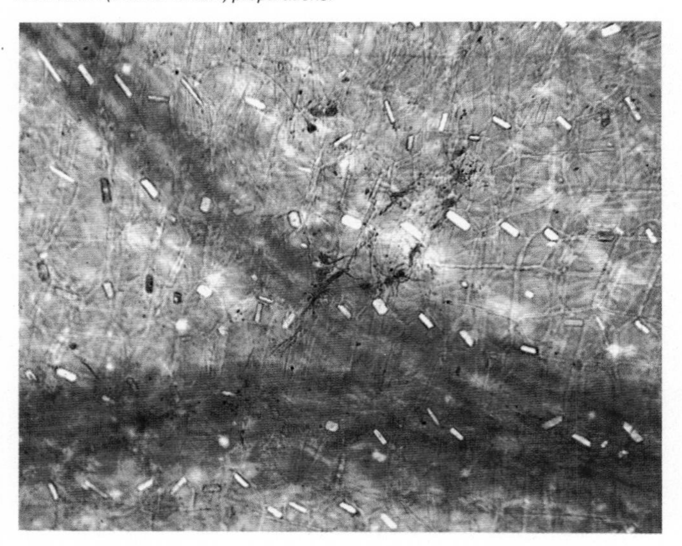

Homoeopathy

Although homoeopathy has only been systematized for about two centuries, its roots go back much further. As a method of treatment, it is quite different from any other and wholly unconventional in concept. The term was first introduced into England in 1827 and derives from the Greek words *hómoios* meaning similar, and *páthos* meaning pain. This literal meaning, however, of 'similar to the pain', fails to give any practical clue as to how an illness can be cured by means of the same illness.

The Hippocratic concept that 'like can be treated with like' makes it clearer and it is on this concept that homoeopathy is based. Accustomed as we are today to an almost constant stream of new discoveries emerging in various scientific areas, it is difficult for us to grasp the full significance of this Hippocratic statement and its fortunate rediscovery by the German physician, Christian Friedrich Samuel Hahnemann (1755-1843).

With this Hippocratic concept in mind, Hahnemann regulated the methods of diagnosis and the homoeopathic procedure that is still practised today. By the age of twenty he was already a qualified doctor and, like all eighteenth-century physicians, was prescribing preparations and procedures (including traditional blood-letting) consistent with contemporary pharmaceutical knowledge and methods. Being keenly observant, however, he came to doubt the efficacy of these centuries-hallowed treatments.

These hairs of Urtica dioica *(stinging nettle), here seen greatly enlarged, contain a liquid whose histamine content makes this a valuable plant in treating several complaints.*

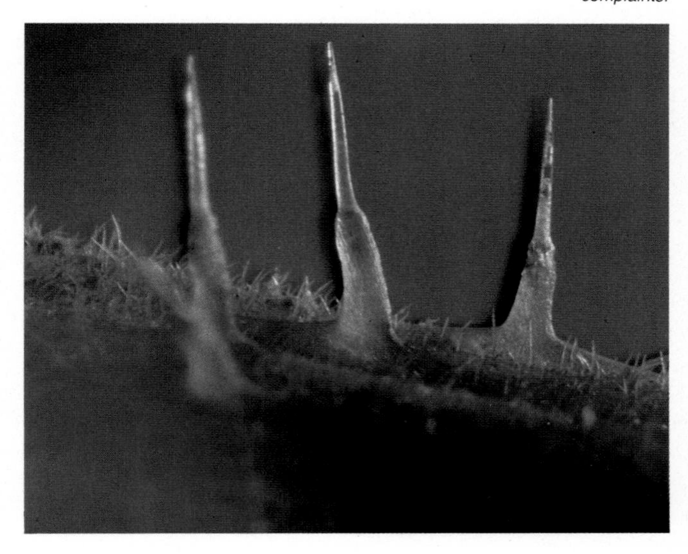

He remarked, too, that medicines often prescribed in good faith only tended to aggravate the illness. He began, therefore, to criticize openly many of the common practices of contemporary medicine pointing out that the use of certain medicines was not always founded on sound scientific reason.

In his main work, *Organon* (1810), he wrote as follows: '... Allopathic treatment [a term created by Hahnemann to highlight the contrast between the current school of thought and his own; it derives from the Greek *àllos* meaning different and *páthos* meaning pain, and indicates how illnesses are cured by a different derivative action] without ever being able to remove and cure the original (dissimilar) chronic disease, only develops new artificial diseases beside it. As daily experience shows, this practice renders the patient much worse and more incurable than before ... it could be described as criminal treason against the principles of cure to mix the two systems of medicine according to the pleasure of the patient ... The ordinary physician imagines he can get over the difficulties of antipathic treatment by giving a stronger dose of the remedy at each renewed aggravation of the illness. By this method an equally transient suppression of disease is effected and then there is still greater necessity for giving ever-increasing quantities of the palliative. There ensues either another more serious disease or, frequently, danger to life, and then death itself.'

Hahnemann's mission in life was to discover ways of curing the sick in a natural way, with simple medicines. His determined research led him to read a treatise by a nineteenth-century Edinburgh doctor, William

*Pollen grains from the hazel (*Corylus avellana*) and pellitory of the wall (*Parietaria officinalis*) magnified 180 times. These two types of pollen are only two of the many allergens that are the cause of so many distressing springtime allergic reactions.*

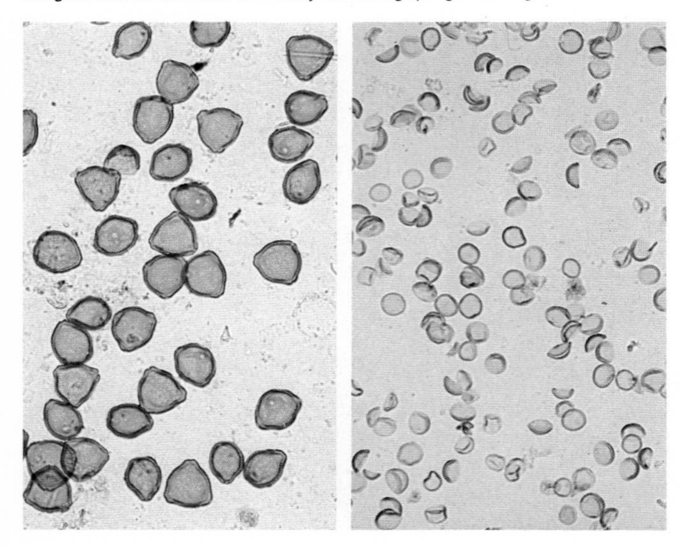

Cullen, on the properties of quinine and on certain 'strangenesses' that became apparent in people who habitually took it. Spurred on by scientific curiosity, he began to experiment on himself, and thus began to formulate the basis of homoeopathy. He observed, in fact, that concentrated doses of quinine produced a fever similar to that of malaria, although it was well known that quinine was used to combat the disease.

In this connection Hahnemann says: '...All the morbid symptoms and alterations in health that each medicine is especially capable of developing in the healthy individual must first be observed as far as possible, before the physician can hope to find among them, and to select, the suitable homoeopathic remedies for most of the natural diseases.'

This was an affirmation of 'like treating like', and it was from this point that the salient features of the homoeopathic doctrine were drawn:

- determination of the symptoms created in a healthy person by the use of various substances;
- comparisons of these symptoms with those relative to known illnesses;
- the use of tested substances, appropriately prepared, in the treatment of a particular illness.

Returning to the concepts of his basic text, Hahnemann says: '... Whichever medicine contains, in the symptoms observed from its use, the greatest similarity to the totality of symptoms of a given case of natural disease, this medicine will be the most certain homoeopathic remedy for the illness ... A medicine selected in this manner produces its own artificial disease on those very parts and points of the organism now suffering from the natural disease ... The instinctive automatic vital force is from that time forward no longer affected by the natural disease, but solely by the stronger similar medicinal disease. Because the moderate medicinal disease is produced by a small dose of the medicine, it is overcome by the increased energy of the vital force and soon spontaneously disappears, leaving the body free from all disease...'

This statement not only encapsulates the certainty he felt in having found a new path, and, in his view, the only one to be taken in dealing with all diseases, but also introduces the new concept of dynamization, here translated from the German by the phrase 'the vital force'. It is important to ponder a little on this term as it is the cornerstone of homoeopathic preparations.

The author experimented on healthy persons with a wide variety of animal, vegetable and mineral substances, cataloguing the symptoms obtained and preparing his earliest remedies, and thus laying the foundations for the first written descriptions of homoeopathy. Once he had established that a particular substance had a specific effect on a disease, Hahnemann went on to the dynamization process. Starting with the mother tincture of the substance, the next step was to dilute one drop of the tincture with 99 drops of alcohol. After being shaken vigorously, one drop of this dilution was then diluted with another 99 drops of alcohol, and so on for as many times as was necessary to achieve the required degree of dilution. This method produced solutions in hundredths but, of course, this could be altered to tenths or fiftieths or whatever strength was required merely by varying the number of drops of alcohol. Each solution obtained would thus have a different degree of dynamization of the product.

To dynamize, therefore, does not mean to dissolve or fraction the initial product as much as possible. Dynamizing enables the substance – by dilution and the shaking given to each dilution – to release its properties, with an emphasis on quality rather than quantity.

The same method is still used for homoeopathic products, although obviously many more aspects are taken into account today than could possibly have been conceived in Hahnemann's lifetime.

It is easy to imagine the dust that would normally have been found in a laboratory as well as the spores and fungi present in poorly washed test-tubes which would have become part of the homoeopathic product and would have been 'dynamized' along with the product itself. The result, of course, would have been quite different from that being sought or, at least, would have considerably reduced the efficacy of the preparation.

Such dangers are avoided nowadays by preparing the products in totally sterile surroundings, with constant levels of temperature and humidity, using tinctures extracted from medicinal plants specially grown in unpolluted soil without fertilizers or other chemical products. Thus both doctor and patient can be completely confident of the purity of the curative product whose action will be based exclusively on the transformed original element.

From a diagnostic point of view, the practice of homoeopathy is not

*Opposite, a splendid field of lavender (*Lavandula angustifolia*), grown for the essential oil that is extracted and used in the perfume industry. The cultivation of such plants for their essence makes it possible to utilize land that is not suitable for other crops.*

restricted simply to the study of the actual disease but also takes into account the patient's state of mind, treating the person as a whole. Rather than investigating the illness or disease as something contracted by the person in question, it studies the actual patient. The diagnosis of a homoeopathic doctor is based on information that is quite outside the usual area of interest, and questions are put to the patient about his psychological condition, which, to anyone not familiar with the basic philosophy of homoeopathy, might appear irrelevant. In this way, a pattern of symptoms is built up, which enables the practitioner to prescribe the appropriately dynamized homoeopathic medicine which, in a healthy person, would produce the same symptoms as have been diagnosed in the patient.

Thus there is no standard remedy for all patients suffering from a particular disease but a wide variety of medicines which have to be selected carefully for each individual.

This is a remarkable innovative approach that is not always accepted by those practising allopathic medicine. Hahnemann introduced a detailed code of practice for all homoeopathic doctors to follow when examining a patient, which is best summarized in the following paragraph from the *Organon*: '...The examination of each individual case of disease demands of the physician nothing but sound senses and freedom from prejudice, attention in observing and fidelity in tracing the picture of the disease.'

He also stressed that mass-produced prescriptions should be avoided and that it was not possible to effect a proper cure without treating each case in 'a rigorous manner and on a personal level'. This is known as 'individualization'.

The opposition that has been mounted by the conventional medical profession against homoeopathy ever since its discovery, and which continues to this day, is motivated by two developments: the increase in the number of homoeopathic schools, and the high dynamization of the preparations.

After Hahnemann's death, many homoeopathic schools were established because of the novelty of the subject. With a view to giving it greater scientific validity, and in a quest for new knowledge, some detached themselves, to a greater or lesser extent, from the basic methodology created by its originator. The schools, therefore, became divided between 'purists' and 'non-purists'.

The purists adhered scrupulously to the rules laid down in the *Organon* in which Hahnemann had described how every disease could be overcome by a single medicine, by a single substance, used in different dynamizations for different degrees of illness. The non-purists, on the other hand, used a greater variety of drugs which were often linked with non-homoeopathic remedies.

This dissension, apart from causing considerable confusion, was to bring discredit on homoeopathic methodology as a whole; this discredit was increased further by the second development mentioned above: the high dynamization of the products.

Although the remarkable effects of vaccines had already been proved, the medicinal action of highly diluted and dynamized homoeopathic products has not been widely accepted. Even today, the fact that homoeopathy has not made greater strides, or won more

general recognition, is due to the use of these preparations.

It has been scientifically proved that by proceeding with the various dynamizations in hundredths, according to the method already described, after the ninth dynamization not a single molecule of the original substance remains. How, then, is it conceivable to use, as some schools do, dynamizations diluted to a millionth of a hundreth? With justification, the French school and its official pharmacopoeia only recognize as medicinal those preparations diluted to the ninth dynamization of a hundredth, all others being regarded as improvised magistral preparations. Yet facts have shown that even at these latter levels of dynamization remarkable cures have been achieved. Critics of homoeopathy claim that this occurs as a result of a 'placebo effect', that is by suggestion, the preparation itself having no practical effect. But how is a placebo effect possible in people wholly unaware that a dose of medicine has even been given to them, and how can it be beneficial to animals?

There is, unquestionably, something that remains in the preparation that eludes actual chemical-physical analyses yet finds its way into the organism and which is used for curative purposes. One theory holds that such a cure is not so much due to chemical interactions as to vibratory interactions that are typical of various organs and of various products.

These, by and large, are the reasons why homoeopathy and allopathy are so completely at variance.

Homoeopathic schools and hospitals have long been established in

*Pollen grains of sage (*Salvia officinalis*), a labiate plant well-known in both kitchen and pharmacy. Why should a man die who has sage in his garden? was the rhetorical question posed by the medical school of Salerno centuries ago to illustrate its countless medicinal properties.*

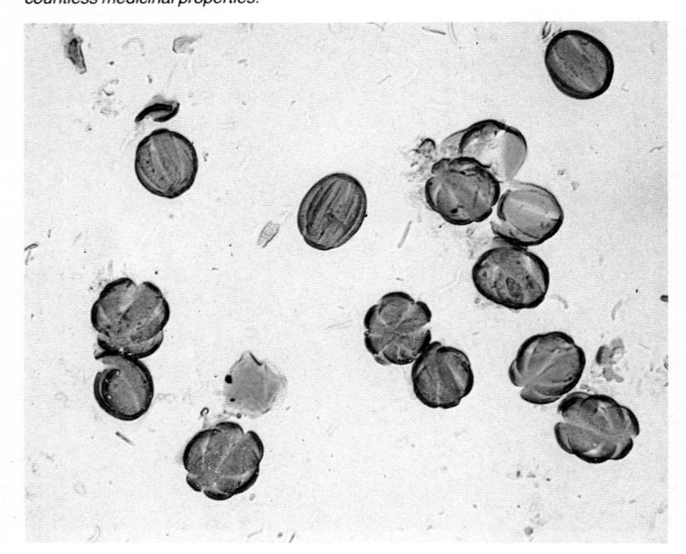

many European countries, and new ones are being set up all the time. Many members of the medical profession as well as the general public are showing increasing interest in homoeopathic theories and practices. Whatever the various reasons for this, they surely stem from a fundamental desire to return, as far as possible, to natural healing methods.

The large majority of homoeopathic preparations contain a plant base which, even if derived from plants containing toxic principles, yield many curative properties, and may be administered with complete safety. Homoeopathy, along with aromatherapy, is firmly establishing itself as a reality, furnishing phytotherapy with a serious scientific basis in a manner that, only a short while ago, would have been deemed impossible.

Aromatherapy

Aromatherapy, which can be regarded as a specialized branch of phytotherapy, concerns the use of essential oils for their healing properties. We have already seen how difficult it is to extract essences, how expensive they are to produce and how extensively they have been used in a variety of ways.

Nowadays essences are nearly always associated with perfumes, which do not come within the scope of this book, but what is seldom realized is that an essence can also be an active medicinal principle. Aromatherapy is often claimed to be a recent discovery, but it would be

*Ginger (*Zingiber officinale*) is an exotic plant used pharmaceutically as a carminative (to relieve intestinal gases). The drug, which has an aromatic odour and a pungent flavour, is found in the rhizome. The powdered root is frequently used in both savoury and sweet English dishes.*

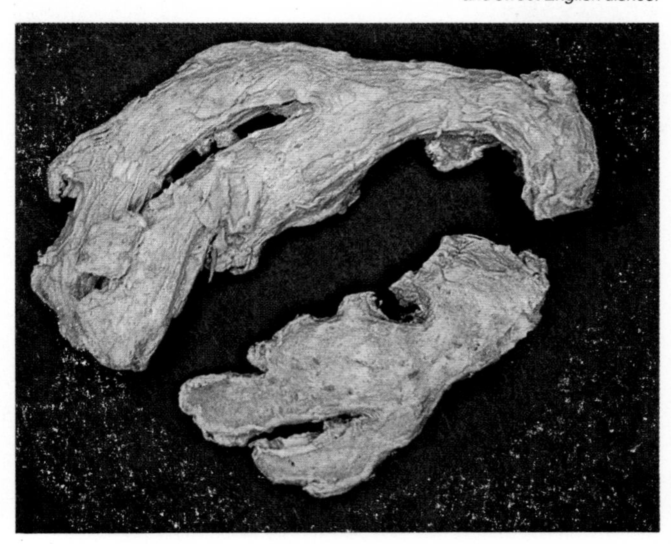

more correct to describe it as a rediscovery. We know that our ancestors used essential oils to embalm their dead, to render putrefied substances more tolerable, and as food preservatives. These examples not only confirm the fact that essences have always had other uses apart from the making of perfume but emphasize what is often a fundamental characteristic – their anti-bacterial qualities. It is obvious that any treatment in which essential oils are used either internally or externally requires a high standard of purity, which is not always maintained in essences produced for the perfume manufacturers. For this reason, all essences that are extracted for medicinal purposes must be obtained, by the processes already described, from plants grown under controlled conditions in which no chemical products of any kind have been used.

All essences can be quite simply divided into three categories: *terpenic, oxygenated* and *sulphurized*. The most important element of a given essence determines the category to which it belongs.

The quintessence, known in modern terms as the active principle, has been sought since the time of Paracelsus as the sole element in the entire plant possessing curative properties. Experiments on guinea-pigs and humans have now established that when only a small – albeit the most important – part of the total essence is used, the medicinal effect on a particular illness often differs from the anticipated result. It is evident, therefore, that an essential oil should be used in its entirety, rather than broken down into its various components, in order to achieve a more vigorous, total synergic action.

Despite the fact that aromatic drugs are recognized as having a valuable antiseptic quality, they are still not sufficiently utilized, even though the results obtained have been extremely successful. Almost any bacterial attack is treated nowadays with antibiotics or other similar-acting drugs. Consequently, although the infection is suppressed, the body becomes debilitated and has difficulty in restoring its natural defence mechanism.

Another factor to be considered is that the action of pharmaceutical drugs does not remain constant over a period of time, as germs become resistant to ever-increasing doses. This makes it necessary, therefore, to create new and stronger drugs which, unfortunately, still have the same harmful side effects on the whole system.

In contrast to this, the results of recent research now show that essences perform a specific antibiotic action and produce no secondary effects whatsoever on the organic functioning of the body. Given this quality (and clinical tests have left no room for doubt), they surely deserve wider use. As an example, essence of thyme has greater antiseptic power than hydrogen peroxide and guaiacol, due to its thymol content. A water solution of essence of thyme kills the typhus bacillus in two minutes, streptococcus in four minutes and the tuberculosis bacillus in one hour. Similarly, essence of lemon kills the meningitis bacillus in a quarter of an hour, and staphylococcus and pneumococcus in one hour.

It is interesting to recall that in olden days people sprinkled themselves with the essences of rosemary, thyme, sage and other fragrant plants as a protection against contagious diseases during

*Opposite, the lemon (*Citrus limon*) is not only a familiar fruit everywhere but also provides, by means of the* écuelle *process, a very delicate essential oil that plays an important part in the making of eau de Cologne* *(see p. 00).*

epidemics. The good sense of this practice is today fully endorsed, as is proved by our own current use of atomized sprays comprising a mixture of essences with a phenolic (carbolic acid) content which can easily sterilize a room full of bacilli. Were such a procedure to be adopted in hospitals and operating theatres, almost total asepsis could be achieved.

Furthermore, germs do not become resistant to the action of the essences, so that the latter's effect on them does not diminish during their active life. This is the determining factor in differentiating between essential oils and antibiotics. Although essences do not act directly on germs, they have an unfavourable effect on their habitat, causing them to disappear as a result of the unsuitable environment thus produced. This is the manner in which conditions such as festering sores and the early stages of necroses have been healed when treated with solutions of essential oils.

It has been suggested that the fragrance of the solution merely masks the foul smell of the sore, but this is not so. What really happens is that the essence suppresses the sore by blending with the products of deterioration to yield non-toxic compounds. In addition, many people have, at some time, suffered from a form of skin inflammation which, when treated with an appropriate solution, has healed quite quickly without the tissues being in any way affected. A great many tests have, in fact, been carried out on both superficial and deep burns, in all instances with positive results.

A further important factor, absent in other types of medication designed for the same purpose, is the speed of absorption, which makes essences particularly suitable for the comprehensive treatment of a wide variety of infections. This rate can actually be measured in many different essences and is an invaluable quality in cases requiring the fastest possible curative action.

It is only right to mention that many women have had unhappy experiences of this rapidity of action. After using a new perfume, they have noticed allergic reactions or other phenomena almost immediately on a part or all of the skin, which is entirely due to absorption of the essential oils. A simple test can be carried out by spreading some garlic essence on the sole of one foot; after only a few minutes, the breath will have the characteristic garlicky odour. The essence has been absorbed by osmosis and has quickly entered the bloodstream. This is clearly a vital factor in cases when speedy action is necessary, and oral or parenteral (otherwise than through the digestive system) adminstration of the medicament is impossible. Even disregarding the curative properties of the essence, it could become the vehicle for the administration of the medicament through osmosis.

Essences, however, are not only effective because of their bactericidal action. There is much evidence to show that their healing effect is, in fact, obtained by means of a range of activities. Essences can be categorized according to these activities: antispasmodic or spasmolytic, stimulatory, cicatrizant, antifermentative and hormonal. In this connection, it is remarkable how the traditional use of certain plants has now been justified by qualitative analyses of their essences.

It has been proved that many plants, for example, produce substances with hormonal qualities similar to the female ovarian

*Opposite, a camphor tree (*Cinnamomum camphora*) from which camphor, once widely used as a moth-repellent, is extracted. Currently, natural camphor is only used pharmaceutically in anti-rheumatic preparations, synthetic camphor having supplanted it in the battle against moths.*

hormones and, therefore, behave in the same way. Sage, hops, willow and liquorice have long been popular remedies to increase the milk-flow of a nursing mother or to correct and stabilize the menstrual flow, and science has now confirmed their efficacy and revealed the reasons for it. There are probably many other types of plant that produce such hormones, or others that are akin to them. It is important, therefore, that these valuable natural resources should be discovered, classified and used, under strict medical control, to avoid dependence on ill-tolerated synthetic preparations.

Many people have personal experience of the antiputrefactive and antifermentative uses of certain essential oil-producing plants such as fennel, anise and coriander, which are especially effective remedies against such complaints as gastritis and colitis.

Why do essences possess such curative powers? How can their action be explained? Science still has to find the definitive answers to questions such as these, although there is no shortage of theories. One important hypothesis, propounded by the Russian surgeon, V.P.F. Filatov, is based on the principle that every tissue, before it dies, attempts to prolong its life by producing special substances known as biostimulants.

In current pharmacology these substances are obtained from the female placenta, which produces them in considerable quantities. When used on sick organisms, biostimulants excite the organic defence mechanisms and thus encourage the healing process. It is deduced, therefore, that essences, too, when separated by the distillation process from the plant that has produced them, must themselves create stimulants, since they possess the healing action just described. This theory is supported simply by our sense of smell, as it is most unusual for the fragrance of a living plant to be the same as that of the essence extracted from it. This necessarily suggests that some kind of modification must take place during the extraction process.

Another plausible explanation, expounded by Georges Lakhovsky, is based on the rate of vibration. According to this theory, every organ has an established wavelength and any variation in its frequency could cause a specific disease. The essence would be able to reverse the variation, restoring the frequency to normal, and thus effecting a cure.

Without examining such theories any further, the fact emerges that essential oils act quickly and safely; so there seems to be a valid argument in favour of restoring them to a prime position in the pharmacopoeia.

In this broad survey of the efficacy of essential oils, one indirect consequence seems worth mentioning. Many of these oils are used in the cosmetic and perfume industries, which disregard their medicinal action unless that action is an obvious one. In such cases, a thorough check of the cosmetic preparation, in which the essential oil is contained, must be made because there may be a hidden secondary action, which may prove harmful. The cosmetic expert, therefore, must work closely with someone who has a sound knowledge of aromatherapy. This will ensure that the product is not only suitable for its purpose, but that any potentially harmful side effects can be recognized and eliminated.

Equally important is the commercial aspect of the production of

essential oil, which, although on the increase, is below the levels necessary for the correct and economic use of such oils.

Mediterranean countries that grow a variety of crops, often in excess of demand, would do well to devote some of their efforts to growing essence-producing plants. These would give good harvests and be economically worthwhile.

As has already been said, though, there is also a need for laboratories that specialize in the production of high-quality natural essences for curative purposes. The revival of aromatherapy marks the final stage in the affirmation of the scientific importance of this branch of phytotherapy.

Notes on cultivation and plant morphology

The importance of modern herbal medicine has encouraged many farmers to start growing medicinal plants. This has been done to meet the heavy market demand and to bring into production those odd pieces of land which, either because of their size, shape or unsuitability for other crops, have been left uncultivated.

The production of these new crops has not been easy, and attempts at cultivation have brought their own problems. Bans on chemical fertilizers in order not to adulterate or modify the medicinal compounds of the plants, the fear of a poor harvest, and the novelty of this type of cultivation have resulted in the importation of these plants on a large scale. For the most part, imports have come from those countries which, aided by government subsidies and a large and cheap labour force, have set aside a large section of their agricultural production to just such crops.

The cultivation of medicinal plants requires an in-depth knowledge of many variables which, unfortunately, is seldom found in any single area of specialized research. One of these variables is the choice of site, which must be based on the biological needs of each type of plant in order to ensure that its growing conditions are as similar as possible to those of its natural habitat. Temperature, the degree of humidity and the elevation of the ground are all factors to be borne in mind if the best possible yield is to be obtained. The reproductive phase and the best methods of propagating young plants must also be studied carefully. Last, but by no means least, is the question of what quantities of each medicinal plant should be grown in order not to flood the market. Some research into potential domestic and foreign demand is obviously desirable.

It is beyond the scope of this book to include a detailed study of the subject, but a summary description of plant morphology is given here, together with an explanation of some of the propagation methods normally applied in cultivation.

There are many very different types of plants, ranging from the primitive to the more highly developed forms. In the more primitive plant forms such as the algae, fungi and lichens the main vegetative body may be called a thallus. The more highly evolved groups, however, may be formed of three major parts: root, stem and leaves.

The root is the organ that anchors the plant in the soil and enables it to absorb water and dissolve nutrients: it usually consists of a main root and secondary roots. The root has a prospective capsule covering the apex of its growing point which is called a pileorhiza or 'root cap'. Root hairs, which are small extensions of single outer cells of the roots, have absorbent walls and grow out at different angles, and in various directions from the roots. Some plants, like the ivy, have adventitious roots, which are roots that develop above ground from any point except the main root.

Roots are divided into several types: *taproots*, if the primary or first root is more developed than the secondary roots that develop from it; *fibrous root system*, when many roots of approximately the same size develop; *tuberous roots*, when the root becomes an organ of reserve; *aquatic roots*, when they are completely immersed in water; *aerial roots*, when they are not in contact with the ground at all but absorb water from sources above the ground, such as the atmosphere.

The stem is the second most important part of a plant. It is an organ of support for the branches, leaves, flowers and fruit, as well as providing conducting tissue for the sap. There can be a main stem and secondary stems although, strictly speaking, the latter are branches which, like secondary roots, grow at an angle to the main stem.

Each point at which one or more leaves or new shoots emerge from a main or secondary stem is called a node; the space between two successive nodes is an internode.

The terminal bud is situated at the apex of the stem and determines its growth. Inside this bud can be distinguished the cataphylls, which are tiny leaves closely overlapping each other, while at its axil are the

A morphological study of a plant showing: 1. terminal (or apical) bud); 2. axillary bud; 3. petiole; 4. stipule; 5. leaf margin; 6. leaf blade; 7. venation; 8. stem; 9. main root; 10. calyptra; 11. secondary roots or rootlets.

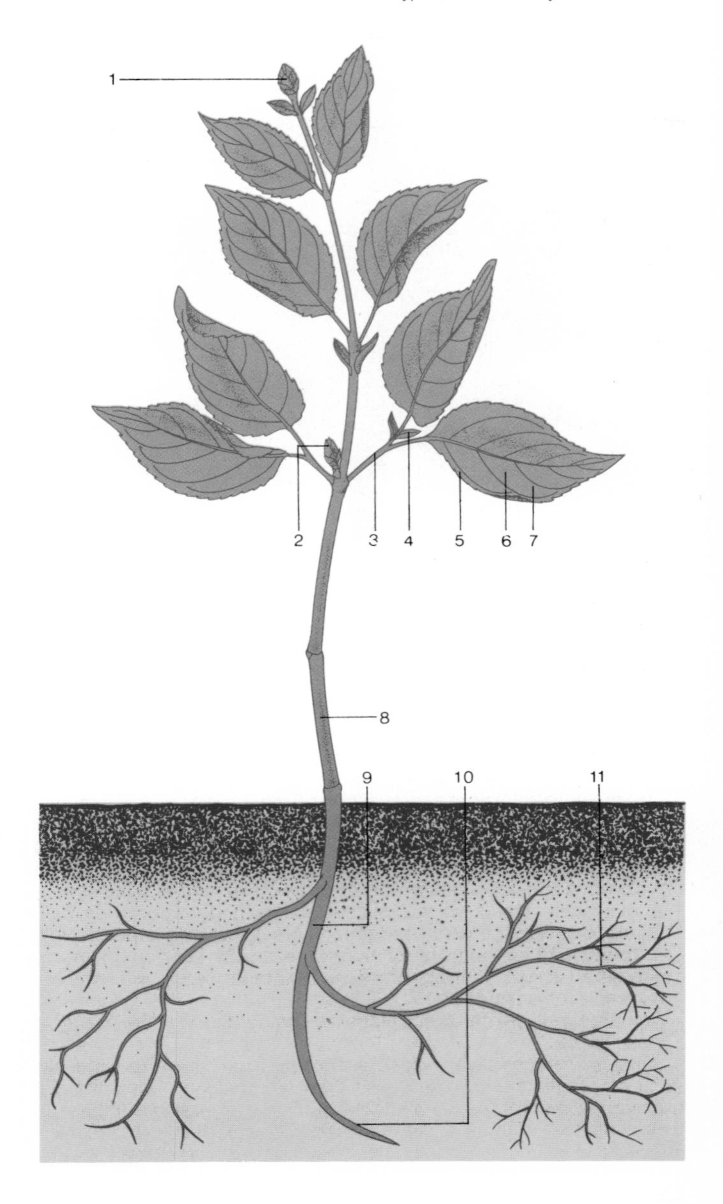

Section of a flower with petals and sepals: 1. style; 2. corolla; 3. petals; 4. stamens; 5. ovary; 6. sepals; 7. calyx; 8. receptacle.

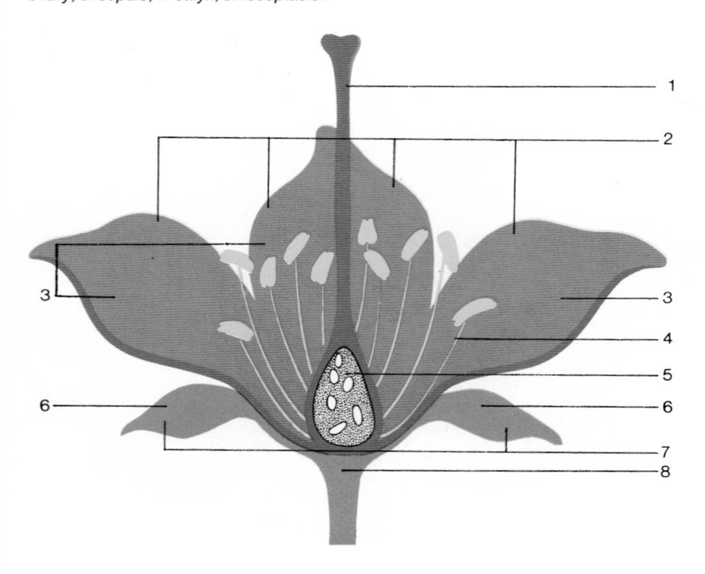

axillary buds from which the new branches will grow. As a result of overfeeding or injury, buds may also develop in places other than the apex. These axillary buds will become the terminal buds and so on. Stems of these new axillary branches may be classified as follows:

- Aerial (standard) stems which include woody or shrubby stems where all or part of the stem has become hard and woody (example: elm and blackberry); stipitate, borne on a very short stalk but with the sheathing leaf-bases above appearing to mimic a stem or trunk (example: palm); culm, the stem of grasses, usually hollow except at the nodes (example: maize); herbaceous, non-woody (example: *Euphrasia* or eyebright); stolon, an above ground horizontal stem or runner (example: strawberry); and scape, leafless stem arising from the ground and bearing flowers but not leaves (example: hyacinth).
- Subterranean stems which include rhizomes, underground horizontal stems (example: butcher's broom); tubers, locally expanded ends of rhizomes that are adapted for storage (example: potato); and bulbs, shortened stems to which thickened storage leaves are attached (example: onion and lily).
- Aquatic stems are of various types, all submerged in water (example: water lilies).

Aerial stems may also be classified according to other characteristics such as length of life, shape and branch formation. The pattern of growth of a stem or trunk may be described as *monopodial* if the main axis continues to grow in one direction but bears lateral branches at intervals, such as the fir tree; *sympodial* if the apex does not grow and

Leaves which differ in type according to margin shape; leaf type is determined by lobe depth in relation to the central venation: 1. lobate; 2. fidus or cleft; 3. parted; 4. sect.

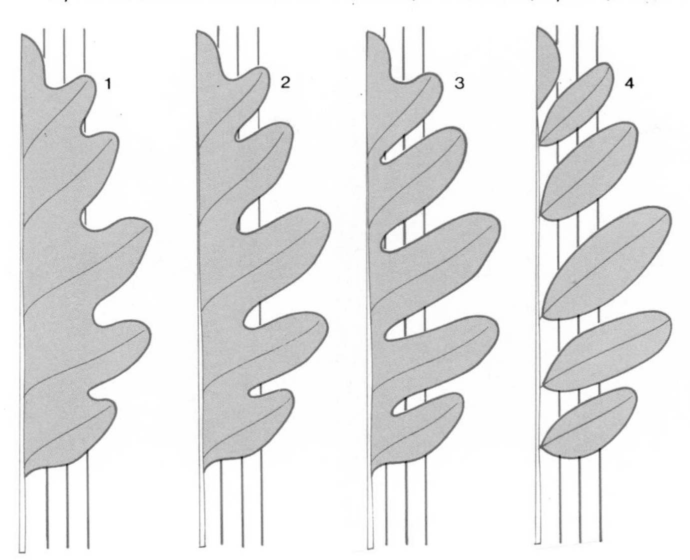

the branches below the apex develop with atrophied apexes, such as the lime tree; *dichotomous* when two branches form from the apex and these, in turn, fork out at their apex, such as the thorn apple and jimson weed.

A leaf is an appendix, usually green and having a broad flattened blade which is attached to a branch or stem by means of a petiole or 'leaf-stalk'. It is usually the organ of food manufacture for the plant, the centre of its chlorophyllous photosynthesis.

The main features of a leaf are normally the blade (lamina), petiole, sheath and stipules. It is rare to find all these features on any one type of leaf, but combinations of the blade with any one or more of the other characters are usually present.

The shape of the blade denotes the geometric structure of the leaf and may be prismatic, cylindrical or laminar (see pp.66-68). A petiole is an organ that supports the blade and joins it to the stem. A sheath is a petiole with a broaded base that either totally or partially envelops the stem. Stipules are two small leaf-like appendages at the base of the petiole which may remain or fall after the bud has opened.

Vascular tissues and their supporting fibrous tissues in the leaf-blade form the venation, or 'veins', and this is classifiable according to its pattern.

As with a stem, a leaf can be classified as to shape, length of life, margin, arrangement on the stem and its various modifications. The classifications that follow are only indicative and do not give a full description of each type of leaf.

Left, section of a bud in which can be seen: 1. cataphylls or cataphyllary leaves; 2. apex; 3. embryo stem buds. Some buds are used as a basis for glycerinate preparations in gemmotherapy, a branch of phytotherapy. There is a tendency nowadays to attribute remarkable curative properties to buds as this is the vegetative part of the plant.
Right, an example of a compound imparipinnatisect leaf. On the opposite page, various definitions of leaves based on their venation: 1. campylodrome: the venation curves up

The characteristics and divisions of every type of leaf are, in fact, different. Some leaves, for example, may have similar leaf-blades but their margins, venation or insertion on the stem will differ slightly. A single leaf may even be part of a larger, compound leaf. This is why some illustrations may appear to be the same but are classified differently.

The ideal classification would be one that took into account all the characteristics of a leaf, thus describing it fully in all its complexity. The illustration on page 64 demonstrates this. It shows a compound leaf with leaflets growing on either side of the stem, and with a terminal leaflet, which makes it an imparipinnate; the overall shape would be regarded as elliptic. It can, therefore, be classified as a compound imparipinnatosed leaf.

Although, unfortunately, it is not possible to enter into a discussion of the sexual reproduction of plants or their floral characteristics, certain forms of vegetative propagation must be mentioned as they are of particular relevance to the subject matter of this book. In some cases there are natural methods, such as layering, while others are the result of technical experimentation. The latter category has produced many techniques, the main ones being propagation by cuttings, air layering, layering (induced) and grafting, all of which are illustrated on pp.76-79.

from the base to the apex following, equidistantly, the line of the margin; 2. rugose: the venation is indented into theleaf blade; 3. reticulate: the venation has a haphazard appearance, like a closely-meshed net; 4. rectinerved: the venation runs in straight parallel lines; 5. venose: the primary and secondary venations stand out in relief from the foliar lamina; 6. pinnately veined: the venation resembles the barbs of a feather; 7. parallel-veined: the main veins run parallel over most of the leaf; 8. palminerved: the venation follows the hand-shape of the leaf.

Various examples of leaf outline, defined according to geometrical shapes: 1. orbicular: circular; 2. spathulate: shaped like a spatula or spoon; 3. rhomboidal; 4. pentagonal; 5. reniform: kidney-shaped; 6. deltoid; 7. cordate: heart-shaped; 8. mucronate: tipped with a short sharp point (mucro).

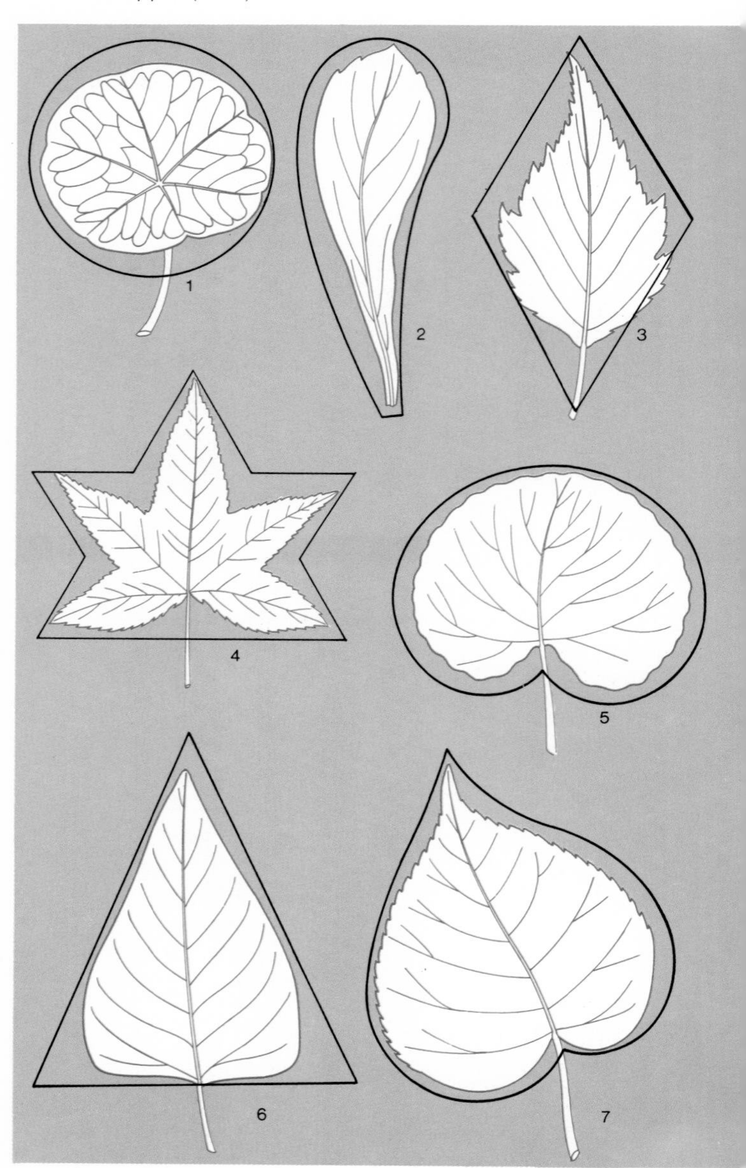

9. pandurate or panduriform: fiddle-shaped; 10. apiculate: tipped with a very small, sharp point; 11. acicular: needle-shaped; 12. flabellate or flabelliform: fan-shaped; 13. hastate: arrow-head or halberd-shaped but with the basal lobes pointed and narrow and standing nearly at right angles; 14. asymmetrical; 15. oval.

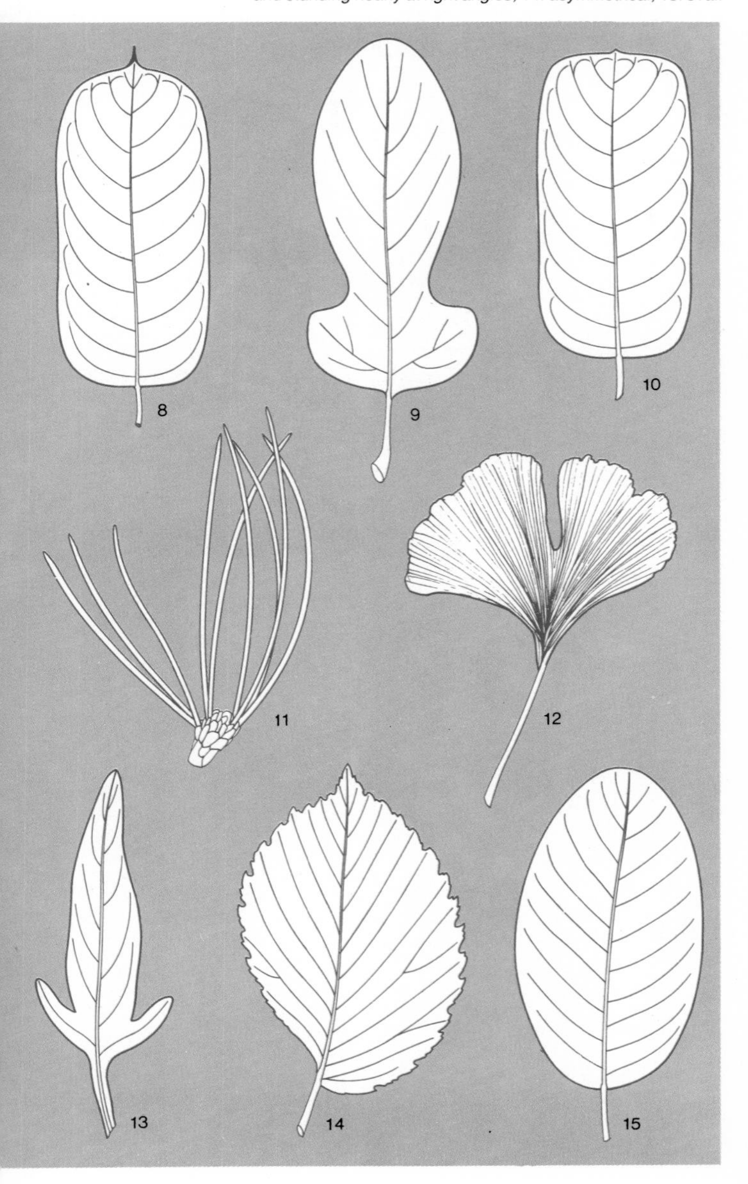

16. emarginate: with a slight notch at the tip; 17. ligulate or liguliform: strap- or ribbon-shaped; 18. elliptical; 19. obovate: having the general shape of the longitudinal section of an egg; 20. cuspidate: with an apex somewhat abruptly constricted into an elongated sharp-pointed tip; 21. ensiform: sword-shaped; 22. sagittate: shaped like an arrow-head, triangular, with the basal lobes pointing downwards or towarads the stalk; 23. cuneate: wedge-shaped.

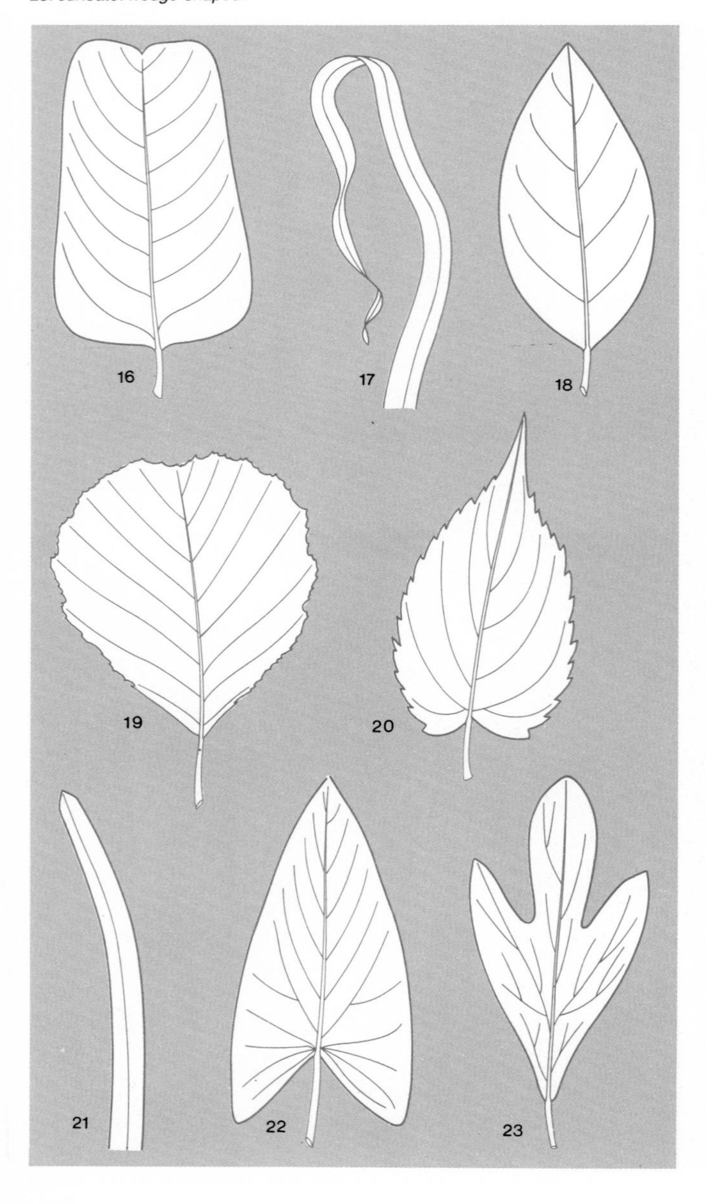

Examples of leaf arrangements: 1. imbricate: overlapping; 2. basal leaves in rosette form; 3. decussate: opposite, each pair at 90° to those above and below; 4. verticillate: arranged in whorls; 5. connate: similar parts united (the basal parts of two leaves almost forming a sheath around the stem); 6. alternate: arranged singly and alternately on opposite sides; 7. opposite: in pairs at each node, with one leaf on each side of stem; 8. distichous: two-ranked, with leaves on opposite sides and in the same plane.

Examples of different types of leaf margin: 1. dentate: toothed; 2. palmate-parted; 3. lobate, lobed, lobose or lobulate; 4. wide-serrate; 5. trilobate: 3-lobed; 6. serrulate; 7. crenate: edged with shallow, rounded teeth, scalloped; 8. lacerate: irregularly cut. 9. serrate; 10. pinnate-parted; 11. laciniate, pinnatified: as if cut into bands; 12. bipartite: split into two, almost to the base; 13. pentalobate; 14. runcinate: hooked; 15. palmatifid:

the leaf-blade is cut about half-way to form several lobes; 16. tripartite: divided almost to the base into 3 parts; 17. digitate: diverging from a central point, like the fingers of a hand; 18. palmatisect: the leaf-blade being cut to the base to form several diverging lobes.

Examples of compound leaves: 1. tripinnatisect; 2. bipinnatisect; 3. compound-elliptical; 4. imparipinnate; 5. paripinnate; 6. palmate; 7. trifoliate; 8. compound-obovate; 9. lyrate: pinnately lobed, the terminal lobe being much larger than the lateral lobes; 10. pinnatisect: pinnatifid but with cuts reaching mid-rib; 11. aristate or awned: terminal leaflet replaced by a stiff bristle.

7
8
9
10
11

Examples of different ways in which leaves are inserted on the stem: 1. amplexicaul: a sessile leaf with base clasping the stem horizontally; 2. overlapping sheathing: leaves partially cover each other; 3. decurrent: extending down and uniting to the stem; 4. sessile: having no petiole; 5. perfoliate: sessile, with a leaf base that surrounds the stem; 6. peltate: the petiole is in the centre of the leaf blade. On the opposite page, the definitions and descriptions of some stem and leaf modifications: 1. cladode: a flattened stem with a leaf-like appearance; 2. utricle: leaves with a globose shape.

*3. phyllode: a flattened, broadened branch or petiole that has become leaf-like; 4. spines and 5. thorns: resulting from a transformation in the outer tissue of a stem, leaf or branch-end; 6. ascidium: a leaf shaped like a cup or pitcher designed to capture insects; the pitcher plant (*Nepenthes*) is a good example; 7. tendril: a stem, leaf or part of a leaf modified into a long, slender, clinging, filamentous structure; this may twine around a support, within a radius of about 20 inches (50 cm), or it may have adhesive terminal discs for attachment to a nearby wall.*

Air layering. *Having removed the leaves from a section of branch, a slanting, upward cut is made into the wood. The incision is treated with a growing medium and covered with a plastic sleeve. After a relatively short time, roots will appear and the new plant can be separated from the parent. This method can only be used on large shrubs or medium-sized branches.*

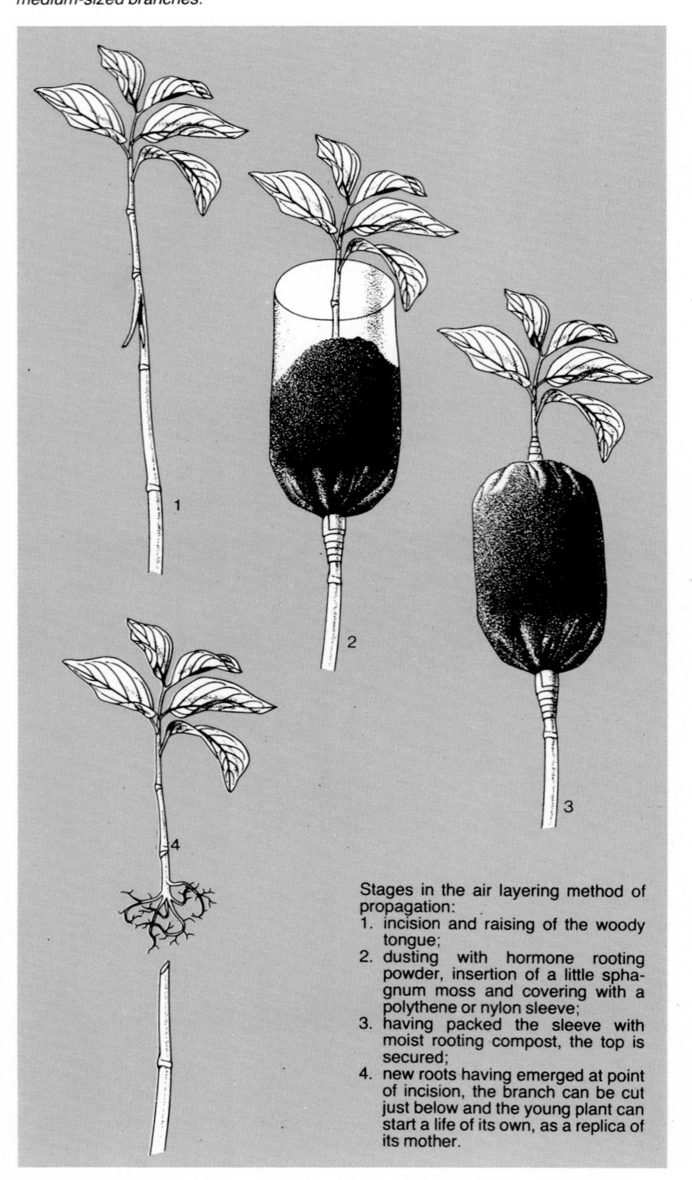

Stages in the air layering method of propagation:

1. incision and raising of the woody tongue;
2. dusting with hormone rooting powder, insertion of a little sphagnum moss and covering with a polythene or nylon sleeve;
3. having packed the sleeve with moist rooting compost, the top is secured;
4. new roots having emerged at point of incision, the branch can be cut just below and the young plant can start a life of its own, as a replica of its mother.

Layering. *This method enables roots to be formed on stems that are still connected to the main plant and can be carried out in any season. Having chosen some young, healthy branches, they are then bent and anchored into the ground so that the apex is standing upright. After some time, new roots and shoots will emerge and the young plants can be separated from the parent and replanted.*

Top, rhizome division. *Many plants can be propagated by splitting up their naturally-produced underground stems at the right time. Bottom,* softwood and hardwood cuttings. *This is the simplest method of vegetative reproduction. Pieces of young branches or stems, planted outdoors in a sheltered position, will slowly form roots. They should be cut, just below a node, to a length of between 6-16 inches (15-40 cm), depending upon the type of plant. This sytem can be used on biennial and perennial plants (such as geraniums and hydrangeas.)*

Top, leaf-bud cuttings. *A widely used method for many types of plants that do not bear visible buds at the base of their leaves. It is particularly successful if these 'eye' cuttings are taken when the plant is in active growth. The leaf is scooped out complete with petiole, small bud and sliver of wood from the stem; after dusting with hormone rooting powder, it should be planted firmly in a flowerpot with the appropriate compost for cuttings. The new roots will eventually appear at the base of the petiole.*
Bottom, leaf cuttings. *If the leaves are more than 4 inches (10 cm) long and thick and fleshy, they can be divided into two or three pieces, each one being treated as a cutting.*

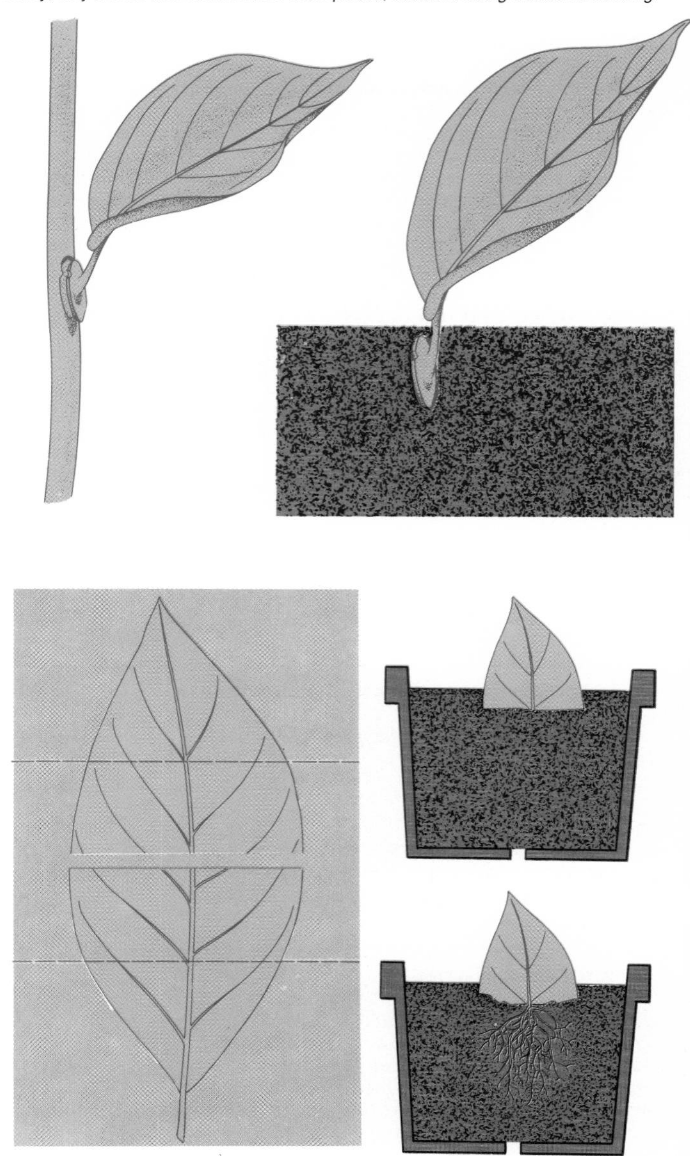

HERBAL RECIPES TO TRY AT HOME

Warning: In the preparation of these recipes great care must be taken to ensure that the correct plant is used, as any confusion could have damaging effects on the health. In an attempt to avoid this, the Latin name of each herb is given so that it may be checked against the corresponding entry in the book, where more information will be found. The other ingredients used in the recipes are all easily obtainable from good chemists or health-food shops. As these preparations are all made using natural, and therefore easily perishable ingredients, it is essential that they be covered and stored in a cool dark place, preferably in an airtight container. Long term storage is not recommended. Unless otherwise indicated, all the following recipes should be made up using fresh or, if these are not readily available, freshly dried ingredients.

Cough syrup

½ tsp lobelia (Lobelia inflata)
4oz (100g) clear honey
½tsp cloves
½pt (300ml) boiling water
Put the lobelia, honey and cloves in a bowl and pour over the boiling water. Stir and leave the liquid to stand. Take a dessertspoonful every two hours until coughing ceases.

Spiced peppermint drink for sickness and nausea

1oz (25g) peppermint (Mentha piperita)
pinch cloves
pinch cinnamon
1pt (600ml) boiling water
sugar to taste
Place the peppermint, cloves and cinnamon in a bowl and pour over the boiling water. Add sugar and leave to stand until cool. Drink one wineglassful every half hour until nausea subsides.

Tonic to calm the nerves

1oz (25g) hops (Humulus lupulus)
1oz (25g) lavender flowers (Lavandula officinalis)
1oz (25g) balm leaves (Melissa officinalis)
1oz (25g) primrose (Primula officinalis)
Add 1 teaspoon of the mixture to ½ cup of boiling water. Sip this amount slowly, twice a day, without sugar.

Treatment for halitosis

½oz (15g) wormwood (Artemisia absinthum)
½oz (15g) red sage (Salvia officinalis)
½oz (15g) angelica root (Angelica sylvestris)
½oz (15g) rue (Ruta graveolens)
½oz (15g) horseradish root
Place the above ingredients in a covered saucepan. Boil in 3 pints (1.5 litres) of water for 20 minutes. Cool and leave to settle until liquid is clear. Adults should drink half a teacupful three times a day, children half that quantity. Repeat until breath smells sweet.

Herbal remedy for headache and sickness

1oz (25g) betony (Stachys officinalis)
1oz (25g) rosemary (Rosmarinus officinalis)
1oz (25g) sage (Salvia officinalis)
1oz (25g) peppermint (Mentha piperita)
1oz (25g) marjoram (Origanum vulgare)
Mix the above ingredients in a large saucepan and boil for 30 minutes in 4 pints (2 litres) of water. Remove from the heat, and leave to stand until cool and clear. Take one cup three times a day until the pain is eased. This drink will also help soothe an upset stomach.

Tonic for purifying the blood

2oz (50g) elder shoots (Sambucus nigra)
2oz (50g) primrose flowers and leaves (Primula officinalis)
1oz (25g) dandelion root (Taraxacum officinale)
1oz (25g) young nettle leaves (Urtica dioica)
Use freshly dried ingredients for this tonic. Put 1-2 teaspoons of the mixture into a cup and pour on boiling water. Allow to stand for several minutes, then strain. Drink one cup of the hot liquid a day, sweetened with sugar. This tonic helps to eliminate toxic substances, such as uric acid, from the blood.

English tea

4oz (100g) raspberry leaves (Rubus idaeus)
1oz (25g) balm leaves (Melissa officinalis)
Use freshly dried ingredients for this tea. Mix leaves together and pour boiling water onto them, as for China tea. Add sugar if required, but no milk. This tea is a pleasant alternative to ordinary tea, and aids the digestion.

Yarrow tea

yarrow leaves (Achillea millefolium)
cayenne pepper
treacle
This tea relieves the symptoms of the common cold. Make the tea in the usual way, and sprinkle with a little cayenne pepper. Sweeten with the treacle. This will cause profuse perspiration and thus speed recovery.

Dandelion coffee

½lb (225g) dried dandelion roots (Taraxacum officinale)
Collect dandelion roots early in the year, dry them over a gentle heat and grind them to a powder in a pestle and mortar. Used in the same way as ordinary coffee, dandelion coffee is very similar in flavour and much more wholesome, in that it is caffeine-free.

Lemon rinse for highlighting blonde hair

2 lemons (Citrus limonum)
warm water
Squeeze the juice from the lemons, strain and make up to double the quantity with warm water. Apply to hair and leave on for 15 minutes, sitting out in the sun if possible. Rinse thoroughly in warm water. This rinse is also good against greasy hair.

Sage rinse for darkening hair

½oz (15g) sage leaves (Salvia officinalis)
2pt (1 litre) water
Steep leaves in water for 2 hours then strain. Pour over hair and leave on for half an hour then rinse out.

Herbal remedy for cystitis

1oz (25g) parsley seed (Petroselinum crispum)
1oz (25g) lovage root (Levisticum officinale)
2oz (50g) bearberry leaves (Arctostaphylos uva-ursi)
Use freshly dried ingredients for this remedy. Put 1½ teaspoons of the mixture into a pan with approximately ½ pint (300ml) of water and bring to the boil quickly. Remove from the heat and allow to cool. Drink half a teacupful twice a day until symptoms subside.

Footbath for colds and influenza

½lb (225g) freshly ground mustard seed
boiling water
Put the ground mustard seed into a muslin bag and boil in 2 pints (1 litre) of water. Add the liquid to a hot footbath to relieve the symptoms of colds and influenza.

Elder flower face mask

2oz (50g) fresh elder flowers (Sambucus nigra)
5oz (150g) carton natural, unsweetened yogurt
Mash the elder flowers to a paste using a pestle and mortar. Add this to the yogurt, mix together thoroughly and apply generously to the face. Massage in well and leave for 20 minutes then rinse off with cold water. The mildly astringent action of the flowers helps smooth the skin, bleach freckles and relieve sunburn.

Lavender pot pourri

Note: Flowers and leaves for making pot pourri should be picked when quite dry, preferably mid morning on a sunny day. Old or damaged flowers should never be used.

1lb (450g) lavender flowers (Lavandula officinalis)
10oz (275g) peppermint (Mentha piperita)
4oz (100g) rosemary (Rosmarinus officinalis)
2oz ((50g) summer savory (Satureja hortensis)
2oz (50g) benzoin
5 drops lemon essence
20 drops lavender essence
Mix together the dried ingredients, then add the benzoin, lemon essence and lavender essence. Placed in a shallow dish, the pot pourri mixture will impart its fragrance to a room. Store any unused pot pourri in an airtight jar until needed.

Fragrant herbal bath

1lb (450g) hops (Humulus lupulus)
1oz (25g) thyme (Thymus serpyllum)
1oz (25g) sage (Salvia officinalis)
1oz (25g) lavender (Lavandula officinalis)
Put the ingredients into a muslin bag and tie securely. Hang the bag from the hot tap while the bath is running, so that the hot water passes through it, extracting the natural oils and fragrance of the herbs. This bath will help relax tired muscles and relieve rheumatism.

MEDICINAL PLANTS

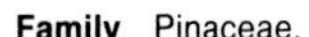

1 ABIES ALBA Mill.

Abies pectinata DC., *Pinus picea* L., *Pinus pectinata* Lem.
Silver fir

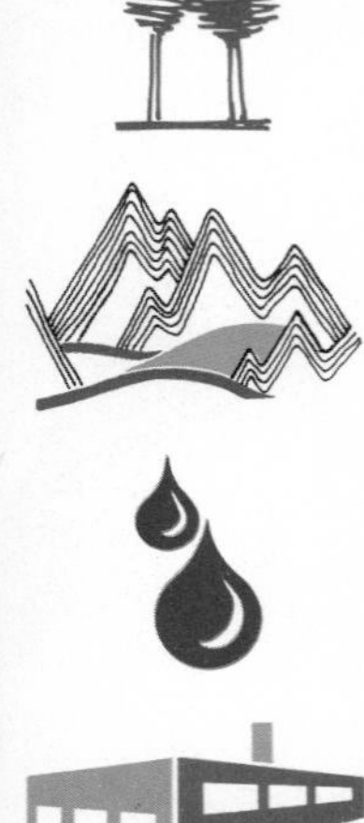

Family Pinaceae.
Description This tree, which may reach a height of about 130 feet (40m), has a pyramidal crown and a straight trunk with almost smooth, greyish bark. The branches grow nearly horizontally. The persistent, linear leaves (needles) have two narrow white bands on the underside and are arranged in pairs in opposite rows. The yellow catkin-like structure (male flowers) are cylindrical while the upright female flowers form an oval, greenish structure in the spring, ripening into long, brown cones by the autumn. The tree's native habitat is the mountain forests of Europe although it has been extensively planted in northern and western Europe and is naturalized in Britain. Gathering is done in spring or summer.
Parts used Buds, needles, bark, resin.
Chemical compounds Buds: resin, limonene, pinene. Leaves: glycoside pitch pine, essence. Bark: cellulose, minerals, tannin, phlobaphene. Resin: oil of turpentine, abietic acid (oil of turpentine, obtained by distillation, containing pinene, camphor, phellandrene, bornyl acetate, salicylic acid).
Properties Buds: antiseptic, balsamic, antibiotic. Leaves: expectorant, bronchial sedative. Bark: antiseptic, astringent. Resin: balsamic, vulnerary, vasoconstrictive, eupeptic, antiseptic.
Forms of use Suffumigation, decoction, infusion, inhalation, powder, distilled water, oil of turpentine in capsule form, syrup.
Notes The timber from this tree is especially sought after for its lightness and for its bark which provides very good extracts for tanning. The resin, obtained by tapping the bark, is used to make the turpentine known as Strasbourg turpentine. Essential oils from the buds are used to give many bath products their familiar pine scent.

---

2 PICEA ABIES (L.) Karst.

Abies excelsa (Lam.) Poiret., *Pinus abies* L., *Picea excelsa* Link
Norway spruce

Family Pinaceae.
Description From the Greek *abios*, a long time. A tall-trunked tree which may reach a height of 164 feet (50m). It is erect and resinous with a reddish-brown bark. The regularly placed main branches have secondary branches which grow upwards at first and then hang down. The short, straight leaves (needles) are persistent and grown in all directions, arranged uniformly on the main and secondary branches. There are male and female inflorescences; the small, male ones produce the pollen while the cone-shaped females are red and, unlike those of the silver fir, pendulous with caducous scales. The seeds are equipped with a membranous wing. This tree is endemic in northern Europe and in the mountains of the southern Alps. It is naturalized in Britain.
Parts used Buds, leaves, resin.
Chemical compounds Resin: essence, pitch pine, phlobaphene, tannin. The main compounds found in the essence are: pinene, phellandrene, camphene, bornyl acetate.

Properties Antiseptic, balsamic, expectorant, sedative, anti-inflammatory, antibiotic.
Forms of use Infusion, distilled water, powder, ointment.
Notes 'Burgundy (or white) pitch' is obtained by making an incision in the trunk. The distillation of the pitch is used to make oil of turpentine from which ointments are prepared for external application.

3 ACANTHUS MOLLIS L.

Acanthus sativus Dod.
Acanthus

Family Acanthaceae.
Description A plant usually found under cultivation rather than growing wild, it has a black, branched tap-root and a sturdy, cylindrical stem. The glossy, dark green basal leaves are large, oblong, supple and pinnatifid-sinuate. The white, purple or light blue flowers are arranged in a terminal pubescent spike among leafy bracts. The capsule is dehiscent and the seed ovoid. The stem may grow to over 40 inches (1m) in height. Commonly found in damp areas of low-lying ground and in gardens throughout Europe, it was naturalized in Cornwall but is very rare now. The leaves are gathered from sping-summer.
Parts used Leaves.
Chemical compounds Mucilage, tannin, glucose, pectic substances.
Properties Emollient, astringent, vulnerary, detergent.
Forms of use Infusion, trituration, fluid extract.
Notes Mallow leaves can be replaced by acanthus leaves for their mucilaginous content. It is said that the Greek architect, Callimachus, was inspired to create the Corinthian capital by looking at the perfect symmetry of an acanthus plant.

---

4 ACER CAMPESTRIS L.

Field maple

Family Aceraceae.
Description A tree that may reach 50 feet (15m) or more in height but is also frequently found as a shrub. Its bark has a rough surface and corky winged seeds arise from the branches. The opposite, leathery, palmate leaves have obtuse lobes and are slightly pilose. The greenish-yellow flowers grow in erect clusters. The fruit consists of two opposite samaras, each containing a flat, round seed. This tree grows wild in most of Europe and is a native of the British Isles; its favourite habitat is calcareous ground between the sea and upland or mountainous areas. It is often used in continental Europe to support vines and lends itself well to making hedges as it puts out a great many shoots which layer easily. The bark is gathered in March-April.
Parts used Bark.
Chemical compounds Phytosterols, choline, allantoin, tannin.
Properties Astringent, slightly anticholesterolemic.
Forms of use Decoction.
Notes The bark is dried in the sun and stored in a dry place. The wood is much sought after by cabinet-makers and carpenters because of its fine grain and very light colour. It is seldom attacked by insects. Knots and excrescences, due to defoliation, are often reproduced artificially by a water-marking process on thin veneers used in cabinet-making. It is a honey-yielding plant and, therefore, to be encouraged in agriculture. Even the European varieties of maple, like the American *Acer saccharinum* L., the sugar or bird's eye maple, produce a sugary sap but, if tapped, the life of the tree is endangered. The astringent properties of the bark have been used as an application for sore eyes.

5 ACHILLEA MILLEFOLIUM L.
Yarrow

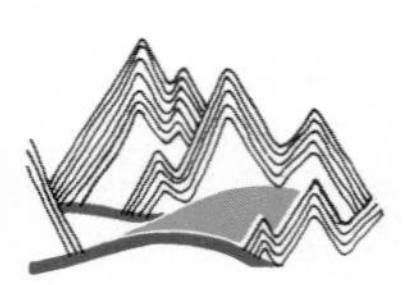

Family Compositae.
Description The genus is named after Achilles who used it to heal his wounded soldiers. A rhizomous herbaceous plant with a straight stem, which may grow to a height of about 40 inches (1m), it branches out at the top into several clusters of many pink or white heads. The dark green, pinnatisect leaves are finely cut and are pilose on the underside. They range from 1-2 inches (2-5cm) to over 8 inches (20cm) long and from ½-1½ inches (1-4cm) wide. The receptacle is covered in small green scales. The achenes are almost oval but foreshortened at the top. The plant is commonly found growing wild in the British Isles, southern Europe, Asia, Australia and North America. Its favourite habitats are untended meadows, fields, roadside verges and grasslands up to an altitude of about 6560 feet (2000m). The plant is gathered from June-September.
Parts used Whole plant.
Chemical compounds Achillein, choline, valeric acid, formic acid, methyl alcohol, and an essence composed of limonene, pinene, thujone, borneol, eucalyptol, azulene. It yields about 0.2% of essential oil, the density of which varies from 0.92 to 0.95.
Properties Antispasmodic, emmenagogic, cicatrizant, tonic, eupeptic.
Forms of use Infusion, tincture, fluid extract, juice.
Notes It is used in cosmetics as a distilled water. As it contains azulene it can be used instead of camomile. It is to be found in many alcoholic preparations. It should not be taken by pregnant women.

---

6 ACONITUM NAPELLUS L.
Aconite (Common monkshood)

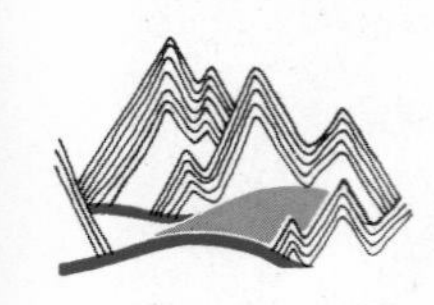

Family Ranunculaceae.
Description A perennial plant with a tap-root that puts out tubercles or 'daughter' roots with many rootlets. The green stem, which may grow to 5 feet (1.5m), is stiff, cylindrical and seldom branched. The leaves, which are dark green on the upper surface and whitish on the lower, are glabrous except for those under each inflorescence which are pubescent; they have petioles and are palmate-parted, alternate and incised. The dark blue, bisexual flowers are arranged in terminal racemes. Each flower has 5-8 petals and a calyx made up of 5 sepals. The fruit is composed of several follicles and the seeds are small, flat and rough. Usually seen as an ornamental, cultivated plant, in Europe it grows wild in high mountainous pasturelands. It is a native of damp shady areas in south Wales and south west England. The plant is gathered from summer-autumn.
Parts used Tubercles or 'daughter' roots.
Chemical compounds Aconitine, mesaconitine, neopelline, hypaconitine, indaconitine, aconitic acid, malic acid, acetic acid.
Properties Analgesic, sedative, antineuralgic, antirheumatic, antidiarrhoeic, antitussive in homoeopathy.
Forms of use Tincture, semi-fluid extract, syrup, titrated fluid extract.
Notes A highly poisonous plant! It acts on the nerve centres and paralyzes them. The symptoms of aconite poisoning are a burning sensation on the tongue, vomiting, abdominal pains and diarrhoea, leading to bradycardia, tachycardia, mydriasis, paralysis and death. Emergency antidotes are atropine and strophanthin. The leaves are less poisonous than the tubercles.

7 ACORUS CALAMUS L.

Acorus odoratus Lam., *Acorus aromaticus* Gilib.
Sweet sedge

Family Araceae.
Description From the Greek word *akoron*. This aquatic plant originates in India but has become naturalized in America and Europe, including Britain. The European plants do not bear fruit because they are probably triploids. Reproduction is by rhizome division. The rhizome is large, branched, cylindrical and creeping, and bears the scars of fallen leaves. The leaves can be over 40 inches (1m) long; they are only about 1 inch (2.5cm) wide with a central rib protruding on both surfaces. The stem is triangular with the yellow, cylindrical-conical spadix set at an angle and covered with tiny yellowish-green flowers. The spathe does not envelop the spadix completely and can easily be mistaken for a flower. The fruit is a red capsule with a few ovate seeds. The plant likes damp, marshy sites, ditches and irrigated fields. It is gathered in August-September.
Parts used Rhizome.
Chemical compounds Acorin, tannin, choline, essence containing asarone, eugenol, pinene. Cetylic acid, palmitic acid, vitamin B_1. The yellowish essence, which becomes viscous after a time, has a density of 0.36 and yields 1-4% of essential oil.
Properties Bitter eupeptic, antithermic, emmenagogic, tranquillizer.
Forms of use Infusion, tincture, fluid extract.
Notes Sweet sedge is used a great deal in the making of alcoholic drinks and in perfumery to give a bitter tang to the former and those special nuances to the perfumes; it is also used in toothpaste. The essence, which contains asarone, has a tranquillizing action. When very fresh, it can be poisonous. It is often adulterated with the rhizome of the yellow water iris (*Iris pseudacorus*).

---

8 ADIANTUM CAPILLUS-VENERIS L.

Maidenhair fern

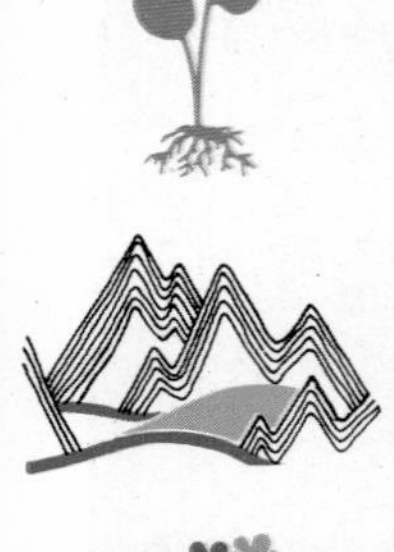

Family Polypodiaceae.
Description From the Greek work *adianton*. A perennial fern with a scaly rhizome and rootlets, it grows wild in fairly warm areas, in western and southern Europe, including Britain, near natural springs or among rocks and streams where water can play on it. It is also cultivated and grown as an indoor or greenhouse plant. The delicate, yellowish-green leaves are bi-tripinnate, fan-shaped, lobed and densely veined. The ochre-coloured sporangia are arranged along the upper edges of the leaves, on the underside, in kidney-shaped sori. In exceptional instances, this plant may grow to a height of about 20 inches (50cm) but usually remains at about 4-6 inches (10-15cm). It is gathered in June-July.
Parts used Whole plant.
Chemical compounds Gallic acid, tannic acid, a bitter substance, essential oil, gum, mucilage. Although the plant has a pleasant fragrance, this cannot be utilized because of the low content of essential oil.
Properties Antitussive, expectorant, galactagogic, antidandruff, detoxicant in alcoholism.
Forms of use Infusion, syrup, fluid extract, tincture, poultice.
Notes The galactagogic (increasing the flow of milk) and detoxicant actions of this plant are due to compounds which have not yet been isolated but there may well be some flavaspidic acid present. The pleasant-tasting infusion known as Bavarian tea is merely a mixture of ordinary tea, maidenhair fern and milk; claims that it is a diaphoretic (inducing perspiration) have not yet been tested.

9 ADONIS VERNALIS L.

Adonis helleborus Crantz
Spring pheasant's-eye

Family Ranunculaceae.
Description A rhizomous plant with a great many rootlets, it has a simple branched stem with light green, palmate, very incised, alternate leaves, either with a small petiole or sessile. It has a single, apical, yellow flower with a 5-sepalled calyx and many dentate, ovate-lanceolate petals. The fruits are greenish, pubescent achenes. It averages about 8 inches (20cm) in height. An uncommon plant, it may be found growing wild in the undergrowth of mountainous pasturelands of most of Europe, although not in Britain. The plants are gathered every third year in May.
Parts used Whole plant.
Chemical compounds Cimarine, adonidin, adonitoxin, protein, starch, choline, resin, adonitol, levulose, acids.
Properties Cardiotonic, vasoconstrictive, sedative.
Forms of use Infusion, fluid extract, powder, tincture.
Notes It is inadvisable to take adonis preparations in cases of cardiopathy, nephritis and aortitis. In all other instances it should only be used under strict medical control because of its highly poisonous nature. it is a rather rare plant and, therefore, completely protected.

---

10 AESCULUS HIPPOCASTANUM L.

Hippocastanum vulgare Gaertn.
Horse-chestnut

Family Hippocastanaceae.
Description A tree about 82 feet (25m) in height with a rough bark that has deep surface cracks. It has a thick crown and its opposite leaves are borne on long petioles; they are palmate-compound consisting of 5-9 obovate leaflets with acute tips and serrate margins. The fragrant pink or white flowers are bisexual and arranged in erect clusters. The tubular calyx has 5 lobes; its corolla has 5 petals; the androecium has 7 stamens with the 3 lower ones curving down; the gynaecium, with the ovary, has 3 loculi with a simple style. The fruit is spheroidal, prickly and trilocular; it contains 1-2 smooth reddish-brown seeds with a white mark. This tree originates in the Balkan Peninsula and was taken to Italy by the Sienese doctor, P.A. Mattioli, whence it spread throughout Europe to be grown as an ornamental tree on large estates and parklands and to line avenues. It is now naturalized throughout western Europe, including Britain. Gathered in summer-autumn.
Parts used Bark, pericarp and seeds.
Chemical compounds Bark: esculin, ash, tannin. Pericarp: ethereal oil, saponin, pectin, potash, calcium, phosphorus. Seeds: phytosterol, starch, sugar, linoleic acid, palmitic acid, stearic acid.
Properties Bark: astringent, vasoconstrictive, antithermic. Pericarp: peripherally vasoconstrictive. Seeds: tonic, decongestant.
Forms of use Decoction, powder, tincture, medicinal wine, ointment, fluid, dry and semi-fluid extracts; suppositories, poultice (in powder form).
Notes Horse-chestnuts can be made into a type of edible flour. If the seeds are roasted they can be used as a substitute for coffee.

11 AGRIMONIA EUPATORIA L.

Agrimony

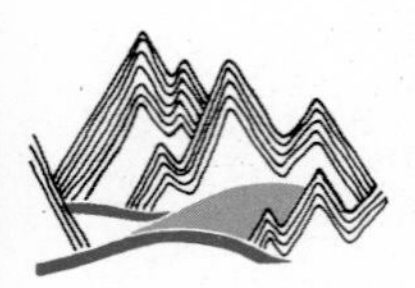

Family Rosaceae.
Description There is some disagreement as to the etymology of the generic name; some say it derives from the Greek *arghemon*, albugo – an eye disease which this plant can cure – while others maintain that it is from the Latin *agri-moenia*, defender of the field – because of its propensity for growing around the edges of fields. The specific name, on the other hand, immortalizes a king, Mithridates Eupator, who was experienced in herbal remedies and seems to have used it as an antidote to poisons. A very downy perennial herb, it has a small, contorted rhizome covered in rootlets. The erect, furrowed stem is nearly always simple. It has many close-growing basal leaves arranged in a rosette while the fewer stem leaves are alternate and pinnatosect with oval, dentate leaflets. Incised stipules arise from the axils. The yellow flowers, which have triangular sepals and obovate petals, grow in a terminal spike and open from the base of the flowering stem upwards. The fruits consist of 2 cone-shaped achenes with a ring of hooked bristles at the top. Commonly seen growing in the wild throughout Britain and Europe, in neglected fields, on roadside verges, stone walls and waste ground, this plant may grow as high as 40 inches (1 m). It is gathered in September.
Parts used Whole plant except the rhizome.
Chemical compounds Tannin, phytosterol, eupatorin, vitamins C and K, essence.
Properties Astringent, vulnerary, cholagogic, anti-aphonic.
Forms of use Infusion, medicinal wine, syrup, tincture.
Notes The bruised plant is used in veterinary work to heal sores. Its light, aromatic fragrance is lost in the drying process.

---

12 AGROPYRUN REPENS DB.

Triticum repens L., *Gramen caninum vulgatius* Mor.
Couch-grass

Family Gramineae.
Description An invasive plant with a slender, creeping leathery rhizome with many stoloniferous rootlets. The thin culms are glabrous and both sterile and fertile. The narrow, linear leaves are pilosect and slightly serrate with a short ligule at the junction of leaf-sheath and leaf-base. The flowering stems bear 4-9 flowers, each with 2 stamens and 3 stigmas, on terminal spikelets from spring to autumn. The caryopses are oval-oblong. This plant, which grows to about 8 inches (20 cm) high, prefers dry, uncultivated land, especially rough grassland and is found growing wild in most of Europe, including Britain. It is gathered throughout the year.
Parts used Rhizome.
Chemical compounds Starch, mucilage, levulose (or fructose), mannitol, saponin, carvone, a little essence, triticin glucoside. When burnt, the ash contains a considerable amount of silicon.
Properties Diuretic, emollient, lithontriptic, antiphlogistic.
Forms of use Fluid, semi-fluid and dry extracts, tincture, syrup.
Notes Apart from its phytotherapeutic value, this plant is used in the making of home-brewed beer because of the starch and enzymes present in its rhizome. In some countries, the young shoots are also eaten raw in spring salads, and flour is made from its seeds for a kind of bran mash for feeding livestock. A little sugar can also be obtained from it. After being cleaned and dried in a warm, shady place the rhizomes must be stored in a dry place to avoid germination. To obtain the starch, long boiling is required to break down the leathery membrane that covers the rhizome.

13 AILANTHUS ALTISSIMA (Mill.) Swingle

Ailanthus glandulosa Desf.
Ailanthus

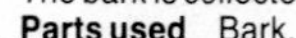

Family Simaroubaceae.
Description A tree with a greyish bark growing to a height of about 65 feet (20 m), with whitish lenticels. The leaves are imparipinnate with up to 12 lanceolate leaflets. It bears small flowers, with little bracteoles, in terminal panicles from May to July. The calyx is short with overlapping lobes and the 5-petalled corolla is light green. The androecium has 10 stamens with double-locular anthers and the gynaecium is formed of 4 carpels borne on a short stalk. The fruit is a membranous samara which contains a flat seed. The plant exudes an unpleasant odour. The ailanthus, which originated in China, has become extensively naturalized in some parts of Europe, including Britain, both as a garden and field tree. The bark is collected in spring.
Parts used Bark.
Chemical compounds Glucoside (not fully researched), resin, bitter essence, tannin, mucilage.
Properties Astringent, anthelminthic, antidiarrhoeic, rubefacient, emetic.
Forms of use Powder, fluid extract, infusion, poultice.
Notes Its leaves were once used as a yellow dye for wool and in paper-making for their cellulose content. The plant was introduced into Europe, however, to help develop the silk industry but was found to be unsuitable. The ailanthus has become increasingly widespread as it throws up suckers freely. Care should be taken in using this plant internally as insufficient experiments have so far been carried out. An excessive dose has first a purgative and then an emetic action.

---

14 AJUGA REPTANS L.

Consolida media Fuchs
Common bugle

Family Labiatae.
Description A stoloniferous, pilose, perennial plant, about 12 inches (30 cm) high. Its rhizome is short with several rooting runners. The basal leaves, arranged in a rosette, are oval, narrowing towards the petiole; the margins are slightly dentate. The stem leaves are small with almost no petiole, becoming bracts, sometimes coloured, as they near the apex. The purplish-blue flowers are arranged in spikes and arise from the axils of leafy bracts. The calyx is 5-toothed. The tubular corolla has 2 lips, the lower being very much larger than the upper. The fruit consists of 4 rough achenes. In Europe this plant is frequently found in mountainous areas and in Britain it often occurs in damp, grassy fields. It is gathered in May-early June.
Parts used Whole plant.
Chemical compounds Tannin, saponin, organic salts.
Properties Astringent.
Forms of use Compress, lavage, ointment.
Notes It is preferable to use this plant externally although the young shoots can be mixed with salads. In some countries it is gathered as cattle fodder. It is widely used in homoeopathy in various preparations against throat irritation and especially in cases of mouth ulcers.

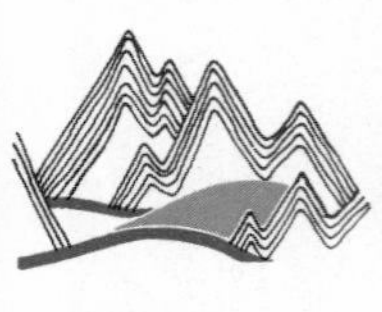

15 ALCHEMILLA VULGARIS L.

Alchimilla vulgaris Clus.
Lady's mantle

Family Rosaceae.
Description The name of the genus reflects the fact that this plant was once used in alchemy. A small herbaceous plant, it has an oblique rhizome with a number of rootlets. The kidney-shaped leaves, delicately pleated like little fans, are arranged in rosettes. The basal leaves are borne on long petioles but its stem leaves are sessile and its stipules are amplexicaul. The greenish-yellow flowers are insignificant; they have a calyx, 2 or 4 stamens but no corolla. The plant, which is native to Britain and Europe, grows to 4-12 inches (10-30 cm) high and prefers damp, mountainous sites such as north Scotland and Cumberland. It is gathered in summer and dried in the shade.

Parts used Leaves, stripped of their petioles.
Chemical compounds Tannin, salicylic acid, phytosterol, saponin, palmitic acid, stearic acid.
Properties Astringent, diuretic, tonic, vulnerary, haemostatic, tranquillizer, antirheumatic.

Forms of use Infusion, decoction, fluid extract, tincture.
Notes Apart from its phytotherapeutic use, this plant is used commercially in Switzerland in the blending of tea. In many mountainous areas, the young leaves are mixed with other salad ingredients. It has also given good results as a forage plant; cows have produced a higher yield of milk, and cheese made from such milk has a most distinctive flavour.

---

16 ALLIARIA PETIOLATA (Bieb.) Carara & Grande

Alliaria officinalis Andrz. ex Bieb., *Erysimum alliaria* L., *Sisymbrium alliaria* Scop.
Garlic mustard (Jack-by-the-hedge)

Family Cruciferae.
Description The name of the genus derives from the Latin word for garlic, *alium* or *allium*, because of the unmistakable smell of this herb. It is a glabrous, herbaceous annual, smelling of garlic. The leaves are cordate-ovate and crenate-dentate with long petioles on the lower leaves and shorter ones on the upper. The stiff, cylindrical stem is 8-28 inches (20-70 cm) high. The inflorescence is corymbose with white flowers. The fruits are erect siliquae which may be as long as 2 inches (5 cm). The black seeds are striate. This plant prefers uncultivated, damp sites; under cultivation, it grows best on the rich, alluvial soil of the plains or foothills and is found in Europe, Australia and Africa. A native of England and Wales where it is found in hedgerows and on the edges of woods, it is occasional in Scotland and Ireland. It is harvested in August.

Parts used Whole plant.
Chemical compounds Sulphurous essence which, under the action of myrosin, produces sulphate of allyl. Pectin, simigrin (potassium myronate), carotene.
Properties Anticatarrhal, vermifuge, antiscorbutic, anti-asthmatic, antiseptic, vulnerary.
Forms of use Juice, decoction.
Notes This plant was used in the past to obtain a particular yellow colour. The young leaves are mixed with other salad ingredients to impart a garlic flavour.

17 ALLIUM CEPA L.

Cepa rotunda Dod.
Potato onion

Family Liliaceae.
Description The bulbous root of this plant consists of layers of fleshy scales covered by white, yellow or violet-coloured tunics. The erect stem is hollow with a swelling at the lower end and can grow as high as 40 inches (1 m). The hollow leaves, which are almost cylindrical or slightly flattened, have a glabrous surface. The flowers, which have white or purple tepals, are clustered into rounded heads. The fruit consists of one capsule and 3 loculi with flat, black seeds. Although originating in Persia, it is frequently grown, both privately and commercially, in gardens throughout Britain and Europe for the edible root (onions). It is gathered from midsummer onwards, depending on time of planting.

Parts used Bulb.
Chemical compounds Essential oil containing allylic disulfides, sugar, inulin, quercetin, calcium, bioflavonoids. Distillation gives a yield of 0.015%.

Properties Diuretic, antibiotic, hypoglycaemiant, hypotensive, dechlorurant, anti-inflammatory, antithermic, lithontriptic, anthelminthic, antisclerotic, analgesic, antineuralgic, expectorant, antirheumatic, corn remover, cosmetic.
Forms of use Decoction, fluid extract, tincture, poultice, ointment, medicinal wine, juice.

Notes The juice is a moth repellent, rust-preventive and a polish for copper and glass. It will allay several types of hysterical attack and when rubbed into the skin it encourages hair growth. A few drops in the external auditory meatus will improve the hearing. It gets rid of freckles and soothes the pain of insect stings; when applied to the skin it repels mosquitoes and it aids scar formation on wounds.

---

18 ALLIUM SATIVUM L.

Porrum sativum Reh.
Garlic

Family Liliaceae.
Description The name of the genus derives from the Celtic word *al*, caustic. It is a very well-known, bulbous, herbaceous plant which grows to about 40 inches (1 m) high. The bulb consists of 8-10 curved bulblets (cloves). The stem is erect and hollow. Originating in central Asia, garlic has been cultivated in Mediterranean countries for many centuries and in Britain since the beginning of the 16th century. It is gathered in July-August.

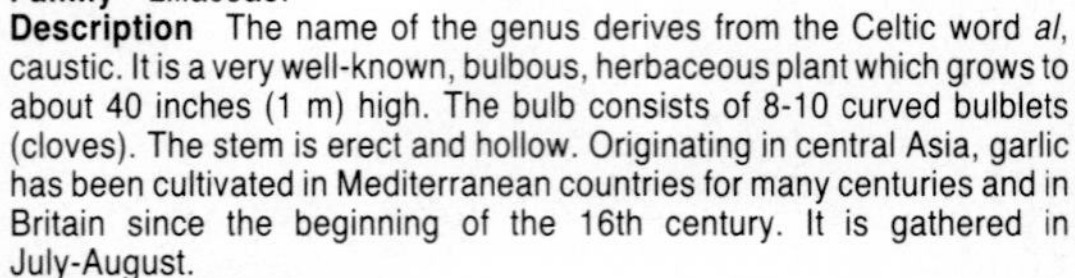

Parts used Bulb.
Chemical compounds Alliin, allicin, inulin, essence, vitamins A, B and C. Distillation gives an average yield of 0.25% of essential oil.
Properties Antibiotic, hypoglycaemiant, hypotensive, anthelminthic, carminative, intestinal disinfectant, antirheumatic, corn-remover, balsamic, antimalarial, rubefacient.

Forms of use Tincture, fluid and semi-fluid extract, ointment, poultice.
Notes The juice acts as an insect repellent and neutralizes the poison of their bites and stings; it is an excellent glue and it also enables holes to be made cleanly in glass. It was used during the First World War by the French for its antiseptic properties. The cloves have always been regarded as a source of strength. Chickens will lay more eggs when garlic is mixed with their food. When storing fruit, a few cloves of garlic sprinkled among it will delay rotting. It is also thought to have an anticancerous action. A decaying tooth will hurt less if packed with garlic pulp until treatment can be obtained. A little rubbed behind the ear will alleviate the pain of trigeminal neuralgia; and a little pulp introduced into the ear will ease rheumatic otalgia.

19 ALLIUM URSINUM L.
Ramsons (Wood garlic)

Family Liliaceae.
Description A perennial herb with a white bulb bearing a floral stem. The oval, dark green, glossy leaves emerge directly from the bulb on long petioles. The flowers, grouped in an apical umbel on the stem, are white and consist of 6 tepals; they are enclosed in a spathe which unfurls as they open. The fruit is a trilocular capsule containing angular seeds. It is often found growing in damp, shady sites throughout most of Britain and Europe, especially on the banks of streams, and is recognizable by its strong oniony smell. The stem can be as tall as 16 inches (20 cm). It is gathered in May-June.
Parts used Bulb.
Chemical compounds Essence, vinyl sulfide, salts, unstable aldehyde.
Properties Depurative, rubefacient, hypotensive, antiseptic, anthelminthic.
Forms of use Tincture, syrup, decoction, juice, pulp poultice, essence.
Notes Medicinally, ramsons can be used instead of cultivated garlic. It is currently much used in juice form for slimming diets. A few young leaves are sometimes used to give an aromatic tang to wild-plant salads. Its essence used to be used as a rubefacient in rheumatic diseases and, in solution, as a liquid household disinfectant.

---

20 ALNUS GLUTINOSA (L.) Gaert.
Betula alnus L., *Betula glutinosa* Vill.
Common alder

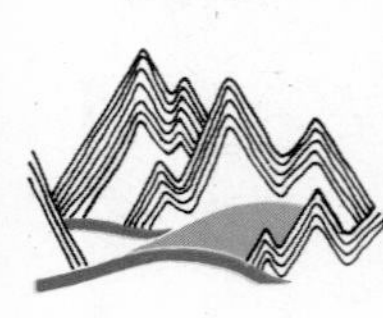

Family Betulaceae.
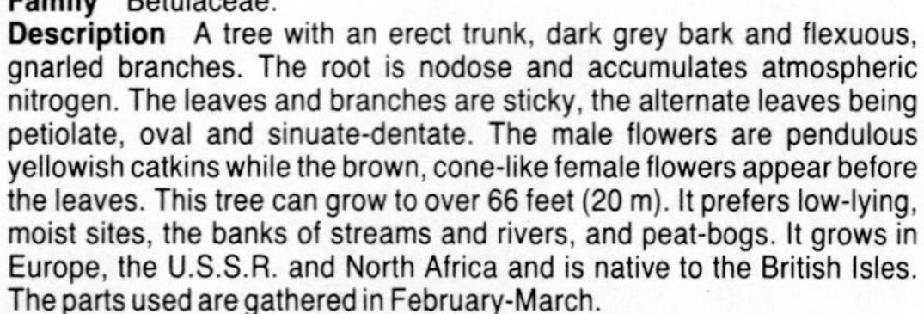
Description A tree with an erect trunk, dark grey bark and flexuous, gnarled branches. The root is nodose and accumulates atmospheric nitrogen. The leaves and branches are sticky, the alternate leaves being petiolate, oval and sinuate-dentate. The male flowers are pendulous yellowish catkins while the brown, cone-like female flowers appear before the leaves. This tree can grow to over 66 feet (20 m). It prefers low-lying, moist sites, the banks of streams and rivers, and peat-bogs. It grows in Europe, the U.S.S.R. and North Africa and is native to the British Isles. The parts used are gathered in February-March.
Parts used Leaves and bark of the young branches.
Chemical compounds Tannic acid, gluten, alnuline, fatty substance. In the bark: tannin, emodin, alnuline, salts, colouring material.
Properties Leaves: galactagogic, vermifuge, astringent. Bark: febrifuge, astringent.
Forms of use Infusion, powder, tincture, decoction, medicinal wine.
Notes Common alder-wood is much used by cabinet-makers and has the quality of being able to retain its hardness for many years when used under water (for example for sluices and pumps). Its bark is also employed in the making of printers' inks and its tannin content has been utilized in tanning leather, to which it imparts a characteristic dark red shade. Branches of alder leaves having a sticky surface, due to their gluten content, are used in country districts instead of flypapers.

21 ALOE FEROX Mill.
Aloe

Family Liliaceae.
Description A plant with a simple woody stem, its fleshy triangular, convex leaves have a spiny margin and are arranged in rosette form at the top of the stem. The flowers have short peduncles and 6 red tepals. The fruit is a trilocular capsule with flat, ellipsoidal seeds. It grows up to about 12 feet (4 m) tall and is to be seen growing wild along the shores of the Mediterranean and on the dry plains of East and South Africa. Its juice is collected throughout the year.
Parts used Juice of the leaves.
Chemical compounds Aloin, aloe-emodin, resin, essence.
Properties Laxative, cholagogic, stomachic, aperient.
Forms of use Infusion, dry extract, tincture.
Notes The aloe is also used in the making of some alcoholic drinks in which its bitter taste is blended with other bitter ingredients. Applied externally, it has an absorbent action on serious ulcers and purulent ophthalmia. It is also used as a cream for reddened skin. A decoction of its juice acts as a mosquito-repelling lotion.

---

22 ALTHAEA OFFICINALIS L.
Marsh mallow

Family Malvaceae.
Description The generic name of this plant derives from the Greek *althein*, to cure. A herbaceous plant with a whitish, spindle-shaped root and a number of rootlets, the simple or slightly branched stem may grow to a height of 6-7 feet (2 m), with palmate-lobate, irregularly dentate leaves covered in down to give a whitish surface. The flowers arise from the axils of the leaves singly or in groups of 2-3. Each one has 5 inner sepals, lobed outer sepals and 5 white petals tinged with pink. Its smooth, dark seeds are arranged like rays in the spheroidal fruit. This plant, a native of the British Isles, germinates easily in ditches or in moist ground near the sea and grows wild throughout Europe.
Parts used Root.
Chemical compounds Mucilage, starch, fatty oil, asparagine and betaine.
Properties Very emollient, slightly laxative, antitussive.
Forms of use Cold maceration, infusion, poultice, extract.
Notes Marsh mallow is also used in the cosmetic industry and in mouthwash preparations related to odontology. The decorticated root is sometimes given to children to chew when they are cutting teeth. The powdered root is used in the making of confectionery. The leaves are used in poultices for abscesses and are also distilled to obtain a water which, with the addition of camphorated spirits, is an excellent eye-lotion for acute or chronic eye inflammation. It is said, too, that infusions of marsh mallow leaves will give some relief in cystitis by eliminating the spasm. Enemas of a cold maceration of leaves make a gentle purgative for small children although care should be taken if it is taken internally.

23 AMYGDALUS COMMUNIS DULCIS DC.

Prunus communis Arch., *Prunus dulcis* Mill.
Sweet almond

Family Rosaceae.
Description A highly branched tree growing to a height of about 33 feet (10m) with a rough, scaly, greyish bark. Its greenish branches carry alternate, oblong, acuminate leaves with a serrate margin; the upper surface of these leaves is a glossy green while the underside is opaque; their short petioles and the numerous teeth around their edges contain a number of glands. The flowers, which bloom before the leaves unfurl, have a 5-sepalled calyx and a pink and white 5-petalled corolla. The fruit is an oblong drupe which has a green, pilose outer skin with a lateral channel; the woody and pitted endocarp has a reddish-brown seed, containing firm white pulp with 2 cotyledons, which has a distinctive flavour. Seldom found in the wild, it is often cultivated with olive trees in the Mediterranean area. The almonds are gathered in July-September.
Parts used Seeds.
Chemical compounds Fructose, fatty oil, emulsion, salts, vitamins A and B, protein. The oil consists of olein, peptone, calcium, phosphorus, potassium, sulphur, magnesium.
Properties Nutritive, emollient, laxative, vitamin-rich, antitussive.
Forms of use Oil, lactate, pulp.
Notes The seeds (almonds) are used in the confectionery and cake-making industries. Almond oil, which contains tocopherol, does not go rancid and makes an excellent skin lotion. For home use, only the sweet almond should be used as it does not contain the hydrocyanic acid which is found in the bitter almond. The residue left after the oil has been extracted makes excellent fodder for livestock.

---

24 ANAGALLIS ARVENSIS L.

Scarlet pimpernel (Shepherd's weatherglass)

Family Primulaceae.
Description The name of the genus derives from the Greek word *anagalein*, to laugh; this stems from an old saying that if chickens ate the plant they would cackle, that is to say 'laugh'. An annual plant with a creeping stem, the root is spindle-shaped and contorted. The leaves are sessile, opposite, ovate-lanceolate and entire with small spots on the underside. The flowers grow singly, on a long peduncle, being erect or recurving according to the stage of their maturity. The calyx is 5-lobed and the brick-red corolla is small, its tube cut into crenulate lobes with 5 stamens set at their base. The superior ovary consists of a single locule with a simple style. The fruit of the scarlet pimpernel is capsule-shaped like a tiny, closed urn, the upper half of which opens like a hinged lid to release its numerous ripe seeds. It is commonly found growing wild throughout Europe, its habitat tending to be any small piece of untended ground, preferably on rather sandy soil. A native of Britain, it is commonly found in England, Wales and Ireland, and less frequently in Scotland. The plant is gathered in August.
Parts used Whole plant.
Chemical compounds Cyclamides, in the spring; tannin, saponin.
Properties Antitussive, vulnerary, cholagogic.
Forms of use Fluid extract, poultice.
Notes Massive doses provoke polyuria and tremor. It is inadvisable to use this plant for medicinal purposes in the home.

25 ANCHUSA AZUREA Mill.

Anchusa italica Retz., *Anchusa paniculata* Ait.
Anchusa

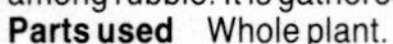

Family Boraginaceae.
Description A herbaceous, bristly-haired plant with a spindle-shaped root, its erect stem reaches a height of about 28 inches (70cm). The leaves are entire, the lower ones being ovate-lanceolate, acute and petiolate while the apical ones are sessile. The flowers are in cymes; they have a bristly-haired calyx with lanceolate and acute lobes. The corolla is 5-lobed and usually bright blue although occasionally purple. The fruit is a rough-textured achene. This plant, which is rare in Britain, can frequently be seen growing wild in Europe on waste ground, at the roadside and among rubble. It is gathered at the end of the summer.
Parts used Whole plant.
Chemical compounds Cynoglossine, consolidine, tannin, salts, colouring material.
Properties Antitussive, diaphoretic, depurative, diuretic.
Forms of use Infusion, tincture, syrup, fluid extract.
Notes This plant, when ground down, is used externally in poultices applied to areas of inflammation. A red colouring substance can be extracted from the root which, at one time, was used as a basis for various cosmetics. The tender leaves and young cymes can be boiled and eaten with other green vegetables. It is important not to exceed the prescribed doses in order to avoid any unpleasant effects due to the cynoglossine, which has a paralyzing effect.

---

26 ANEMONE HEPATICA L.

Hepatica nobilis Mill., *Hepatica triloba* Chaix
Hepatica

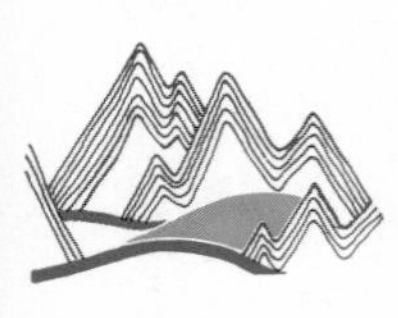

Family Ranunculaceae.
Description A herb which grows to little more than 4 inches (10cm) high, it has a rhizome with many rootlets which sends up a number of flowering stems. Its basal leaves are 3-lobed, cordiform, glossy and petiolate; they are green on the upper surface and purplish-red underneath. Each stem bears a flower which, in the wild, has sky-blue petalloid sepals; in cultivation, pink, white and other colours are also seen. The fruit of the hepatica consists of oblong achenes with a terminal style. This plant is frequently found growing wild in continental Europe, in damp undergrowth near trees, on calcareous ground. The medically useful parts are gathered in spring.
Parts used Leaves.
Chemical compounds Anemonin, hepatotrilobine, anemol, saponin.
Properties Antineuralgic, diuretic.
Forms of use Powder, ointment, oily solution, tincture, medicinal wine.
Notes A plant which has only quite recently become recognized in the pharmaceutical world, it had formerly been categorized, due largely to its appearance, as a remedy for liver ailments. In fact, it is poisonous with a rubefacient (counter-irritant) effect like cantharides and can only be used externally and, even then, under strict supervision. It is taken internally by some people in the form of a medicated wine as a diuretic but its use is not recommended because of the poisonous element already mentioned.

27 ANEMONE NEMOROSA L.

Ranunculus sylvarum Clus.
Wood anemone (Windflower)

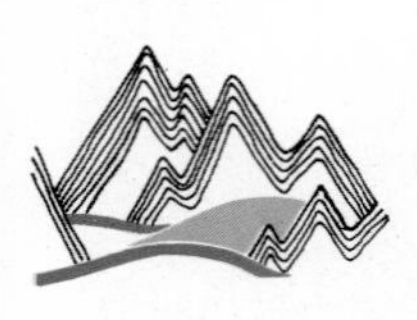

Family Ranunculaceae.
Description The name of the species derives from the Greek *nemus*, a wood. It is a low-growing herb with a creeping rhizome and numerous fragile rootlets. Floral stems grow to a height of about 12 inches (30cm) bearing white, pink or even purple 6-sepalled flowers. One or two pubescent, incise-dentate leaves carried on long petioles appear after the stem. The fruits are achenes. Its natural habitats are woodlands, foothills and mountain slopes and it is commonly found growing wild in Britain. It is gathered in spring, before flowering.
Parts used Whole plant.
Chemical compounds Proto-anemonin and anemonin.
Properties Rubefacient, toxic.
Forms of use Externally in allopathic medicine and internally in homoeopathic medicine.
Notes This plant is only used externally for rheumatic complaints in the form of a local friction, as it is caustic. It has been used as a home-made remedy for toothache – some of the herb was macerated in wine to make a mouthwash – but this is not at all advisable.

---

28 ANGELICA SYLVESTRIS L.

Imperatoria sylvestris Lam., *Selinum sylvestre* Crantz
Wild angelica

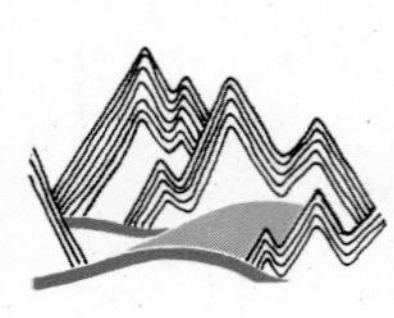

Family Umbelliferae.
Description The generic name derives from the Greek *anghelos*, an angel, so called because of its medicinal properties. A herbaceous plant, up to 10 feet (3m) tall, it has a large, blackish taproot. The stem is erect, branched, hollow and heavily striate. It is tinged with purple and covered with a whitish down. The lower leaves are bitripinnatifid; the others are oval, dentate and often cordiform. The basal leaves, like the upper ones, are sheathed. The greenish flowers are 5-petalled, have 5 stamens and are clustered into terminal umbels. The fruit is ovoid with flattened seeds. This plant, which is native throughout Europe, including Britain, is often found growing in moist fields and hedgerows, and is particularly common in the Fens. Harvesting is carried out in September.
Parts used Root and seeds.
Chemical compounds Essence, angelic acid, resin (Angelicin), tannin, pectin. The following have been identified in the essence: phellandrene, furan, methyl alcohol and ethanol. The leaves give a yield of 1%. The density varies from 0.80 to 0.90; it is soluble in 3 volumes of alcohol at 90%.
Properties Aromatic, carminative, emmenagogic, antispasmodic.
Forms of use Essential oil, tincture, infusion.
Notes The young leaves can be used as aromatic herbs in salads and the seeds are used by confectioners and pastrycooks. Angelica is one of the ingredients in alcoholic distillates such as vermouth and liqueurs like Chartreuse. Large doses have the effect of despressing the central nervous system.

29 ANTENNARIA DIOICA (L.) Gaert.

Gnaphalium dioicum L.
Cat's foot (Mountain everlasting)

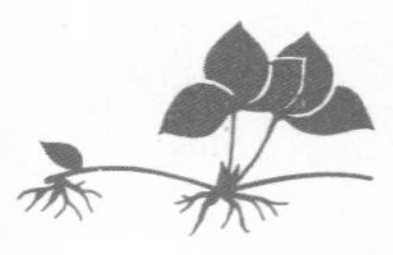

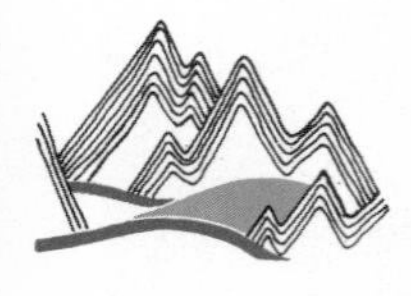

Family Compositae.
Description The name of the genus derives from *antenna*, as the pappus hairs of the florets resemble the antennae of a butterfly. A small, stoloniferous, perennial plant, it is light grey and cottonwool-like in appearance with erect stems of up to 8 inches (20cm). The spoon-shaped, basal leaves, in rosette form, are wooly on the upper surface but less so underneath. The stem leaves are alternate, lanceolate, whitish and wooly. The heads are clustered into an apical corymb. The flowers are yellow and tubulous; in the male the corolla is 5-toothed and in the female it is crimson in colour. The fruits are achenes with a protruding bristly pappus. Its natural habitat is among the wooded fields in the mountains of Europe, Asia and America, up to about 10,000 feet (3,000m). It is also a native of the heaths and dry mountain slopes of the Scottish Highlands and western Ireland. This plant is usually gathered in May, before its flowering-time which starts in June.
Parts used Whole plant.
Chemical compounds Tannin, essential oil, phytosterol, mucilage.
Properties Antitussive, cholagogic, emollient.
Forms of use Infusion, syrup, fluid extract.
Notes It is included in almost all chest remedies because of its high mucilage content. It is also used as an 'everlasting' cut flower as it dries well and keeps its colour. The plant can be propagated by division.

---

30 ANTHEMUS NOBILIS L.
CHAMAEMELUM NOBILE (L.) Au.

Chamomilla nobilis GG.
Common camomile

Family Compositae.
Description The name of the genus derives from the Greek *anthemis*, a little flower. It is a branched, erect, perennial herb which grows up to 16 inches (40cm). The lower leaves are petiolate and the upper ones are sessile; they are all bipinnatifid and lobed. Each head is about ¾-1 inch (20-25mm) in diameter. The peripheral female flowers are ligulate and white; those in the centre are tubular and yellow. The fruits are yellow-green, obovate achenes. Although it is rare to find this plant growing wild in Britain, it is widely cultivated throughout Europe in well-exposed, moist ground and in gardens. It is gathered in summer.

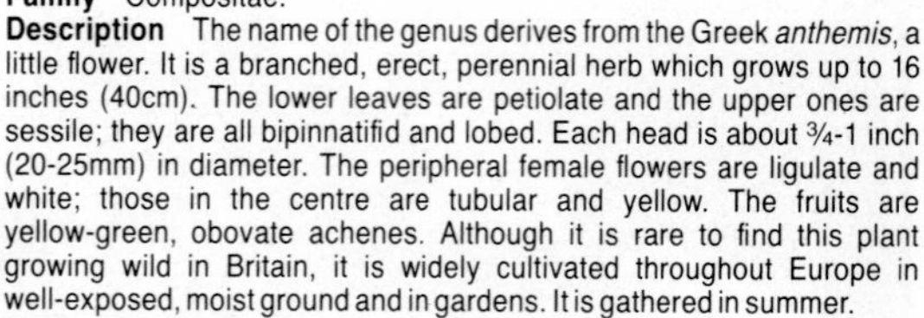

Parts used The head.
Chemical compounds Ethereal oil, isobutyric acid, methyl crotonic acid. Azulene, anthosterol, anthosterine. Glucosides, anthemic acid, free fatty acids, inositol. The essence is obtained with a yield that varies from 0.5% to 1%. It gives off a strong aromatic fragrance. It has a density of 0.90 and an acid reaction. It dilutes in 1 volume of alcohol at 90%.
Properties Aromatic bitter, emmenagogic, anthelminthic.
Forms of use Infusion, essence, tincture, syrup, powder, fluid extract.
Notes The administration of the active principles of this plant is incompatible with the administration of products containing extracts of Peruvian bark, tannin or silver salts (s. nitrate, s. protein, mild s. protein). It is useful to note that common camomile is not just a different variety of wild camomile – otherwise known as scented mayweed *(Matricaria chamomilla)* – but is a different species altogether.

31 ANTHYLLIS VULNERARIA L.
Common kidney vetch (Lady's fingers)

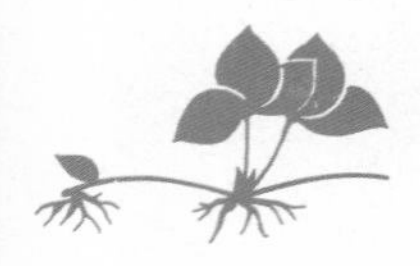

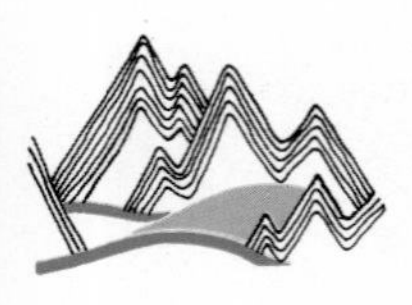

Family Leguminosae.
Description The specific name derives from the Latin *vulnus*, a wound, alluding to the scar-forming properties of this herb. It has a spindle-shaped rootstock and a procumbent, pilose stem more than 40 inches (1m) long. The lower leaves are simple while its upper ones consist of narrow, lanceolate pairs of leaflets about 1 inch (2cm) in length. The terminal leaf is broader and may be as long as 2 inches (5cm). The flowers are yellow, white, red or violet depending on the type of soil. They are clustered into heads with 2 palmate-parted or palmatisect leaves at the base. The corolla is yellow. Each small pod contains a single seed. It grows best on calcareous and sandy soils in hilly and mountainous districts. It is native to Britain and commonly found on sea cliffs. The plant is harvested in summer.
Parts used Roots, leaves and flowers.
Chemical compounds Saponin, tannin, mucilage.
Properties Astringent, vulnerary, antitussive, laxative.
Forms of use Decoction, infusion, fluid extract, poultice, tincture.
Notes These flowers dry very well and are, therefore, often used in arrangements of dried flowers with *Gnaphalium stoechas* (eternal flowers).

---

32 ANTIRRHINUM MAJUS L.
Snapdragon

Family Scrophulariaceae.
Description A perennial herb, it has a branched taproot and pubescent stem that is woody at its base. The leaves may have very small petioles or may be sessile; their arrangement on the stem may be whorled or alternate. The upper surface of each leaf is slightly pilose and the shape is lanceolate. The flowers, which range in colour from white through yellow, orange, pink, scarlet and dark red, are grouped in racemes; each one has a bilabiate corolla and a 5-lobed calyx. The fruit consists of ellipsoidal capsules containing oval, crested seeds. This plant may grow to about 20 inches (50cm) high. Although it not a native of Great Britain it is widely cultivated because of its attractive flowers. The parts required are gathered in summer.
Parts used Leaves and flowers.
Chemical compounds Mucilage, gallic acid, resin, pectin, rhynantine, bitter.
Properties Antiphlogistic, resolvent.
Forms of use Infusion, poultice.
Notes Effective with all types of inflammation, this plant can also be used on haemorrhoids where its decongestant effect is similar to that of *Linaria*. It was once used as a gargle in cases of mouth ulcers and internally for colitis and pyrosis. Externally, a poultice of the plant applied to areas of the skin affected by erythema is said to be most beneficial.

33 APIUM GRAVEOLENS L.

Sium apium Roth., *Sium graveolens* Vest., *Seseli graveolens* Scop.
Wild celery

Family Umbelliferae.
Description A biennial herb, it is about 20 inches (50cm) tall and has a taproot. Its stem is erect, ridged, shiny and branched. The glossy leaves are pinnatisect and incise-dentate. The greenish-white flowers are grouped in umbels of 6-12 unequal ray florets, each flower having 5 petals and 5-ribbed carpels. The ovoid fruit is flat with 2 brownish achenes. In the wild, this plant, which is native to Britain, grows best in marshlands, by waterways and other damp sites and is especially common along the English and Welsh coasts. It is widely cultivated but is less fragrant than in its wild state. It is gathered from June-October.
Parts used Roots, all green parts, ripe seeds.
Chemical compounds The roots contain: an essence consisting of limonene, sedanolic and sedanonic acids; mannitol, pentosan, mineral salts. The green parts: calcium, phosphorus, iron, carotene, vitamins B_1, B_2, C and K, proteins, glycidol. The fruits: apiine glucoside, oleoresin and a colouring substance.
Properties Diuretic, minerals, vitamins, carminative, aperient.
Forms of use Decoction, infusion, syrup, juice, fluid extract.
Notes This plant is used in '5-root syrup' (asparagus, butcher's broom, celery, parsley, fennel), an excellent diuretic. The leaves contain 0.1% of essential oil and the root contains 0.3%. It is rarely used as a carminative (a remedy to relieve intestinal gases). There is also a variety with an enlarged root known as celeriac or turnip-rooted celery.

---

34 AQUILEGIA VULGARIS L.

Common columbine

Family Ranunculaceae.
Description The generic name derives either from the Latin word *aquilegus*, something that draws water, or from *aquila*, an eagle, because of the sweeping curve of its pointed petals and spur. It is a herbaceous plant with a long rootstock and rootlets. The graceful, erect, branched stem is glabrous. The basal leaves are biternate with green cuneate-crenate segments and a pubescent petiole. The bluish-purple flowers are in apical agglomerates, each having 5 sepals, 5 petals and a hooked spur. The fruits are one-follicled, terminating in a point, and contain many smooth, shiny seeds. The plant grows wild in most of Europe on mountain slopes, in woodlands, copses and in shady sites in damp, hilly areas, preferably on calcareous soil. Although a native of Britain, especially found in the south of England, it is uncommon in the wild though often cultivated in gardens. It grows to about 40 inches (1m) or more. It is gathered from spring-autumn.

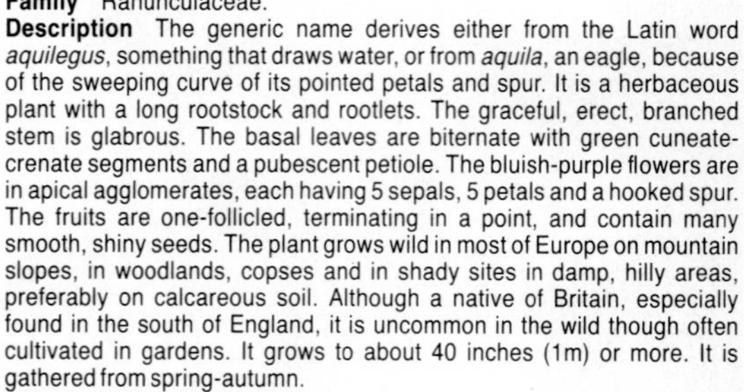

Parts used Whole plant.
Chemical compounds Aquilegine, cyanogenetic glycoside, emulsin, enzyme.
Properties Depurative, diuretic, diaphoretic, urocolitic.
Forms of use Infusion, tincture, distilled water.
Notes This is now a protected plant in the wild. In any case, it should never be used in home-made remedies because the presence of hydrocyanic acid makes it dangerous. It has been used in homoeopathy, in various preparations for affections of the nervous system. It can be applied externally in poultices to treat the commoner skin diseases.

35 ARACHIS HYPOGAEA L.
Groundnut

Family Leguminosae.
Description An erect, tufted, herbaceous plant, it is about 20-35 inches (50-90cm) high. Its leaves consist of 4 sessile oval segments, arranged in pairs on a long petiole, the flowers arising from the axils. These have a tubular calyx and a corolla consisting of a standard (vexillum), wings and carina. The petals are yellow with reddish striations. The stalk of the ovary is elongated in order to deposit its fruit on the ground. The fruit consists of a closed shell containing up to 4 rough, fibrous seeds. This plant prefers a warm, moist atmosphere typical of tropical areas but will bear fruit even in a temperate climate. It is cultivated for groundnuts in southern Europe and only 'rogue' plants are found growing wild. The crop is harvested in September.
Parts used Fruit.
Chemical compounds Starch, sugar, choline, arachin, oil, proteins, betaine.
Properties Nutritive, fluidifier.
Forms of use Flour, peanut butter, margarine, roasted or salted nuts.
Notes Extensively used to obtain oil for industry, human foodstuffs and pharmaceuticals such as anticholesterolaemic substances. It is often adulterated with sesame and cotton oils. Groundnut oil is composed of oleic, palmitic, stearic, eicosanoic, myristic and lignoceric acids. An excellent coffee substitute is made from the roasted seeds (peanuts). The flour is used a great deal for diabetics in prepared foodstuffs such as biscuits and sweetmeats.

---

36 ARBUTUS UNEDO L.
Arbutus (Strawberry tree)

Family Ericaceae.
Description A glabrous shrub, it usually grows to 15-20 feet (4.5-6m) high. The main stem is erect and branched with a reddish bark. The oblong, elliptical leaves are alternate, persistent and leathery with a finely dentate margin. The pink or white flowers are borne in pendulous racemes. The rotund, warty berries are a reddish-brown colour and contain a yellow pulp. This plant grows on the rocky shores of the Mediterranean (especially Liguria and Sardinia), in southern Europe, Africa and Australia; it also grows wild in north west Ireland. The parts required for medicinal purposes are gathered in July-August.
Parts used Leaves.
Chemical compounds Arbusterine, tannin, gallic acid, oil of wintergreen.
Properties Astringent, diuretic, renal antiseptic.
Forms of use Decoction, fluid extract.
Notes The fruit averages a 20% sugar content and is used to make delicious and nourishing jams and preserves. An excellent alcoholic distillate and aromatic vinegar can also be made from the fruit. Its numerous seeds are rich in fatty oil which unfortunately cannot be used.

37 ARCTIUM LAPPA L.

Lappa major Gaert., *Lappa tomentosa* Lam., *Arctium majus* Bernh.

Great burdock

Family Compositae.
Description The generic name derives from the Greek *arktos*, a bear, alluding to the rough burrs, and the specific name from *lappa*, to seize, referring to the 'hugging' propensity of the burrs. A biennial plant, which only puts up its basal leaves in the first year, it has a brown, branched taproot which has a distinctive smell. The branched stem can grow to a height of about 7 feet (2m) and ¾-1¼ inches (2-3cm) in thickness. The basal leaves, which are larger than the stem leaves, may grow to 20 inches (50cm) long and 16 inches (40cm) wide. The heads are globose, arranged in apical clusters, with scaly bracts ending in hooked tips except in the centre. The flowers are purple. The plant prefers waste ground and calcareous soil. There are many varieties and it is to be found wild throughout Europe, America and Asia. In Britain it is most common in southern England, but absent from Scotland and northern England. It is gathered in summer and dries quickly.
Parts used Root and leaves.
Chemical compounds Inulin, lappoline, essential oil, bitter principle, sugar, antibiotic, compounds of calcium and magnesium.
Properties Root: dermatopathic, diaphoretic, hypoglycaemic. Leaves: vulnerary, dermatopathic.
Forms of use Decoction, powder, juice, poultice, ointment.
Notes The young, first-year roots are boiled and eaten as a root vegetable in some places, as are the fleshy, young petioles of the basal leaves. The juice of this plant, when used as a friction, has a stimulating action against baldness.

---

38 ARCTOSTAPHYLOS UVA-URSI (L.) Spr.

Arbutus uva-ursi L.

Bearberry

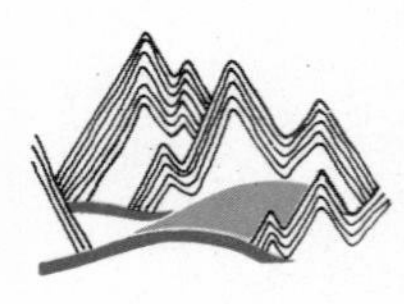

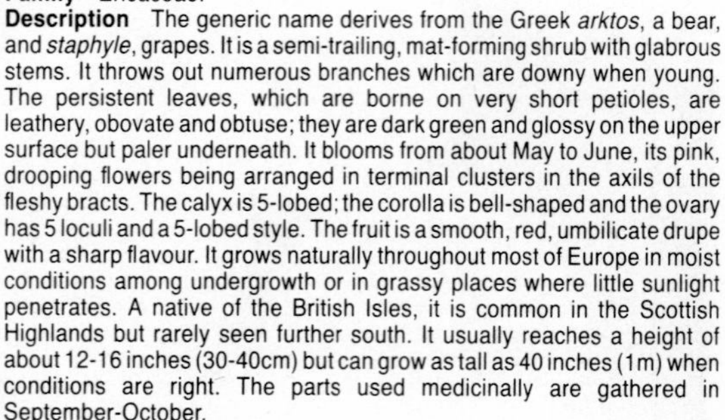

Family Ericaceae.
Description The generic name derives from the Greek *arktos*, a bear, and *staphyle*, grapes. It is a semi-trailing, mat-forming shrub with glabrous stems. It throws out numerous branches which are downy when young. The persistent leaves, which are borne on very short petioles, are leathery, obovate and obtuse; they are dark green and glossy on the upper surface but paler underneath. It blooms from about May to June, its pink, drooping flowers being arranged in terminal clusters in the axils of the fleshy bracts. The calyx is 5-lobed; the corolla is bell-shaped and the ovary has 5 loculi and a 5-lobed style. The fruit is a smooth, red, umbilicate drupe with a sharp flavour. It grows naturally throughout most of Europe in moist conditions among undergrowth or in grassy places where little sunlight penetrates. A native of the British Isles, it is common in the Scottish Highlands but rarely seen further south. It usually reaches a height of about 12-16 inches (30-40cm) but can grow as tall as 40 inches (1m) when conditions are right. The parts used medicinally are gathered in September-October.

Parts used Leaves.
Chemical compounds Arbutin and methylarbutin glucosides, ericoline, ursolic acid, tannin, gallic acid, citric acid, quercetin essence.
Properties Diuretic, astringent, lithontriptic, renal antiphlogistic.
Forms of use Decoction, fluid extract.
Notes The leaves are often adulterated with red myrtle, box, dark myrtle and common myrtle leaves. Bearberry leaves are used as an aromatic in pipe tobacco while the fruit is used in home-made jams.

39 ARISTOLOCHIA ROTUNDA L.
Snakeroot

Family Aristolochiaceae.
Description The generic name derives from the Greek *lochos*, parturition, a herbal aid to childbirth. It has a globose, tuberous rootstock with a great many rootlets. The stems emerge from the root with a few erect, delicate, simple branches to reach a height of about 20 inches (50cm). The ovate-cordate leaves are entire, reticulate, sessile and amplexicaul. The yellow flowers, which arise from the leaf axils on a short pedicel, terminate in a deep-coloured oblong, emarginate limb. The fruit is ovoid, with lines running lengthways, and contains numerous albuminous seeds. This plant is often found in southern Europe growing by the roadside and in fields and meadows although less frequently than its close relation *Aristolochia clematitis* (birthwort) which grows extensively in Europe. It is extremely scarce in Britain. The roots are dug up in May.
Parts used Root.
Chemical compounds Aristolochic acid, humin, tannin, sugars, malic acid, colouring substance.
Properties Bronchosedative, antitussive, emmenagogic, vulnerary.
Forms of use Infusion, tincture, powder, fluid extract.
Notes If the root is taken in strong doses the results can be drastic; it can provoke abortion as well as poisoning with inflammation of the mucuous membranes, enteritis and vomiting, resulting in respiratory paralysis. A decoction can be used externally on ulcers that are proving difficult to heal or, in the case of a sacral fistula, in a hip-bath. Good results have also been obtained in cases of eczema and other skin complaints.

---

40 ARNICA MONTANA L.
Doronicum oppositifolium Lam., *Doronicum arnica* Desf.
Arnica

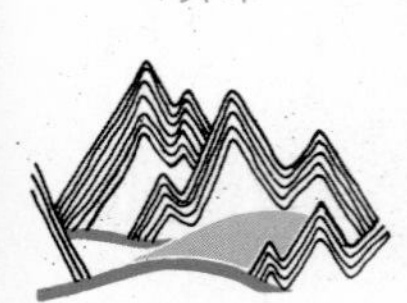

Family Compositae.
Description The name derives from the Greek *ptarmikos*, sternutatory, because it causes sneezing. It is a perennial, rhizomatose herb reaching an average height of 8-12 inches (20-30cm). The rhizome tends to grow horizontally. The pilose stem is stiff and usually simple. The leathery, elliptical leaves are sessile, glabrous on the underside, 5-veined and entire, forming a basal rosette. Several pairs of leaves may spring from each stem. The heads are terminal and up to 3¼ inches (8cm) in diameter; their peripheral, ligulate flowers are orange-yellow with a 3-toothed tongue and the central flowers are tubular. Its habitat is in the calcareous soil of mountain pastures in central Europe. This plant is gathered in summer.
Parts used Flowers and rhizome.
Chemical compounds Arnicin, arnisterin, inulin, essence, tannin, phytosterol as well as palmitic, stearic and lauric acids. A greenish-yellow essence with a pungent odour is produced from the rhizomes, giving a yield of about 1%. The flowers also yield an essence which is orange-coloured due to the presence of stearoptenes.
Properties Anti-ecchymotic, antiphlogistic, scar-forming, sternutatory, nervous system stimulant.
Forms of use Tincture, infusion, fluid extract.
Notes Arnica is incompatible with iron and zinc salts as well as with lead acetate and magnesium carbonate. Taken in large doses it can provoke paralysis and tachycardia. It is used as a substitute for tobacco by mountain dwellers in central Europe. It is used in homoeopathy to treat bruises, ecchymoses, articular effusions, lumbago and sciatica.

41 ARTEMISIA ABROTANUM L.

Southernwood

Family Compositae.
Description A sub-shrubby herb with a woody, creeping rootstock. It has an erect, irregularly branched stem covered with down, and grows to a height of about 40 inches (1m). The silvery-white leaves are pubescent and bipinnatisect with linear lobes. The yellowish flowers, in heads, are arranged to form a panicle. The semi-spherical involucre is formed of lanceolate bracts. The fruit is a compressed achene. It is rare to find this plant growing wild but it is sometimes grown on a small commercial scale in kitchen gardens. The part used medicinally is gathered in summer.
Parts used Flowering tips.
Chemical compounds Essence, abrotanin, tannin.
Properties Anthelminthic, stomachic, cholagogic, emmenagogic.
Forms of use Infusion, powder, tincture, essence, syrup, distilled water.
Notes The essence is frequently used in the perfumery trade to add certain subtle tones. The plant is also used in salads, as a culinary herb and in the preparation of commercial and home-made aromatic vinegars. Because of its emmenagogic (restoring the menstrual flow) effect, no product made from southernwood should be taken during pregnancy. In some country districts of continental Europe an infusion of it is traditionally given to small children as a disinfectant against parasitic worms. It is used to stop small wounds bleeding and help them heal. It is also a deterrent against flies and other insects when rubbed on the skin.

---

42 ARTEMISIA ABSINTHIUM L.

Common wormwood (Absinthe)

Family Compositae.
Description The specific name derives from the Greek-rooted Latin *absinthium*, without sweetness. It is a perennial plant, about 40 inches (1m) high with a taproot. It has a woody stem with many alternate leaves, the basal leaves being lobed with a long petiole and the stem leaves bipinnatifid, all covered with a whitish down. The yellowish flowers are tubular and grouped in globose heads forming terminal panicles. The fruits are smooth, obovate achenes. It grows throughout Europe preferring uncultivated and waste places. In England and Wales, where it is a native, it is common on roadsides. The parts required for medicinal use are gathered in May and August.
Parts used Leaves and flowering tips.
Chemical compounds The plant contains glucoside absinthin, tannin and potassium nitrate; its essential oil has been found to contain mainly thujone, phellandrene and a sesquiterpene. There is a yield of essential oil of 0.4% with a density of 0.93; this is bluish-green when extracted from the fresh plant and yellow when taken from the dried plant.
Properties Anthelminthic, splenobiliary, emmenagogic, cholagogic, antisaturnismic.
Forms of use Powder, tincture, infusion, oily solution, medicinal wine.
Notes This plant is mainly used for alcoholic distillates and macerates with a bitter base; it is also used, in carefully measured amounts, as a substitute for hops in the brewing of beer. When taken in large doses or over a long period of time, absinth-based liqueurs will provoke a toxic condition and may result in epileptiform convulsions. The use of absinth-based preparations has been shown to have a marked antitoxic effect on saturnine poisoning.

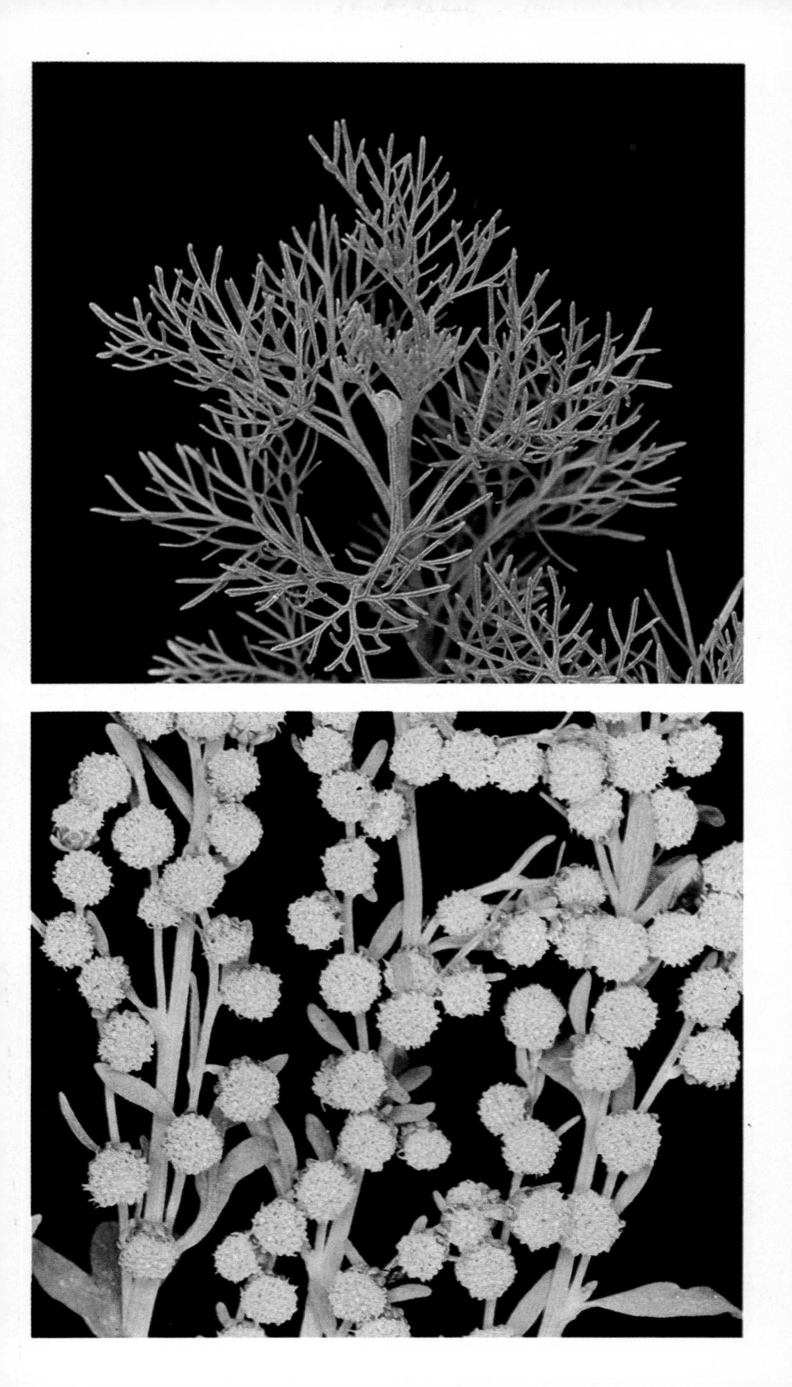

43 ARTEMISIA GLACIALIS L.

Glacier wormwood

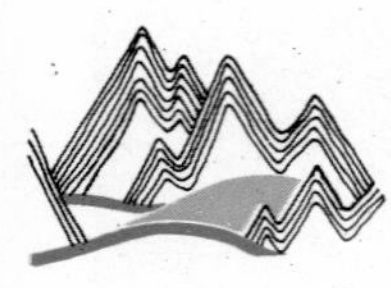

Family Compositae.
Description The generic name is derived from the Greek *artemes*, healthy. It is a small silvery, aromatic plant, about 4 inches (10cm) high with a small taproot. It has an erect, simple stem and its deeply divided leaves are either lobed or entire. The flowers are grouped into small golden heads with velvety bracts forming their involucres. The fruits are flattened achenes. This plant is found in the south western Alps on rocky sites at about 5000 feet (1500m) or higher. It is gathered in summer.
Parts used Whole plant.
Chemical compounds It contains a bitter principle, essential oil (eucalyptol), resin, tannin. The essence obtained from the plant gives a yield which varies from 0.1 to 0.3%. It has an aromatic fragrance and a buttery consistency.
Properties Digestive, antimeteoric, sedative, stomachic, expectorant.
Forms of use Infusion, tincture, syrup, fluid extract.
Notes It is widely used, alongside other varieties of a similar kind, in the preparation of original liqueurs such as 'genepi liqueur'. From a medicinal point of view, its use is limited to the areas in which it thrives and thus has only local importance for home-made remedies. It would also seem that preparations made with this herb have a marked effect on mountain sickness. Indiscriminate collection of the glacier wormwood has brought it within the category of an endangered species and it is now protected. Poultices of the ground-down plant are used as a first-aid remedy for wounds.

---

44 ARTEMISIA VULGARIS L.

Mugwort

Family Compositae.
Description A perennial plant with a woody rhizome and an erect, angular stem, branched at the top. The alternate, sessile leaves are green with whitish undersides; they are pinnate in form with incisions, dentate and acute towards the tip. The heads are grouped into glomerules to form reddish or yellowish terminal branched spikes. The achenes are smooth and have no pappus. The whole plant exudes a characteristic odour. In continental Europe it is extensively found in the wild from coastal to mountainous areas, with a preference for uncultivated and waste land. A native of Britain, it is most commonly found in hedgerows and roadsides, though rare in Scotland and northern England. It can grow to a height of over 5 feet (1.5m). It is gathered in summer.
Parts used Whole plant.
Chemical compounds Essence, inulin, resin, artemisin. An average yield of 0.3% of essence is obtained, containing mainly eucalyptol and terpene.
Properties Emmenogogic, digestive, antispasmodic, anthelminthic, antidiabetic.
Forms of use Infusion, tincture, powder, fluid extract, essence, distilled water.
Notes It is inadvisable for pregnant women to take any preparation containing this herb because of its strong uterine decongestant effect. The essence is used in insecticides, often being mixed with pyrethrum. Cattle are never allowed to eat this plant as it would taint their milk. Like absinthe, it is used as a bitter in the preparation of some alcoholic liquors.

45 ARUNDO DONAX L.

Donax arundinaceus Beauv.
Giant reed

Family Gramineae.
Description A very tall herbaceous plant, the largest grass indigenous to Europe, it grows to a height of about 16½ feet (5m) or more. The rhizome is fat, nodose and wavy. The hollow stem is woody and bears light green, sheathed leaves which are lanceolate at the base and up to about 2 feet (60cm) long. The flowers are arranged in apical panicles over 20 inches (50cm) in length; these are green at first, turning a deep purple as they mature. The glumes are keeled and equal. The fruit is a caryopsis. This type of reed is common in ditches and marshlands throughout southern Europe and can be found, rarely, in Britain as a cultivated ornamental plant. It is gathered in autumn.
Parts used Rhizome.
Chemical compounds Resin, essence, sugars, silica, salts of calcium and potassium.
Properties Diuretic, galactofuge, diaphoretic.
Forms of use Decoction, powder.
Notes The stems of this plant are well known as they are frequently used as plant supports by horticulturalists and gardeners. A particular type of cellulose is also obtained from them. The leaves are used in some areas of continental Europe as makeshift fodder for livestock. Besides their medicinal uses, the rhizomes can be ground into flour and used to make bread. In southern Europe, the terminal panicles were, at one time, used in country districts to make brooms.

---

46 ASARUM EUROPAEUM L.

Asarabacca

Family Aristolochiaceae.
Description The genetic name derives from the Greek *asaron*, nausea. From its small, low-growing branchlets spring long petioles bearing persistent leaves which are kidney-shaped except for their cordate base. The flowers, hidden by the petioles, are bisexual with a purplish-green, bilobate bell-shaped perianth. The androecium has 12 stamens while the gynaecium has 6 loculi with a 6-lobed stigma. The fruit is a trivalved capsule which contains 2 rows of ovoid, rough-textured seeds. It grows in moist, woodland areas with a preference for beech-woods. It is possibly a native to the woodlands of England and Wales but is very rare. It is gathered in spring.

Parts used Rhizome.
Chemical compounds Essential oil, sucrose, camphor, asarin, tannic acid.
Properties Emetic, expectorant, diaphoretic, sternutatory.
Forms of use Infusion, fluid extract, semi-fluid extract, tincture, syrup.

Notes The powder is equal to that of the oleander as a sternutator. Although this plant is used in the making of spirituous liquors there is some doubt as to its toxicity when taken in other than very small amounts. It can cause nephritis and metritis and, in a few known cases when large amounts have been taken, even death. If crushed when freshly cut, the plant gives off the smell of turpentine. The rhizome, if chewed, produces a burning sensation on the tongue and deadens the feeling. It is completely non-toxic when dry. A vibrant, apple-green pigment can also be obtained from the asarabacca which, at one time, was used in the dyeing of wool.

47 ASPARAGUS OFFICINALIS L.

Asparagus altilis Asch.
Asparagus

Family Liliaceae.
Description The generic name derives from the Greek *spargao*, turgid. A perennial plant with a small rhizome, the stems can grow to over 6½ feet (2 m). It has many long, delicate branches and subulate branchlets which resemble leaves. The male and female flowers are borne on small pedicels and have campanulate perianths with greenish-white tepals. The androecium has 6 stamens. The shoots grow directly from the rhizome and are covered in scales derived from metamorphozed leaves. The fruit is a red berry which contains up to 4 seeds. Normally a cultivated plant, it is often found growing wild throughout Europe, including Britain, in sandy areas such as sea cliffs or in hedgerows. The medicinal part is gathered after the shoots have been cut.
Parts used Rhizome.
Chemical compounds Asparagine, mucilage, sugar, essence, phosphoric anhydride, potassium phosphate, vitamins B_1, B_2 and C, gallic acid and tannic acid.
Properties Diuretic, antiplethoric, antidropsical.
Forms of use Decoction, syrup, fluid extract.
Notes One of the ingredients of '5-root syrup'. It is inadvisable for anyone suffering from kidney stones, cystitis, diabetes, nephritis or gout to take asparagus preparations. It has a similar sedative effect on the heart as the false hellebore (*Adonis helleborus*). L-asparaginese, an enzyme of asparagine, has a remarkable antileukaemic effect

---

48 ASPHODELUS ALBUS Mill.

Asphodel

Family Liliaceae.
Description A herbaceous plant with enlarged tuberous roots, a simple stem which grows to about 40 inches (1 m) and sword-shaped basal leaves which are fleshy and glabrous. The flowers are in dense spikes each emerging from a bract; each flower has 6 tepals with white or reddish venation. The fruit is a tripartite, oval capsule with blackish seeds. It is commonly found growing in ploughed fields and on rough ground in southern Europe and around the shores of the Mediterranean. It is gathered in September.
Parts used Tubers.
Chemical compounds Asphodeline, resin, asphodeloside, mucilage, sucrose.
Properties Detergent, vulnerary, antidermatosic, emollient.
Forms of use Decoction, tincture, pulp.
Notes At one time, the tubers were eaten but, in view of the presence of asphodeline, this is not advisable and any preparation containing asphodel should never be taken internally by anyone suffering from nephritis or gastritis. Alcohol can be obtained from fermented tubers. Asphodel is mainly used externally for the treatment of skin conditions and for lightening freckles as well as in the manufacture of cosmetics. It was also used, in the past, as a cough remedy because of its mucilage content.

49 ASPLENIUM RUTA-MURARIA L.
Wall rue

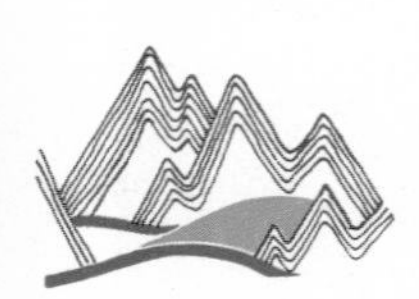

Family Polypodiaceae.
Description A cryptogamic plant with a small scaly rhizome that has a dense growth of rootlets. The olive green fronds are leathery, persistent and bipinnatisect with many obtuse sub-divisions. The sori are linear on the underside of the fronds. Its average height is 4 inches (10 cm). Quite commonly found on old walls, in rocks and crevices, it grows wild throughout most of Europe, including Britain, mainly in hilly areas. The parts required for medicinal purposes are gathered in late spring.
Parts used Fronds.
Chemical compounds Tannin, salts, mucilage, gallic acid.
Properties Emmenagogic, ophthalmic, astringent.
Forms of use Infusion, powder, tincture, distilled water.
Notes Distilled water is made with the fronds and as an eye-lotion or -drops, this has always given tangible results in ophthalmic complaints and in many diseases of the orbit. The tannin content renders it suitable to stop the bleeding of small wounds. Attempts have been made to grow this plant ornamentally but it has never been greatly appreciated.

---

50 ASTRANTIA MAJOR L.
Melancholy Gentleman (Astrantia)

Family Umbelliferae.
Description A herbaceous plant about 20 inches (50 cm) high with a dark, aromatic root and smooth stem. The compound, basal leaves are amplexicaul and borne on a long petiole which widens at the stem; they are palmate-lobate with 5 oval, serrate lobes. The apical leaves are smaller and sessile with umbels of rather pale flowers arising from their axils, either singly or in groups of 2 or 3. The floral components are clearly visible, as are the dark grey, striate bracts. The fruit is large, rough and variegated. Its natural habitat is in moist woodlands and along the banks of streams but it is also cultivated. It is rare in Britain but has become naturalized in woods and on wood edges in certain areas of England. It flowers and is gathered from June-September.
Parts used Roots.
Chemical compounds Colouring materials, salts, tannin, purgative substance, resin.
Properties Purgative.
Forms of use Decoction.
Notes The flowers of this plant can be dried and used in floral arrangements. An infusion made from the whole plant makes a gentle diuretic.

51 ATROPA BELLA-DONNA L.

Deadly nightshade

Family Solanaceae.
Description The specific name of this plant, which means 'beautiful woman', probably derives from the use women made of the juice of its berries to make their eyes sparkle; the generic name comes from one of the three Fates, Atropos, who held the scissors to cut the thread of life – a reference to the fact that it is deadly poisonous. This perennial plant has a greyish, fleshy root which springs from a thick rhizome dotted with purplish buds. The fruit is a black, glossy berry with 2 loculi containing kidney-shaped seeds. It is now found mainly in the less frequented mountainous areas of Europe, preferably in shady sites. It is native to the woods and thickets of England and Wales, being most common in south eastern England and rare elsewhere. The leaves are gathered in May and the roots in September.

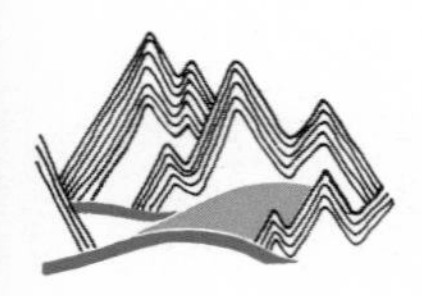

Parts used Leaves and roots.
Chemical compounds Hyoscyamine, atropine, scopolamine, (hyoscine), pyridine, chrysatrophic acid, tannin and starch are the main principles.

Properties Antispasmodic, narcotic, mydriatic, parasympathetic, analgesic, anti-asthmatic.
Forms of use Tincture, fluid extract, powder, ointment, suppository, eye-lotion, medicinal wine.

Notes Preparations made with the root are more active than those made with the leaves. It is used in cases of mushroom or toadstool poisoning. It stimulates the bulbar centre and the central nervous system and causes tachycardia and mydriasis. No preparation containing deadly nightshade should be used by heart sufferers or neurotic patients. It is incompatible with iodate compounds, alkalis, pilocarpine, tannin.

---

52 AVENA SATIVA L.

Oat

Family Gramineae.
Description The generic name derives from the Latin *avidus*, sought after. An annual plant, it is about 40 inches (1 m) in height, with hollow, smooth, nodose culms. The leaves are alternate and acuminate with an amplexicaul sheath. The flowers form a curved, branched panicle at the extremity. Each spikelet of the panicle consists of 2 flowers with glumes. The caryopsis is cylindrical and slightly ridged. The glumellae are aristate. This plant originates in northern Europe although, according to some botanical authors, it is said to have been brought over from southern North America where it had been found growing wild. It is cultivated extensively in Britain and Europe. It is gathered in summer.

Parts used Seeds and leaves.
Chemical compounds Starch, nitrogenous substances, cellulose, mineral salts, vitamins A, B_1, B_2, PP.

Properties Diuretic, nutrient, nerve sedative.
Forms of use Decoction, tincture.
Notes In some parts of continental Europe, oat straw was once used, and possibly still is, to fill mattresses and palliasses, with great benefit to rheumatic conditions. With small children, oats, in various forms, have been found to be remarkably effective against insomnia, in addition to being nourishing. A handful of grains thrown in the bath-water keeps the skin soft because of its emollient action. It is also one of the cereals used as a basic ingredient in the making of certain types of whisky.

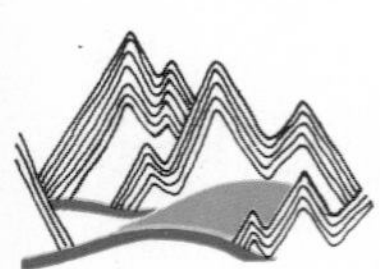

53 BELLIS PERENNIS L.
Daisy

Family Compositae.
Description A perennial herb with a small taproot and a great many rootlets, it grows to no more than 4 inches (10 cm) high. The simple stem, which is delicately downy, bears one head with tubular, yellow, central flowers and white peripheral ligulate flowers. The obovate, slightly crenate, basal leaves grow in rosette form. The fruit is an ovoid achene. This plant grows wild in most of Europe virtually wherever grass grows, from the coast up into hills and mountains, and is extremely common throughout the British Isles, where it is a native. It is gathered in May-June.
Parts used All the parts above ground.
Chemical compounds Tannin, resin, essence, colouring material, saponin.
Properties Ophthalmic, emollient, antitussive, anti-ecchymotic, bactericidal.
Forms of use Infusion, tincture, distilled water, oily solution.
Notes A popular home-made remedy for delicate and listless children. Some authorities claim that it has a cytostatic action on breast tumours. Oil of daisy (bellide) is used in homoeopathy and was, at one time, used in ointments for local application in cases of eczema. A tea made from daisies and primroses has a gently hypnotic effect in cases of slight insomnia. The young, tender leaves are, in some rural areas of Europe, mixed with other early vegetables to make spring salads.

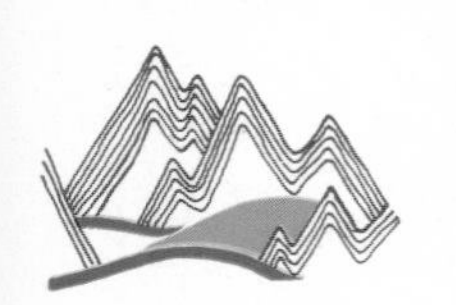

54 BERBERIS VULGARIS L.
Barberry

Family Berberidaceae.
Description The generic name derives from the Phoenician *barbar*, glossy, referring to the sheen on the leaves. A shrub with thick, creeping roots and a very branched, greyish stem; the branches are spiny and thin. The elliptical, dentate leaves are leathery and shiny; they are carried on small petioles and may be alternate or grouped in fascicles within which grow sharp prickles. Its yellow flowers are 6-sepalled and 6-petalled, falling in loose clusters. The fruit is a wine-red berry which contains 2-3 corneous seeds. It grows in copses, hedges and by-ways of the more hilly and mountainous areas of Europe. It was probably introduced into Britain, where it is occasionally found wild in hedgerows, but is more often cultivated in gardens for ornament.
Parts used Root-bark, phloem of the branches, leaves and fruit.
Chemical compounds Bark: berberine, oxyacanthine, resin, tannin, essential oil. Leaves: berberine, citric and malic acids. Fruit: dextrose, fructose (levulose), pectose, gum, pectin as well as citric, malic and tartaric acids.
Properties Bark: stomachic, cholagogic, febrifuge, purgative. Leaves: astringent, antiscorbutic. Fruit: astringent, antiseptic, nutritive.
Forms of use Decoction, tincture, fluid extract, syrup, powder.
Notes In the past, it was regarded as a pestiferous plant when near wheat, as it transmitted red rust-spores to the crop. A yellow dye can be obtained from it and this is also used to adulterate pomegranate bark. The young shoots and fruit are usually the only parts regarded as edible. The fruit is used to make jams, jellies and syrups. Spirituous liquors are also made, after fermentation, by distillation, to produce a moderately alcoholic drink.

55 BETULA PENDULA Roth.

Betula alba Sensu Coste, *Betula verrucosa* Ehrh.
Silver birch

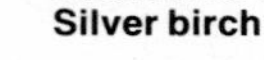

Family Betulaceae.
Description A tree which is not particularly long-lived but which may grow to a height of nearly 100 feet (30 m) with a trunk diameter of up to 28 inches (70 cm). the smooth, pale bark is grey at the base, incised and flakes into thin papery layers. The warted branches are slender and pendulous, with terminal buds. The alternate leaves are deciduous, rhomboidal and acute, with small teeth; the underside is lighter in colour than the upper. The flowers consist of pendulous catkins. The fruits are achenes, each of which has a pair of delicate 'wings'. This tree flourishes on the siliceous ground of woodlands throughout Europe and is found growing wild as well as cultivated. It is a native tree to the British Isles and commonly found everywhere except the Shetlands and the Orkneys.

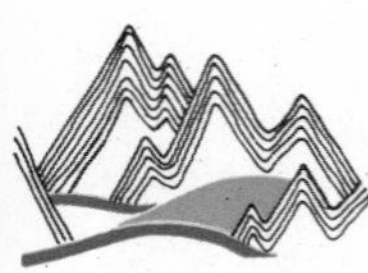

Parts used Leaves, buds, juice, bark of the young branches.
Chemical compounds Bark: betulin, resin, betula camphor. Buds: sugar, betulorentic acid, tannin. Leaves: essence, tannin, resin, sugar, saponin, betulalbine.

Properties Bark: diuretic, laxative. Buds: balsamic. Leaves: diuretic, anti-oedematous, hypocholesterolic.
Forms of use Bark: powder, decoction. Buds: infusion, oily solution.
Notes The leaves contain phytocides which are effective germicides. Their juice, obtained by incision, can also be fermented and made into wine or vinegar. Another use for the juice is as a friction on thick-haired hides. Birch bark tannin is used to make Bulgar tan, which is distilled to produce birch tar (used in the preparation of 'Bulgar' or 'Russian leather') and a balsamic oil similar to vegetable tar.

---

56 BIGNONIA CATALPA L.

Catalpa bignonioides Walt.
Indian bean tree

Family Bignoniaceae.
Description The generic name derives from that of the botanist, J.P. Bignon. This tree grows to 35-40 feet (10-12 m); it has an erect trunk with a rimulose bark. The large leaves, carried on long petioles, have an acute apex and an entire, almost hairless, margin. The white, tubular flowers are bell-shaped, fragrant and gathered in terminal panicles. Each flower has a bilabiate calyx and a 5-lobed corolla. The fruit is an elongated, bivalved siliqua – about 20 inches (50 cm) long – containing numerous flattened seeds. The Indian bean tree originates in North America and is cultivated in the warmer regions of continental Europe.

Parts used Bark and fruit
Chemical compounds Catalpine, p-oxybenzoic and protocachectic acids.

Propeties Febrifuge, slightly narcotic, asthmatic sedative.
Forms of use Decoction and semi-fluid extract.
Notes A quick-growing tree that is widely cultivated on land subject to erosion or landslides, as the roots act as a binding agent. It was once used as a substitute for quinine in treating marsh fever. Distilled water, made from its fruit and mixed with euphrasy (eyebright) and rue, is known to be a valuable eye-lotion in cases of trachoma and conjunctivitis. The roots must never be used as they are poisonous. It is worth noting, too, that this plant, besides having a sedatory effect, also has a slightly narcotic action which never induces a dazed condition and is, therefore, used to advantage in preparations for treating whooping-cough in children.

57 BORAGO OFFICINALIS L.
Borage

Family Boraginaceae.
Description A taprooted annual herb that is covered with whitish, bristly hairs. The large, basal leaves, borne on delicate, hollow petioles, have a marked venation and dentate margin. The size of the flowers gradually decreases towards the apex. The stem is fragile, simple, erect, hollow, hispid and juicy. It becomes branched towards the top. The average height is 20 inches (50 cm) but, in suitable, very nitrogenous ground the author has produced plants as high as 4 feet (1.2 m) with unusually luxuriant foliage. The numerous deep pink or blue flowers are grouped in drooping, terminal clusters. The clayx of each flower is divided into 5 lobes, as is its corolla. The fruit consists of oval, warty achenes. In some regions of Europe it grows freely in the wild in hedgerows, by cart-tracks and on roadside verges from the coast to the foothills. In Britain it is an introduced species, found frequently in the vicinity of houses. It is widely cultivated for culinary use. It is gathered in spring and autumn.
Parts used Whole plant.
Chemical compounds Mucilage, tannin, potassium nitrate, salts, allantoin.
Properties Depurative, emollient, expectorant, diuretic, lenitive.
Forms of use Infusion, juice, medicinal wine.
Notes Borage leaves have been used in salads for centuries. The flowers give a blue dye. A refreshing summer drink can be made with this plant. It is frequently grown near apiaries as it produces a lot of nectar which is attractive to bees. Medically, it can be used as a compress on inflamed or irritated skin.

---

58 BRUNELLA VULGARIS Greene
Prunella vulgaris L.
Self-heal

Family Labiatae.
Description A small, herbaceous plant, which grows to about 10 inches (25 cm) high, with a serpentine rhizome equipped with numerous rootlets. The delicate, pubescent stems bear opposite leaves, the lower ones being petiolate and the upper ones sessile; they are oval to diamond-shaped and either entire or slightly dentate. The flowers are grouped in a spike with 2 basal leaves; there are several overlapping bracts covering each calyx. The purple or violet corolla is bilabiate. The achenes contain a number of seeds. It is commonly found growing wild throughout Britain and Europe in woodland, grassland, clearings and roadsides and it is sometimes cultivated on ground that has a calcareous content. It is gathered in early summer.
Parts used Whole plant.
Chemical compounds A bitter substance, tannin and resinous compounds.
Properties Astringent, stomachic.
Forms of use Infusion, tincture, fluid extract, poultice.
Notes Often seen as a garden border plant, it is also widely used in folk medicine as a mouthwash/gargle and to help fresh surface wounds to heal. It can also be used in the home by macerating it in *eau-de-vie*, Italian *grappa* or brandy to which it gives a pleasant, somewhat bitter, taste. At one time self-heal was used in enemas in cases of haemorrhoids, with doubtful results, as well as in the treatment of rhagades of the breast (a cracked condition of the nipple).

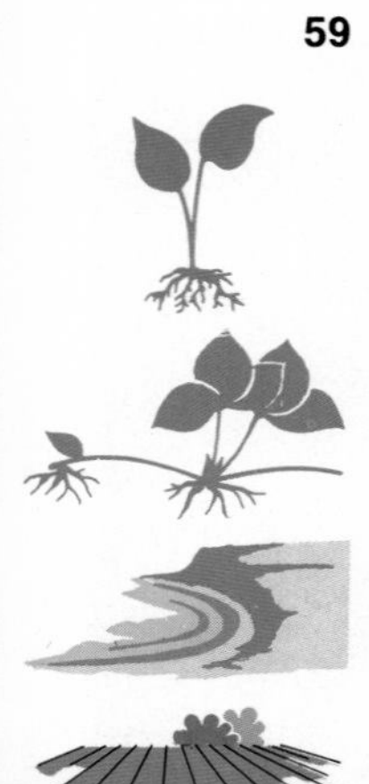

59 BRYONIA CRETICA L. subsp. DIOICA (Jacq.) Tutin

Bryonia dioica Jacq.
White bryony

Family Cucurbitaceae.
Description The generic name is derived from the Greek *bryo*, to thrust, alluding to the speed with which this plant grows. It is a perennial herb with a thick, fleshy taproot containing white pulp, that penetrates to a great depth. The greenish flowers are followed by the fruit, in the form of spherical, red berries about the size of a pea. The seeds are grey and compressed. This plant is native in south west and central England where it is very common in scrub and woodland. The medicinal part can be dug up at any time of the year; it is a difficult plant to harvest in view of the depth of its roots.
Parts used Root.
Chemical compounds Starch, bioresin, phytosterol, bryonin, invert sugar, an amorphous substance of a chemical nature which has not yet been fully researched but is known to have a purgative effect.
Properties Emetic, drastic, hydrofuge, external revulsive.
Forms of use Fluid extract, semi-fluid extract, dry extract, dye and ointment.
Notes If a piece of the root is hollowed out and filled with sugar, a juice is exuded which is used in some rural areas of Europe as a purgative. It is inadvisable, however, to use this plant in any form because of its poisonous nature. White bryony is used a great deal in homoeopathic medicine, in various preparations, in the treatment of arthritis, effusions into joints, hepatic (or biliary) colic, measles, rheumatism, synovitis and coughs. Although not yet sufficiently researched, the use of a decoction of bryony in enemas in the treatment of haemorrhoids is potentially interesting. It must be remembered, however, that any use made of the bryony can be dangerous.

60 BUXUS SEMPERVIRENS L.

Box

Family Buxaceae.
Description The genetic name is derived from the Greek *puxos*, a small box. Very slow-growing, it has a rough bark and extremely hard, yellowish wood. The leaves are opposite, leathery, glossy, entire and carried on a very short petiole. The tiny, greenish flowers arise from the leaf axils. The fruit is a trilocular ellipsoidal capsule from which the black, shiny seeds are forcibly ejected as it splits on ripening. A plant known for its longevity, it is not uncommon for it to live 600 years. It flourishes on limestone ground and is native to the south of England, although it is rarely seen wild, being most commonly cultivated as ornament. It is gathered throughout the year.

Parts used Bark and leaves.
Chemical compounds Buxine, secondary alkaloids, essential oil, tannin.
Properties Febrifuge, antirheumatic, diaphoretic, cholagogic.
Forms of use Powder, decoction, tincture.

Notes The medicinal products of this plant should be used with caution as research into its medicinal properties is fairly recent. Boxwood is a favourite timber with wood-engravers and turners because of its homogenous, non-fibrous structure; the root is especially sought after by cabinet-makers and turners. It is said that the bark has anthelminthic properties. The leaves are known to have been used as a substitute for hops in the brewing of beer in France and as an alternative to quinine in treating malarial fevers. Its distillation provides an essential oil used in odontology and dentistry. Boxwood is heavier than water. The plant is extensively used in homoeopathic medicine as an antirheumatic.

61 CALENDULA OFFICINALIS L.

Marigold

Family Compositae.
Description The generic name derives from the Greek *kalein,* the beginning of the month. An annual, pubescent plant, it averages 16-20 inches (40-50 cm) in height, with a contorted, spindle-shaped root. It has an erect, angular, branched stem, with alternate dentate-mucronate or sinuate-undulate leaves, bearing heads of flowers at the stem apex. The peripheral flowers are orange and ligulate with a 3-toothed apex, while the central flowers are tubular with a 5-lobed corolla. The fruits are achenes with spots on the curved dorsal ridge but with no pappus. In Britain it is grown decoratively in gardens, but it is also found growing wild on uncultivated land from plains to higher ground throughout Europe. It is gathered from June-September.
Parts used Flowers
Chemical compounds Carotenoid, colouring matters, cholesterinic esters, saponin, resin, bitter principle.
Properties Antiphlogistic, emmenagogic, local, cosmetic, vulnerary.
Forms of use Infusion, tincture, fluid extract, distilled water, juice, oily solution, ointment.
Notes The orange ligules are used as a colorant in, for example, butter and syrups as well as to simulate the more valuable saffron stigmas. This plant is sensitive to variations of temperature and dampness, the opening or closing of the flower being an indication of whether it will be a fine or wet day respectively. An application of crushed marigold stems to corns and warts will soon render them easily removable. Some authorities claim that the marigold has the same properties as *Arnica montana* but this has still to be proved. Its essential oil is used fairly sparingly, in view of the difficulty in obtaining it, in perfumes which have a rather sharp tang.

---

62 CALLUNA VULGARIS (L.) Hull

Erica vulgaris L., *Calluna erica* DC.
Heather (ling)

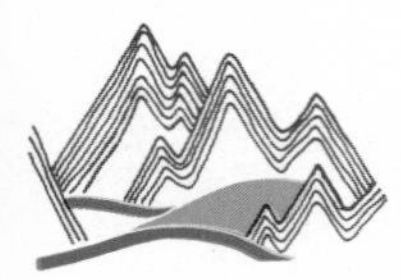

Family Ericaceae.

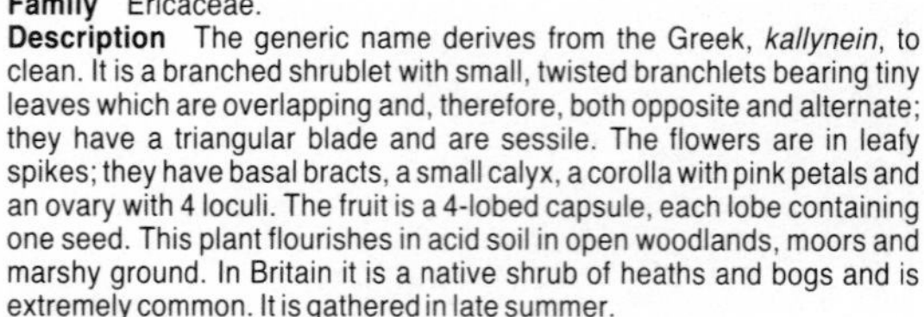

Description The generic name derives from the Greek, *kallynein*, to clean. It is a branched shrublet with small, twisted branchlets bearing tiny leaves which are overlapping and, therefore, both opposite and alternate; they have a triangular blade and are sessile. The flowers are in leafy spikes; they have basal bracts, a small calyx, a corolla with pink petals and an ovary with 4 loculi. The fruit is a 4-lobed capsule, each lobe containing one seed. This plant flourishes in acid soil in open woodlands, moors and marshy ground. In Britain it is a native shrub of heaths and bogs and is extremely common. It is gathered in late summer.
Parts used Flowering tips.
Chemical compounds Ericolin, ericine, ericinol, quercetin.
Properties Diuretic, urogenital antiseptic, depurative, sternutatory.
Forms of use Decoction, fluid extract, powder.
Notes In some regions, the inflorescences have been used to replace hops in the brewing of beer. The branches are used for making brooms and the plant yields a yellow dye. When growing under adverse conditions, the root forms an underground stump which is much in demand for making briar pipes. The soil in which heather has been growing is as rich in flowering-plant nutrients as chestnut compost. The plant produces a great deal of nectar and is, therefore, attractive to bees. In the mountainous areas of Europe this plant is much used to make a liniment for arthritis and rheumatism by macerating it, frequently in conjunction with rhododendron, in alcohol. At one time, boiling-hot poultices of heather were used to treat chilblains.

63 CALTHA PALUSTRIS L.

Marsh marigold (King Cup)

Family Ranunculaceae.
Description The generic name derives from the Greek *kalathos*, a wicker basket. A perennial plant with a short, fleshy rhizome and a great many tufts of thin rootlets. It has an erect, simple, rather spongy stem which is smooth and sturdy, with kidney-shaped, toothed or crenate basal leaves. These leaves have a marked venation and the lower leaves are borne on long petioles, while the apical leaves are smaller and almost sessile. The flowers, growing singly and widely spaced, have a petaloid calyx formed by 5 golden yellow sepals. On ripening, the dry dehiscent fruit expels a number of seeds. The plant is frequently seen in central and northern Europe, including Britain, growing by mountainous brooks and streams as well as in marshes and water meadows. It is gathered in summer.
Parts used Leaves.
Chemical compounds Protoanemonin, flavonoids, tannin, saponin, colouring matter.
Properties Revulsive.
Forms of use Poultice, tincture.
Notes This plant is often grown ornamentally by garden pools or in wet ground. It is dried and sometimes used as a tobacco substitute in smoking cures. The tight buds are sometimes pickled like capers and are even used to adulterate the latter. The marsh marigold should not be used internally to avoid any risk of poisoning from the protoanemonin.

---

64 CANNABIS SATIVA L.

Hemp

Family Cannabaceae.
Description A herb with a taproot and numerous rootlets. The stem is erect, branched, angular, ridged, hollow and woody. The lower leaves are opposite and petiolate while the upper ones are alternate, petiolate and palmatisect with acute, serrate leaflets. The greenish male flowers are in clusters and the female flowers, also green, are in apical panicles. The fruit is a smooth, grey achene with a green seed. A plant that originates in Asia, it is quite commonly seen growing wild in continental Europe but more often cultivated. In Britain it is illegal to grow hemp without a licence. It is gathered in summer.
Parts used Inflorescence tips.
Chemical compounds Cannabinol, cannabidiol, choline, trigonelline, acids, cannabinon essence.
Properties Sedative, narcotic, hypnotic, diuretic.
Forms of use Infusion, fluid extract, syrup.
Notes The medicinal properties of cannabis are overshadowed by its use (illegal in Britain) as a euphorigenic drug. Hemp produces a cortical fibre which is used in rope-making and for weaving coarse fabrics and mats. An inedible, drying oil is produced from the fruit. Birds are particularly fond of the seeds.

65 CAPPARIS SPINOSA L.
Caper

Family Capparidaceae.
Description A subshrubby plant with a woody, branched root from the collar of which arise numerous woody stems. These stems carry alternate, simple, oval or sub-rotund fleshy green leaves, which are borne on a short petiole with 2 spiny stipules at the base; the leaf-margins are entire. The pink-tinged, white flowers are borne on a pedicel that emerges from the axil of the upper leaves. The calyx and the corolla are respectively 4-sepalled and 4-petalled. There are a great many stamens with threadlike violet filaments. The fruit is a globose berry that is green when young, ripening to red; it contains numerous, blackish, kidney-shaped seeds. This plant, which is exclusive to the Mediterranean area of Europe, grows wild in walls, ruins and among any piles of stone and rubble exposed to the sun. The part used medicinally is gathered in spring.
Parts used Root-bark.
Chemical compounds Capparirutin, essence, saponin, pectin, salts.
Properties Diuretic, biliary deobstructive, depurative, antihaemorrhoidal, vasoconstrictive.
Forms of use Decoction, powder, oily solution.
Notes The culinary use of the tightly shut buds pickled in brine is well known, but less so is the fact that the root extract is utilized in cosmetics. It is particularly helpful in treating roseola (any rose-coloured rash) and capillary weaknesses. A decoction of the plant is used to treat thrush. The tincture of its stems is used as a reagent.

---

66 CAPSELLA BURSA-PASTORIS (L.) Medic.
Thlaspi bursa-pastoris L.
Shepherd's purse

Family Cruciferae.
Description The generic name derives from *capsella,* a pocket or purse. It is an annual or biennial herb with a taproot and an erect stem. The pubescent basal leaves form a rosette, the lower ones being pinnate or lanceolate and the upper ones sheathed and sagittate. The flowers have 4 white petals and are arranged in a corymb. The fruits are triangular siliquae with numerous oval seeds. This plant is commonly found throughout Britain and the world and grows profusely as a garden weed and on waste ground. It is gathered throughout the year.
Parts used Whole plant.

Chemical compounds Choline, acetylcholine, fumaric acid, tartaric acid, malic acid, citric acid, sparteine, sulphur compounds, tannin, saponin, potassium.
Properties Haemostatic, emmenagogic, hypotensive, vulnerary.
Forms of use Infusion, fluid extract, tincture, powder, medicinal wine.

Notes This plant has been used to replace extracts of spurred rye in the treatment of uterine haemorrhages, with excellent results. The seedlings are used in livestock fodder, mixed with other edible wild plants. It curdles milk, presumably by means of a weak radioactive effect similar to that of the horse chestnut and of the avena, a factor that makes it particularly suitable for cosmetic preparations. It was used at one time, over a long period, instead of quinine in treating malaria. Homoeopathy makes use of this plant mainly in treating nose-bleeding and urinary calculosis. It is also used as a powdered inhalation in conjunction with the elder *(Sambucus nigra)*.

67 CAPSICUM ANNUUM L.

Capsicum longum DC.
Red pepper

Family Solanaceae.
Description An annual plant with a taproot and an erect, simple, branched stem of up to 40 inches (1m) high. The flowers arise from the branchlet axils of the stem on short, slanting peduncles; they have a small cupular calyx terminating in 5 lobes. Their tubular corolla is usually white and 5-lobed, surrounding yellow stamens with violet anthers. The fruits are large pendulous berries in various shapes from long and narrow to round, conical or quadrangular within which are numerous pale, flat, circular seeds. A native of tropical America, this plant is frequently cultivated throughout Europe for the fruit which is harvested in August-September.
Parts used Fruit.
Chemical compounds Capsaicin, essence, carotene, capsorubine, lutein, copper, vitamin C.
Properties Revulsive, rubefacient, sialogogic, digestive anti-atonic, antihaemorrhoidal, antirheumatic.
Forms of use Fluid extract, tincture, oleoresin, powder, ointment.
Notes The powder is well known as paprika, a culinary seasoning, and is used in the preparation of a great many sauces. It replaces white pepper in Hungarian paprika cheeses. A red colouring substance, which is not rubefacient (counter-irritant), is obtained from the fruit and used in cooking. Paprika is an effective sea-sickness preventative and is also used in the preparation of revulsive (thermal) wadding and ointments. It also has an antihaemorrhoidal effect when taken in very small amounts. Red peppers have a high vitamin C content which is almost completely lost when they are dried.

---

68 CARLINA ACAULIS L.

Carlina caulescens Lam., *Carlina chamaleon* Vill.
Stemless carline thistle

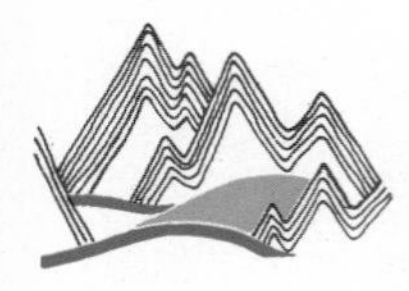

Family Compositae.
Description The generic name, which was originally 'Carolina', derives from the Emperor Charlemagne who used it to cure his army of a pestilence. This plant has a short stem – which may sometimes grow as high as 20 inches (50cm) – and a long, fleshy taproot. The leaves, which form a basal rosette, are pinnatifid with the lobes ending in rigid spines. The flowers are gathered into heads with outer scales which are tightly packed and spiny, and inner scales which are wide-spreading, pale and spineless; the flowers are whitish or purplish brown. The fruits are oblong achenes with pappus bristles around the top. The head opens in dry weather and closes when it is damp. The plant is widely found growing on poor soil in dry, sandy pastures and the mountainous areas of central and southern Europe. It is gathered in autumn.
Parts used Root.
Chemical compounds Essence, inulin, an antibiotic (carline oxide), potassium, calcium and magnesium. It yields about 1.5% of essential oil.
Properties Stomachic, carminative, diaphoretic, antibiotic.
Forms of use Decoction, fluid extract, tincture, powder.
Notes This is a protected plant although it is often destroyed by local inhabitants who regard it as both useless and a nuisance. The fleshy centre is edible and tastes like the thistles belonging to the *Carduus* genus. Excessive amounts have a strong emetic effect. This plant was at one time in great demand in order to produce a distilled water reputed to have aphrodisiac qualities. Popular for dried-flower arrangements, the heads retain their appearance indefinitely.

69 CARPINUS BETULUS L.
Hornbeam

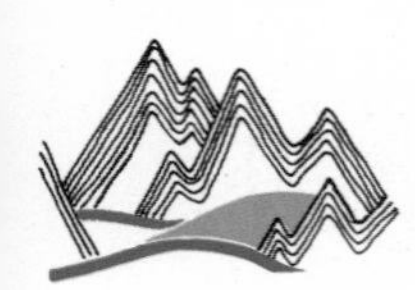

Family Betulaceae.
Description A shallow-rooted tree with smooth, grey bark. The alternate, petiolate leaves are acute, pinnately veined, doubly dentate and glabrous except for hairs in the leaf axil. The male flowers hang in cylindrical catkins with overlapping scales; the female flowers hang in yellowish catkins. The fruit is covered by a trilobate dome; it consists of an ellipsoidal achene complete with seed and wings. This tree can grow to a height of over 66 feet (20m) but also makes an excellent hedge. It is to be found throughout Europe from the lowlands to hilly terrain. A native of the British Isles, it grows most commonly in south east England. It is often cultivated. The medicinal parts are gathered in August.
Parts used Leaves.
Chemical compounds Tannin, salts, resin.
Properties Haemostatic.
Forms of use Powder, decoction, medicinal wine.
Notes This is a tree which seeds itself easily and is often used in reafforestation programmes. It has frequently been used externally as a compress to heal small wounds because of its astringent properties. The timber is used for firewood or for lignite (wood coal). Hornbeam leaves are eaten with relish by goats. Distilled water made from its leaves is an effective eye-lotion.

---

70 CARTHAMUS TINCTORIUS L.
Safflower

Family Compositae.
Description A herbaceous plant with numerous roots and an erect, branched, ridged stem. The oval-lanceolate leaves are spiny, dentate or rarely entire; they are sessile, with a heavily veined surface. The heads bear ovate and oblong scales, the external ones being spiny and the internal, acute. The flowers are sulphur-yellow and the fruit is a tetragonal obovate achene. This plant, which probably originates from Africa, is cultivated mainly on the plains of most of the hot, dry areas of the world and is often found in Europe as an ornamental garden plant. Harvesting lasts from July-October.
Parts used The flowers.
Chemical compounds Lipids, carbohydrates, coagulant enzyme, cellulose, colouring substances, unsaturated oil.
Properties Colouring, anticholesterolemic, purgative.
Forms of use Normal and purified oil, infusion.
Notes This plant, which was at one time in great demand, is nowadays used as a basic ingredient of some margarines and cooking oil. A water-soluble, yellow dye used to be extracted from it as well as an alcohol-soluble red dye which is called safflower carmine. The flowers are sometimes used instead of the much more expensive saffron while, even today, certain oil paints are based on carthamin. The oil content of the seeds is a purgative although, when purified, it can be used as part of the diet of arteriosclerotics, cardiopaths and the obese because of its anticholesterol quality. Safflower seeds are one of the favourite foods of parrots, hence the unofficial name of 'parrot plant'.

71 CARUM CARVI L.

Caraway

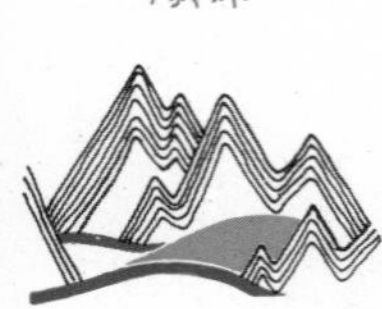

Family Umbelliferae.
Description A biennial plant with a spindle-shaped root and a branched stem reaching a height of up to 32 inches (80cm). The pinnatisect leaves are lobed from base to apex. Each inflorescence consists of an umbel with up to 15 unequal, white ray florets. Within these florets the small flowers, each of which has 5 petals, 5 stamens and a reduced calyx, are grouped into smaller umbels. The fruit is an elongated, ovoid ribbed cremocarp. This plant grows wherever there is grass, even in the mountainous areas of Europe. Possibly a native in Britain, it is increasingly rare in the wild although often cultivated in gardens. It is gathered when ripe.
Parts used Fruit.
Chemical compounds Essence containing: limonene, carvone, carvene; proteins, fatty acids, tannin, oil, resin.
Properties Aromatic, digestive, carminative, antispasmodic, antiseptic.
Forms of use Decoction, tincture, powder, ointment.
Notes A yield of about 5% of essential oil, with a density of 0.9, is obtained by extraction; one of its uses is in the making of the liqueur, Kümmel. This plant is not only used in liquor distilleries but also in perfumeries. It is used, too, in creams and ointments as a parasiticide. Young caraway shoots are often mixed in with salads to add an aromatic tang.

---

72 CASTANEA SATIVA Mill.

Castanea vesca Gaertn., *Castanea vulgaris* Lam., *Fagus castanea* L.

Sweet chestnut (Spanish chestnut)

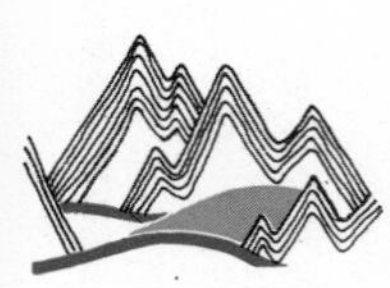

Family Fagaceae.
Description This familiar tree, with its erect, round, branched trunk and deeply ribbed bark can grow to nearly 100 feet (30m) in height. The petiolate leaves are lanceolate, acute, serrate, glabrous and leathery. The male flowers form cylindrical, yellow catkins arising from the leaf axils; the female flowers are grouped in separate catkins or appear as 1 or 2 at the base of the male catkins. The fruit consists of 1, 2 or 3 globular achenes enclosed in a thick, prickly case. This tree grows wild in woodlands throughout southern Europe and is often cultivated in Britain for its timber and nuts. The medicinally useful parts are gathered from May-July.
Parts used Leaves and bark.
Chemical compounds Tannin, gallic acid, inositol, pectin, sugar, phosphorus, magnesium, iron.
Properties Astringent, bronchial sedative, antitussive.
Forms of use Infusion, tincture, fluid extract and syrup.
Notes The flowers are very attractive to bees and are sometimes also used in various blends of aromatic pipe tobacco. The hard timber is widely used by wood-turners and carpenters. The extracted tannin is utilized in the tanning of hides. A natural shampoo, which imparts a golden gleam to the hair, is obtained from its leaves and from the chestnut skins. The leaves have even been used as a substitute for witch hazel. The nutritional qualities of chestnut flour are similar to those of wheat flour; it is used to make a purée to serve with turkey. *Marrons glacés* are a well-known sweetmeat. An infusion of the leaves is one of the most effective remedies for whooping-cough.

73 CATHARANTHUS ROSEUS G. Don

Vinca rosea L.
Madagascar periwinkle

Family Apocynaceae.
Description A typical plant of warm, tropical countries, it has an erect, cylindrical stem which is woody, branched and green in colour; its habit is reclinate for a short way and then erect. The opposite leaves, have a short petiole, are ovate-elliptical or lanceolate with an acute or sub-acute apex. The upper surface of the leaves is glossy and glabrous while the lower one is paler and opaque. The flowers are pedicellate, growing singly at the apex or from the leaf axils; they have a tubular, pink corolla with obovate lobes. The Madagascar periwinkle can grow to a height of 32 inches (80cm). This plant is not found wild in Europe. The medicinally useful parts are gathered while the plant is in flower.
Parts used Leaves.
Chemical compounds Vinblastine, vincristine (Leurocristine), vinroside, vincystine.
Properties Cytostatic.
Forms of use Decoction, fluid extract, tincture, homoeopathic preparation.
Notes The anticancerous possibilities of this variety of periwinkle have only come to light quite recently. For some years it has been used in the treatment of diabetes. The Madagascar periwinkle is a tender species, growing outdoors in warmer regions of Europe but requiring a greenhouse in cooler areas such as Britain in order to control both temperature and moisture.

---

74 CELTIS AUSTRALIS L.

Southern nettle tree

Family Ulmaceae.
Description A long-lived tree with deep, spreading roots that may grow as high as 65 feet (20m), its trunk having a diameter of more than 40 inches (1m). The bark is grey and the trunk is often grooved. The leaves are lanceolate with an acuminate apex and a dentate margin; their upper surface is dark green and the lower a paler colour. The greenish flowers are arranged in axillary clusters on a peduncle. The fruit is a yellowish-green drupe which becomes blackish as it ripens. It grows freely around the Mediterranean and warmer parts of Europe but is not found in Britain outside arboreta. The medicinally useful parts are gathered in June.
Parts used Leaves.
Chemical compounds Tannin, mucilage.
Properties Astringent, lenitive, antidiarrhoeic, stomachic.
Forms of use Decoction, fluid extract.
Notes Nettle tree fruit can be eaten and is used to make country-style jam. The wood, which is widely used by turners, was once used to make whips. An oil can be pressed from the seeds and a yellow colouring essence extracted for dyeing silk.

75 CENTAUREA CENTAURIUM L.

Great knapweed

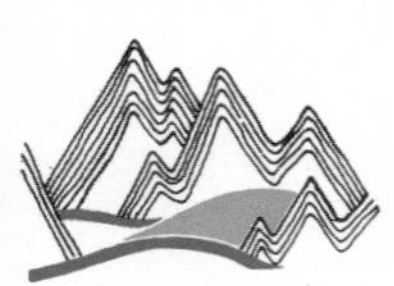

Family Compositae.
Description A herbaceous plant with a fat, white, spindle-shaped root. The erect stem is branched with alternate, pinnatifid, mono or biserrate, green leaves borne on petioles. The purple flowers are tubular and carried in globose heads. The fruit is a flattened achene with a brown pappus. A rather uncommon plant in Britain, it prefers the rich soil of some mountain slopes and wooded areas. It is gathered in October.
Parts used Root.
Chemical compounds Centaurin, phytosterol, inulin, resin, tannin, bitter substance.
Properties Tonic, cholagogic, antitussive.
Forms of use Infusion, syrup, tincture, medicinal wine.
Notes The bitter quality of this plant makes a good basis for home-made spirituous liquors. Externally it is used in decoction as an astringent for skin diseases or for application to wounds, with a remarkable healing effect. A concentrated decoction is also used as a mouthwash in cases of thrush. Distillation of the leaves provides a distilled water that is effective in treating inflamed eyes when used in eye-lotions. In some regions, the tender inflorescences are mixed into salads for their fortifying and digestive effect.

---

76 CENTAUREA CYANUS L.

Cornflower

Family Compositae.
Description The specific name derives from the Greek *kyanos,* sky-blue. It is an annual or occasionally biennial herb, averaging about 40 inches (1m) high, with whitish hairs and a taproot. It has a very branched stem. The basal leaves are pinnatifid and form a rosette while the stem leaves are entire. The flowers are borne on slender peduncles, grouped in heads made up of peripheral, tubular, sky-blue flowers which are deeply lobed and internal, purple flowers. The flowers emerge from a receptacle encased in membraneous scales. The fruit is a cylindrical achene with a bristly, variegated pappus. Found growing wild in many cornfields throughout Europe, this plant is rare in Britain. The cornflower is gathered from May to the end of summer.
Parts used Flowers.
Chemical compounds Flavonoid, centaurin, cyanine dye, cyanidin, tannin, salts of potassium and magnesium.
Properties Ophthalmic, antitussive, bitter diuretic.
Forms of use Distilled water, infusion, tincture.
Notes The young shoots of the cornflower are edible and the long-stemmed flowers are used in dry-flower arrangements as they retain their light blue colour well. The plant is commonly used in some rural areas of Europe as a soothing eye-lotion in cases of conjunctivitis and blepharitis. A decoction of the leaves is sometimes used as an antirheumatic and the seeds as a mild laxative for children.

77 CENTAUREA JACEA L.
Brown radiant knapweed

Family Compositae.
Description A taprooted, herbaceous plant averaging 2 feet (60cm) high, it has an erect, branched, slightly pubescent stem. The alternate leaves, which are lanceolate and wavy-edged, may be petiolate or sessile according to their position on the stem. It has single, apical heads with reddish-purple or, occasionally, white flowers and each head has an involucre of overlapping bracts. The fruit is a white achene. This plant is commonly found in the countryside of temperate Europe, especially in uncultivated areas, hedgerows and on waste ground. It is occasionally found in southern England.
Parts used Root.
Chemical compounds Centaurin, colouring substance, potassium, magnesium, tannin, mucilage.
Properties Bitter tonic, stomachic, diuretic, antithermic.
Forms of use Infusion, tincture, powder, medicinal wine, fluid extract, distilled water.
Notes The brown radiant knapweed is still used, in many rural areas, as a digestive and to reduce the temperature of feverish children. It is an excellent bitter for treating a difficult digestive system. As with the cornflower, distilled water made from its leaves is used as an eye-lotion in cases of conjunctivitis.

---

78 CERATONIA SILIQUA L.
Carob-tree

Family Leguminosae.
Description A small evergreen tree or shrub with a short, thick trunk and a dense crown. The almost round, compound green leaves are paripinnate with very short petioles; they are leathery and glossy with an entire margin and smooth surfaces. The flowers of each sex may be on different trees or the flowers may be bisexual on the same tree, and are arranged in racemes on a peduncle which emerges directly from the trunk. The calyx is small and 5-toothed; there are no petals. The fruit is a reddish-brown leathery pod with 2 long marginal ribs on each side; it is fleshy inside and contains a row of hard, dark-coloured seeds. This plant originates in Asia Minor but is now found growing wild along the Mediterranean coasts and in Portugal. The fruit is gathered when ripe.
Parts used Fruit, from which a type of flour is made.
Chemical compounds Sugars, fats, protein, tannin, pectin, benzoic acid, formic acid, mucilage, vitamins.
Properties Antidiarrhoeic, emollient.
Forms of use Fluid extract, electuary, decoction, syrup.
Notes Alcoholic drinks can be made from the carob-tree stems when the pulp has been fermented. The flour is used in the making of bouillon cubes and as the basis of a cocoa-flavoured drink. It is also used in the cosmetic industry to make face-packs and, in animal husbandry, forms the basis of a mash for animal foods. The timber is well regarded by wood-turners, and tannin is extracted from the bark for use in the preparation of leather.

79 CETERACH OFFICINARUM DC.

Asplenium ceterach L.
Common spleenwort

Family Polypodiaceae.
Description A fern with a very short rhizome and numerous rootlets. Its leathery fronds, which may grow to a length of 8-10 inches (20-25cm), arise directly from the rhizome. They are pinnate-parted with opposite, alternate lobes which are dark green on the upper surface and a reddish-brown on the lower. The sporangia are situated underneath the middle veins and join up in linear sori. This small plant is often to be seen throughout Europe, including Britain, in the cracks and fissures of rocks and walls; in warmer areas it never grows on the ground. It is gathered in May-August.

Parts used Whole plant.
Chemical compounds Tannin, organic acids, mucilage.
Properties Antitussive, diuretic.
Forms of use Infusion.

Notes This plant should be used with caution as it has not yet been sufficiently researched. Preparations made with it have a most disagreeable flavour which has to be disguised with aromatic and sweetening substances in order to make them acceptable to the palate. This plant is often confused with *Asplenium trichomanes* which is very similar but smaller and more delicate. It is worth noting how the common spleenwort grows and thrives in stony places, where the soil has leached away, as this allows for easier dispersal of its spores. When the plant is in full sunlight, the fronds fold up in order to conserve water. In the Mediterranean regions it is widely used to treat gravel in the urine. It is also used frequently, with other mucilaginous plants, to cure bronchial complaints.

---

80 CETRARIA ISLANDICA Ach.

Physca islandica DC., *Lichene islandicus* L.
Icelandic moss

Family Parmeliaceae.
Description This is a lichen, a word deriving from the Greek *leiko,* to lick, which describes, in a figurative sense, the habit of a plant that laps its tongues all over its host. Icelandic moss grows into little erect, odourless tufts about 3 inches (8cm) high and usually lives on rocks or on the bark of trees, especially on the branches of conifers. It can be seen throughout Europe, including Britain, but is especially prolific in the Arctic regions. The thallus, which is greenish or whitish, is divided into leathery, undulate lobes which are fringed and folded; the marginal fringes tend to be a little darker. It is gathered throughout the year.

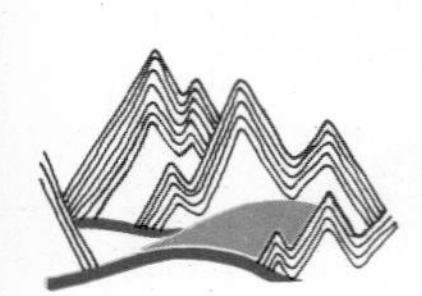

Parts used Thallus.
Chemical compounds Lichen starch, cellulose, mucilage, sugar, gum, cetrarin, salts of potassium, iron, sodium and magnesium, as well as salicylic, fumaric and usnic acids.
Properties Bitter, tonic, antitussive, galactophorous, antibiotic vermifuge, vulnerary.

Forms of use Decoction, jelly, fluid extract, tincture, powder.
Notes Used by pharmacists for chest preparations and in pastilles, the jelly has, on occasions, also been used as a food. Since this iichen is very bitter, it has first to be boiled in potassium carbonate in order to eliminate the flavour. Recent research has revealed a powerful antibiotic quality in the usnic acid and it has become a fundamental ingredient in a wide range of commercially produced disinfectants.

81 CHEIRANTHUS CHEIRI L.
Wallflower

Family Cruciferae.
Description An erect, herbaceous plant with a woody root and short branchlets leading off from the main stems. The basal leaves are grouped to form a rosette while the stem leaves are alternate, lanceolate, entire and almost sessile. The flowers are 4-sepalled and 4-petalled, with a yellow corolla striated in red or brown; they are carried in apical clusters. The fruit is a quadrangular siliqua containing oval seeds. This plant is widely grown by amateur and professional horticulturists throughout Europe. In Britain, although introduced, it is frequently found growing wild in lowland areas. It is gathered in September.
Parts used Leaves.
Chemical compounds Cheiranthin, quercitin, myrosin.
Properties Cardiotonic.
Forms of use Infusion, tincture, powder, fluid extract, dry extract, medicinal wine.
Notes If taken in large doses, this plant can be poisonous because it is more active than digitalin. It certainly should not be taken by anyone suffering from Basedow's disease (Grave's disease or exophthalmic goitre), myocarditis or bradycardia. It has only recently been discovered that cheiranthin has cardiotonic properties; the plant was previously only used as a diuretic, but at some risk. There are two main types of wallflower: the taller varieties which grow to about 15-18 inches (38-45cm) and the dwarf 10-12 inches (25-30cm), some of which are suitable for cutting and some for bedding.

---

82 CHELIDONIUM MAJUS L.
Greater celandine

Family Papaveraceae.
Description The generic name derives either from the Latin *donum coeli,* a gift from heaven, or from the Greek *khelidon,* a swallow, as the plant is in flower during the spring migratory visit of this bird. It is a perennial herb with a taproot that branches out in all directions. Its petiolate leaves are pinnatisect, the segments being either sessile or having very short petioles, broadening out again at the juncture of the segment and petiole. Its small, 4-petalled, golden-yellow flowers have a 2-sepalled calyx and are grouped in small umbel-like clusters. The plant grows wild throughout Europe, western Asia and North Africa, with a preference for rubble, the outer walls of houses and damp places generally. It is probably a native of Britain, although rare in Scotland. This plant may reach 20 inches (50cm) or more in height. It should be gathered in spring and used while fresh.
Parts used Whole plant.
Chemical compounds The alkaloids: chelidonine, sanguinarine, chelerythrin, protopine, berberine, sparteine; phosphate, calcium, ammonium, magnesium, essential oil, enzymes.
Properties Cholagogic, biliary deobstruent, narcotic, coryzide.
Forms of use Infusion, tincture, juice.
Notes It is dangerous to exceed an intake of more than a certain amount of any preparation containing greater celandine extracts due to its effect on the neurovegetative balance and, because of the chelerythrin content, on the heart. The caustic juice is used to get rid of warts and verrucae. It is also used to treat rheumatic complaints and liver disturbances as well as ailments of the respiratory tract and digestive system.

83 CHENOPODIUM BONUS-HENRICUS L.

Goosefoot (Good King Henry)

Family Chenopodiaceae.
Description This variety of goosefoot is named after King Henry IV of Navarre. It is an erect, perennial herb with a woody root and ribbed stems. The whole plant is covered with a yellowish powder. The alternate leaves are hastate, triangular, undulate and petiolate. The greenish flowers, gathered into apical spikes, have 5 sepals. The tightly-packed fruits contain kidney-shaped seeds with endosperm. The plant grows throughout Europe, including Britain, to a height of about 20 inches (50cm) and thrives on flat, waste ground near villages, on roadside verges and in hedgerows. It is gathered in summer.
Parts used Whole plant.
Chemical compounds Mucilage, saponin, iron, salts.
Properties Emollient, laxative.
Forms of use Powder, infusion.
Notes Sufferers with kidney complaints or rheumatism should avoid preparations containing extracts of this plant. Well regarded by macrobiotic dieticians, the young inflorescences are boiled and eaten like spinach. It is particularly recommended for anaemic subjects, because of its iron content. The leaves are also used externally on boils and abscesses. The leaves are pounded to release their mucilaginous content and then applied to the boil to bring it to a head. The seeds have a gentle laxative effect, making them suitable for a slightly constipated condition, especially in children.

---

84 CHRYSANTHEMUM LEUCANTHEMUM L.

Leucanthemum vulgare Lam.
Ox-eye daisy (Marguerite)

Family Compositae.
Description A perennial plant, often grown as an annual, it varies in height from 1-2 feet (30-60cm). It is glabrous, sometimes wooly-haired and slightly branched with longitudinal, red striations on its stems. The petiolate lower leaves are spoon-shaped, the apical ones being narrow and amplexicaul. The flowers are aggregated into heads encircled by the narrow bracts of the involucre with their deep reddish-purple margins. The apex of each outer ligulate flower of the corolla has tiny denticulate ligules. The dark fruits of these are elongated and distinguished by a white line, while the fruits of the central flowers are equipped with a kind of pappus. The ox-eye daisy flowers from April-October and grows wild in Europe, including Britain, in fields and woodland clearings from coast to mountains. It is gathered while in flower.
Parts used Flowers.
Chemical compounds Essence, tannin, gum, resin.
Properties Antispasmodic, antitussive, emmenagogic, vulnerary.
Forms of use Powder, infusion, tincture, poultice.
Notes Applied externally it has a vulnerary action on wounds that are slow to form a scar. Distilled water made from this plant is an effective eye-lotion in the treatment of conjunctivitis. In spring its tender shoots make a useful addition to a mixed green salad. It is often cultivated as an attractive flowering plant.

85 CHRYSANTHEMUM PARTHENIUM Bernh.

Tanacetum Parthenium (L.) Schutz-Bip.

Feverfew

Family Compositae.
Description A perennial plant, sometimes treated as an annual, which may grow to a height of about 28 inches (70cm). The delicate, pale green leaves have an irregular surface and are divided into broad, unequal, obtuse, oval leaflets. The heads are small with an outer ring of square-ended ligulate flowers and small inner disc flowers, although there are some capitula which are only ligulate. The flowering period lasts about 3 months. This plant is frequently found growing wild in Europe, including Britain, where it was introduced from the Balkan Peninsula, and also under cultivation in herb gardens. It is gathered in June.
Parts used Leaves and heads.
Chemical compounds Essence, phytosterol, tannic acid, anthemic acid (the bitter principle).
Properties Stomachic, antispasmodic, tranquillizer, emmenagogic.
Forms of use Infusion, tincture, powder, fluid extract, distilled water, essence, medicinal wine.
Notes This plant is often used in cooking to give a deliciously aromatic, bitter taste to certain foods. The extracted essence is used in both the liquor and perfume industries. As a tincture, it has an anti-ecchymotic effect when used externally. Feverfew thrives in any type of soil.

---

86 CICHORIUM INTYBUS L.

Chicory (Wild Succory)

Family Compositae.
Description A perennial plant about 40 inches (1m) in height with a tapering, taprooted, brown rhizome that has numerous milky sap-producing vessels. The erect stem is branched, with basal, coarsely toothed lobate leaves in rosette form, while its sessile, stem leaves are lanceolate, glabrous and pilose. The flowers are grouped in heads at each foliar axil and have sky-blue, ligulate corollas. The fruit is an ovoidal, angular achene with a short pappus. Probably naturalized in Britain, this plant is common on roadsides in southern England, although it is rare elsewhere. The root can be dug up throughout the summer but is usually left until October.
Parts used Root, flowers and whole plant.
Chemical compounds Bitter substance, choline, sugar, inulin, potassium, calcium, iron.
Properties Depurative, hypoglycaemiant, cholagogic, laxative.
Forms of use Decoction, fluid extract, semi-fluid extract, syrup, powder, distilled water.
Notes Special characteristic: chicory leaves sprout in the autumn but dry off when the plant comes into bloom. Roasted chicory roots are still widely used as an excellent substitute or adulterant for coffee. Diabetics can easily tolerate the boiled root as inulin agrees with them more than starch. The water in which the whole plant has been boiled is useful in relieving constipation due to hepatic insufficiency. The roots, in the form of syrup of succory, make an excellent laxative for children.

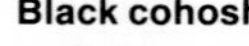

87 CIMICIFUGA RACEMOSA Nutt.

Actaea racemosa L.
Black cohosh

Family Ranunculaceae.
Description A perennial, herbaceous plant with a creeping, fleshy, dark brown rhizome, which grows to an average height of 5 feet (1.50m) with a delicate, angular stem. The basal and stem leaves are bitriternate, each one having 3 pointed, trilobate leaflets. The white flowers are grouped in a racemose inflorescence with a 4-5-sepalled calyx. There may be no petals at all but, if they are present, they may range from 1-8, and are club-shaped. The flowers also contain a great many stamens. The fruit is a pale follicle containing numerous seeds. This is a plant commonly found in North America. The roots are dug up when ripe.
Parts used Rhizome.
Chemical compounds Palmitic, oleic and salicylic acids, bitter, phytosterol, saponin, tannin.
Properties Cardiotonic, antispasmodic, antineuralgic, emmenagogic.
Forms of use Syrup, fluid extract.
Notes The generic name (from the Latin *cimicus,* bug) derives from a belief that this plant had a parasiticidal effect on bugs – a belief long since disproved. Care must be taken not to exceed the prescribed dose of any medicine containing an extract of black cohosh to avoid serious symptoms of poisoning. Its action is similar to that of digitalis and it may be used in conjunction with belladonna to achieve a synergic effect. This drug is incompatible with ferrous salts and alcohols.

---

88 CITRUS LIMON (L.) Burm. fil.

Citrus limonum Risso
Lemon

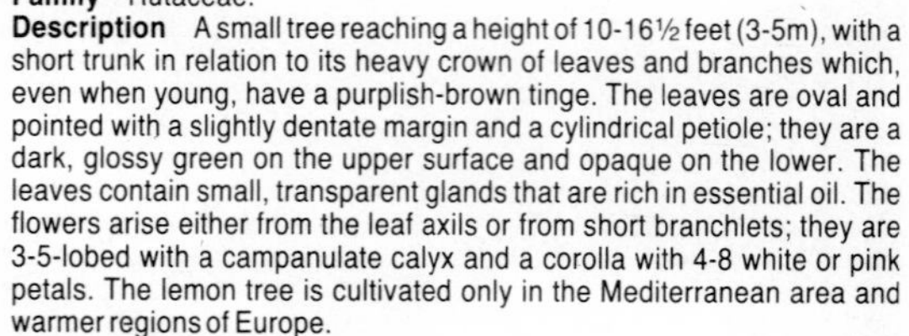

Family Rutaceae.
Description A small tree reaching a height of 10-16½ feet (3-5m), with a short trunk in relation to its heavy crown of leaves and branches which, even when young, have a purplish-brown tinge. The leaves are oval and pointed with a slightly dentate margin and a cylindrical petiole; they are a dark, glossy green on the upper surface and opaque on the lower. The leaves contain small, transparent glands that are rich in essential oil. The flowers arise either from the leaf axils or from short branchlets; they are 3-5-lobed with a campanulate calyx and a corolla with 4-8 white or pink petals. The lemon tree is cultivated only in the Mediterranean area and warmer regions of Europe.
Parts used Peel of the fruit.
Chemical compounds Limonene, citral, pinene, camphene, phellandrene, citronellal, terpinol, octyl aldehyde, linalyl acetate, geranyl acetate, citroptene.
Properties Antiscorbutic, anti-uricaemic, antirheumatic, disinfectant, astringent, vitamin-rich.
Forms of use Juice, essence.
Notes An essence is obtained from the peel which is extensively used in the perfume industry. A better quality essence is made from the flowers. The juice is a very effective bactericide as well as being useful in other ways such as removing inkstains and polishing bronze and other metals that have been neglected. The peel is candied for use as cake decorations and sweetmeats. It will also act as a moth repellent if put into small bags and placed among clothes.

89 CITRUS AURANTIUM L. var. AMARA L.

Citrus bigaradia L isel., *Citrus vulgaris* Risso
Bitter orange

Family Rutaceae.
Description An evergreen tree with a domed crown, it has a rather stocky, smooth trunk of a greyish-green colour and grows to a height of over 26 feet (8m). The green, leathery, elliptical-acute leaves are alternate or spiral with a wing-shaped petiole and a spiny stipule. The flowers, borne at the apex of the branches, have a 5-lobed calyx and a white, 5-petalled corolla; the ovary is superior with a cylindrical style and a spherical stigma. The fruit is a spherical hesperidium with a yellowish-orange, rough skin enclosing several juicy segments which contain ovoid, white seeds. The leaves, shoots and peel of the fruit are rich in oily glands. Originating in the Indies, the bitter orange is rarely found growing wild in Europe but orchards are now well established along much of the Mediterranean coast, especially in the south of France, Sicily, Calabria and Spain.
Parts used Leaves, flowers, peel.
Chemical compounds Leaves: an essence consisting of limonene, aurantiamarin, hesperidin, neohesperidin, acids, stachydrine, glucose, tannin. Flowers: limonene, pinene, linalool, citronellol, nerol, camphene, geraniol, resin. Peel: d-limonene, methyl anthranilate, citral, citronellal, hesperidin, enzyme, vitamins, pectin.
Properties Leaves: digestive, antispasmodic. Flowers: tranquillizer, sedative, antispasmodic. Peel: bitter, digestive, stomachic.
Forms of use Leaves: infusion, essential oil. Flowers: infusion, syrup, essential oil. Peel: infusion, tincture, essential oil, powder, medicinal wine.
Notes The bitter orange is much used both in the making of spirituous liquors, to give a pleasantly bitter-sweet bouquet, and especially in the preparation of 'Curaçao'-type liqueurs. The main use of the plant is in the extraction of essences which vary somewhat according to the part distilled. These essences are in great demand in the perfume industry for their distinctive fragrances. The essential oil obtained from the flowers is known as 'Neroli oil'; from about 1680 this was extracted by distillation but is now obtained with the aid of volatile solvents. The yield is extremely low and the essence is, therefore, often adulterated.

The oil of *petit-grain* is an essence obtained by steam distillation of the leaves and young shoots to give a yield of one part per 400. This oil, too, is often adulterated with synthetic products or with terpenes of lemon. The aqueous portion remaining after the flower distillation is known as orange flower water and has various culinary uses; a similar by-product is obtained from *petit-grain;* both are used in the making of perfumes and, medicinally, as correctives and antihysterics.

The essences mentioned are all employed in the making of various types of *'eau de cologne'*. In recent years, the oil extracted from the seeds has become more widely used as it contains linolenic acid which has an active anticholesterolemic action.

90 CLEMATIS VITALBA L.

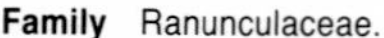

Clematis latifolia dentata JB.

Traveller's joy (Old man's beard)

Family Ranunculaceae.

Description A subshrubby, scrambling or climbing plant, with thin, trailing, channelled stems which can grow to a length of about 50 feet (15m) or so. The opposite leaves are pinnatisect, with small oval, dentate, glabrous leaflets on a twisting petiole. The oblong-obtuse, 4-sepalled white flowers are grouped in panicles. The infructescence consists of aristate, plumose achenes. The plant, a native to southern England and Wales, is frequently to be seen growing wild in woodlands, hedgerows and on rocky slopes throughout Europe. It is gathered in summer.

Parts used Leaves.

Chemical compounds Clemantine, clemetitol, caulosaponin, phytosterol, acids, alcohols, resin, stigmasterin.

Properties Analgesic, rubefacient.

Forms of use Infusion, ointment, fluid extract, poultice, oily solution.

Notes This plant is poisonous if taken internally and should never, therefore, be drunk in any form. The bruised plant will cause inflammation, vesication and even sores if applied externally and is used in homoeopathic medicaments to produce a sympathetic reaction. It has a revulsive and analgesic effect when used as an ointment in many diseases. The young shoots can be eaten like hop shoots but, as well as being bitter, they can be quite dangerous. If the juice is introduced ito the nostrils it will relieve a migraine attack but it can destroy the mucous membrane.

---

91 CNICUS BENEDICTUS L.

Carbenia benedicta (L.) Arcang., *Carduus benedictus* Blak., *Benedicta officinalis* Bernh., *Centaurea benedicta* L., *Calcitrapa lanuginosa* Lem.

Holy thistle

Family Compositae.

Description An annual herb with a white, cylindrical taproot, it grows to more than 2 feet (60cm) high with an erect, angular, pubescent, reddish stem, branched towards the apex. The alternate leaves are leathery and pinnatifid with spiny lobes, those on the stem being sessile and, in a few cases, amplexicaul. The yellow, tubular flowers are grouped in single, tomentose heads. The achenes are cylindrical with a pappus. The favourite habitat of this plant is dry ground, preferably in the Mediterranean region. It is gathered in June-July.

Parts used Whole plant.

Chemical compounds Bitter ethereal compounds, volatile oil, tannin, salts of potassium, resin, mucilage.

Properties Bitter, cholagogic, stomachic, diuretic.

Forms of use Infusion, tincture, distilled water, fluid extract, semi-fluid extract, medicinal wine.

Notes Excessive doses of any mixture containing this plant will cause vomiting. It is used to give a bitter tang to spirituous liquors. It is not advised in cases of hyperacidity but has excellent antithermic properties. The tincture derived from the fresh plant is used in homoeopathic practice for treating hepatitis and jaundice as well as in the relief of arthritis. At one time it was used to treat chilblains. Nowadays it is used externally in cases of shingles, while the 19th-century German botanist Kuntze claimed that a mixture of holy thistle and common centaury was helpful in the various types of epilepsy.

92 COLCHICUM AUTUMNALE L.

Autumn crocus (Meadow saffron)

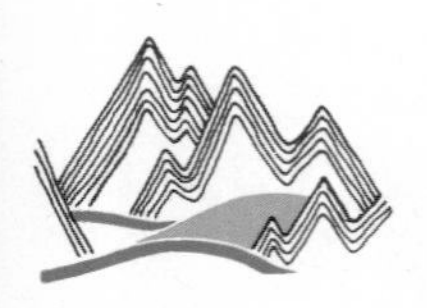

Family Liliaceae.
Description A delightful little herbaceous, colonizing plant with a deeply rooted, oval corm encased in brownish scales. The 2-3 leaves, which arise directly from the corm, are lanceolate, pointed and fleshy with a sheathing base. The 6-tepalled flowers, growing singly, are borne on a long tube which also emerges from the corm; they have 6 stamens joined in the centre to the ovary. The fruits have the unusual biological characteristic of emerging from beneath the ground in spring, at the same time as the leaves; they consist of ovoid capsules containing globose seeds which are lifted up by the elongating pedicels. Autumn crocus grows freely in the lush meadows of fertile valleys of continental Europe. Although a native of Great Britain it is extremely rare except for the area around the Bristol Channel. It is gathered when ripe.
Parts used Seeds and corms.
Chemical compounds Colchicine, colchicoside, fat, tannin, oil, gallic acid.

Properties Analgesic, antipyretic, antigout, emetic.
Forms of use Fluid extract, tincture, pills, ointment.
Notes This plant is particularly toxic, thus making any preparation in which it is used potentially dangerous and only to be taken under medical supervision. Tests have shown it to have a mitotic action on the cells but this has not yet been fully researched. It is contra-indicated with tannin and borax. As an external ointment it has an antipruriginous, antineuralgic and analgesic action.

---

93 CONIUM MACULATUM L.

Cicuta major Lam.
Hemlock

Family Umbelliferae.
Description A biennial herbaceous plant with a thick, white, spindle-shaped root. It has a cylindrical, branched, hollow stem of a light green colour with reddish markings. The sheathed, basal leaves, borne on a hollow petiole, are pinnatifid, mucronate and dentate, fairly dark green on the upper surface but lighter on the lower. On the stem leaves, the petiole is reduced merely to a sheath. The numerous white flowers are grouped in umbels of 10-20 ray florets. The fruits are ovoid cremocarps with ridged seeds. The whole plant has a foetid smell. A native to Britain, it is commonly found growing throughout England and Europe on waste land, among rubble, and in damp ground, from coastal to mountainous areas. It is gathered in summer.

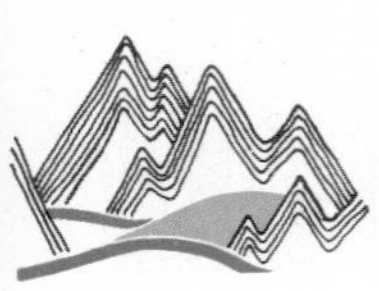

Parts used Leaves.
Chemical compounds Alkaloids, cicutine, methyl-conicine, conhydrine, pseudoconhydrine, gum, pectin, resin, carotene, caffeic and acetic acids, salts.

Properties Analgesic, antineuralgic, antispasmodic, galactofuge.
Forms of use Powder, tincture, syrup, fluid extract, ointment.
Notes A poisonous plant with a paralyzing effect on the motor centres (neuro-muscular junctions); although less toxic when cut and dried, it is still dangerous. Children easily confuse it with parsley but as soon as they pick a few leaves the nauseous smell makes them realize their mistake. A homoeopathic tincture is extensively used to treat arteriosclerosis and prostate complaints.

94 CONVALLARIA MAJALIS L.

Lily-of-the-valley

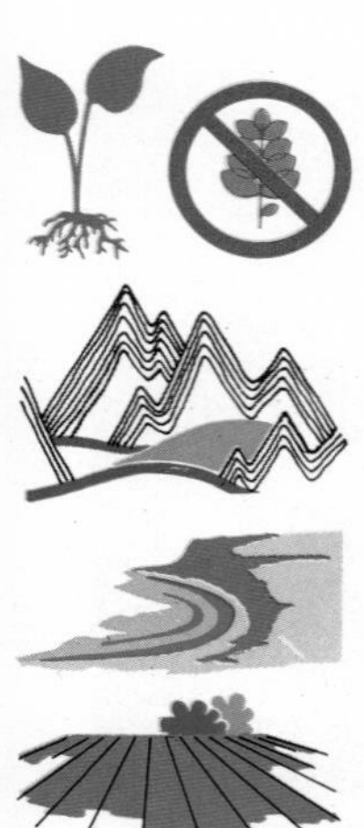

Family Liliaceae.
Description The generic name derives from the Latin *convallium,* of the valleys, and the specific name from *maialis,* of May. A perennial herbaceous plant with a creeping rhizome from which the aerial part arises. Each plantlet has 2 oval leaves with a pointed apex, the leaf base tightly sheathing the long petiole; the blade is smooth, of a rather dark, clear green, with a wavy margin and undulate on the inside. The inflorescence is a raceme with sweetly scented, pendulous, white flowers aligned on one side of the stem and hanging from short pedicels. The flower has no sepals; the bell-shaped perianth is 6-toothed. The fruit is a round, red berry containing a few small seeds. Lilies-of-the-valley grow wild in some regions of Europe, including England (rarely in Scotland), where it is a native, in dry, shady woodlands and the lower slopes of hills or mountains. It is extensively cultivated for both its charming appearance and delightful perfume. It is gathered in May.
Parts used Leaves and flowers.
Chemical compounds Convallatoxin, convallamarin, convallarin, myalin, chelidonic acid, sugar.
Properties Sedative, cardiotonic, diuretic.
Forms of use Powder, fluid extract, tincture, syrup.
Notes This plant is particularly toxic when taken internally and, although it can take the place of digitalin, it is hardly ever used because of the inconsistency of the drug. The powdered rhizome is used as a sternutatory (to cause sneezing) in the treatment of head colds.

---

95 CONVOLVULUS ARVENSIS L.

Field bindweed

Family Convolvulaceae.
Description A herbaceous plant with a creeping root and an erect, thin, twining stem. The petiolate leaves are either hastate or sagittate, acuminate or obtuse-mucronate or entire cordiform. The large, white or pink flowers are trumpet-shaped, borne on a pedicel, with 2 bracts enfolding the 5-lobed calyx with its gamopetalous corolla. The fruit is a capsule with large, black seeds. It is an invasive plant, commonly found throughout Europe, including England, twining itself through hedges and over fences, wherever it can find a roothold in low-lying land, fields and woodlands or the lower slopes of mountains. It is gathered from spring to summer.
Parts used Leaves.
Chemical compounds Resin, glucosides, tannin.
Properties Purgative, cholagogic.
Forms of use Infusion, wafer papers with resin, powder, tincture.
Notes The purgative effect produced by the resin is similar to that of jalap but much less drastic. The powder is a gentle purgative and, when mixed with honey, is readily taken by children. The flowers open in the morning and close in the evening, the long stems creeping or swinging in slow circles to twist themselves around anything with which they come into contact.

96 CORNUS MAS L.
Cornelian cherry

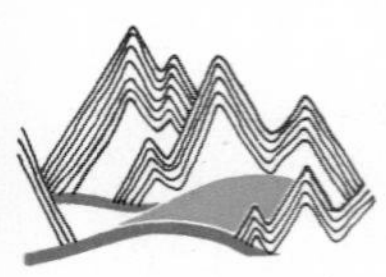

Family Cornaceae.
Description The generic name derives from the Latin *cornus,* horn, because of the hardness of the wood. A branched shrub which grows to a height of about 16½ feet (5m), it has a greenish bark; the opposite leaves are elliptical, simple, acuminate, glossy and slightly pubescent. The flowers appear before the leaves and are grouped in terminal umbels; their calyx is 4-toothed and their pale yellow corolla is 4-petalled. The fruit, which reddens as it ripens, is an ovoid, fleshy drupe with a very hard, pale green kernel. Frequently found in woodlands throughout Europe, it has a preference for calcareous soil. In Britain it is a frequently planted introduction. It is gathered from spring to summer.
Parts used Bark and fruit.
Chemical compounds Cornin, tannin, malate of calcium, tannic and malic acids, glucose, mucilage, colouring substance.
Properties Febrifuge, astringent, nutritive.
Forms of use Decoction, juice, syrup, preserves.
Notes The drupes are preserved in brine to be eaten like olives. They are also used in the confectionery industry to make jellies. Eau-de-vie was, at one time, made from the fruit and the sodium malate used as kitchen salt. A small amount of edible oil is obtained from the seeds. A colouring substance for wool was once extracted from the bark. The leaves have been used in the tanning industry because of their high tannin content. The wood, which is heavier than water, is greatly valued by wood-turners.

---

97 CORNUS SANGUINEA L.
Common dogwood

Family Cornaceae.
Description The specific name derives from the Latin *sanguinea,* sanguine, in an allusion to the blood-red colour of the branches. A very common shrub about 6½-10 feet (2-3m) high, the basal branches are nodose and brown, tending to become redder towards the top. The opposite leaves are oval, acuminate and slightly pubescent with a furrowed petiole. The flowers, which are grouped in dense terminal clusters, are white with a 4-toothed calyx and a 4-petalled corolla. The fruit is a drupe containing fluid and leathery seeds, which is green at first but blackens as it ripens. Dogwood can be seen almost everywhere in the European countryside and is sometimes grown as a hedge. It is native to southern Britain and prefers a calcareous soil. The medicinal part is gathered throughout the year.
Parts used Bark.
Chemical compounds Tannin, cornin, pectin.
Properties Astringent, antipyretic.
Forms of use Decoction, powder, medicinal wine.
Notes Dogwood seeds contain a high percentage of inedible oil which is used in France for soap-making. A colouring substance for a particular shade of green, known as 'vesica green', was once obtained from this plant, but it is now produced synthetically. In some areas the leaves are used as an astringent, nearly always externally. As the fruit has an emetic effect, it is wise to avoid ingesting any preparation in which it is an ingredient. The young branches are very flexible and are still used in some rural areas of continental Europe to make baskets.

98 CORYLUS AVELLANA L.

Hazel

Family Betulaceae.
Description A common shrub or small tree that may grow to a height of 13 feet (4m) or more. The branches, which are flexible when young, are wooly and have glandulous hairs. The male flowers appear before the leaves; they are yellow and pendulous. The female flowers are pale green and arranged in bud-like heads on the upper part of the shoots and branches. The hazel, a native to Britain, is a fairly widely cultivated shrub and can occasionally be seen growing wild. It is found all over the British Isles and continental Europe and prefers hillside slopes although it also grows in the lowlands. It is gathered from spring to autumn, according to the geographical area.
Parts used Bark, amenta (catkins), leaves, fruit (hazelnuts).
Chemical compounds Tannins and resins, flavonoids, proteins, fats, starch, salts, vitamins.
Properties Antipyretic, odontalgic, astringent, antidiarrhoeic, diaphoretic, remineralizing, nutritive.
Forms of use Decoction, infusion, tincture, powder.
Notes This plant is widely grown for its fruit (hazelnuts) which are used in the confectionery and cake-making industries. Apart from using the nuts either whole or chopped, an edible oil is extracted from them. The bark and leaves are used in the tanning of leather as they are rich in tannin, although witch hazel leaves can be substituted to advantage. A fine flour, made from the finely ground nuts, is one of the ingredients used in the cosmetic industry to make cleansing face-masks. The wood is much in demand for the making of small pieces of turned furniture. Many people are allergic to hazel pollen, which is produced prolifically. Hazelnut oil has a very gentle, but constant and effective, action in cases of infection with threadworm or pinworm in babies and young children.

---

99 CRATAEGUS MONOGYNA Jacq.

Crataegus oxyacantha L.
Hawthorn (May-tree)

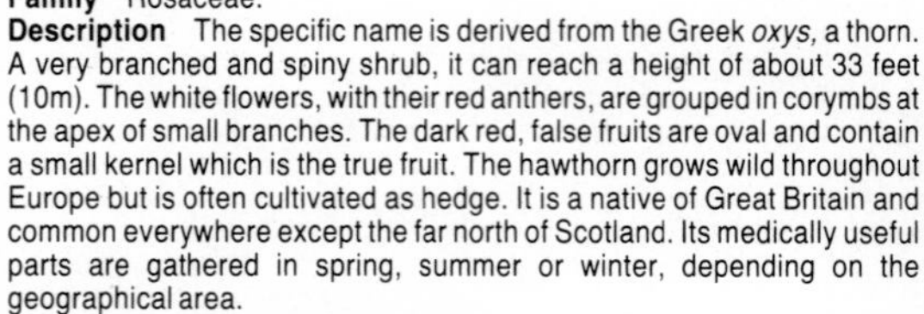

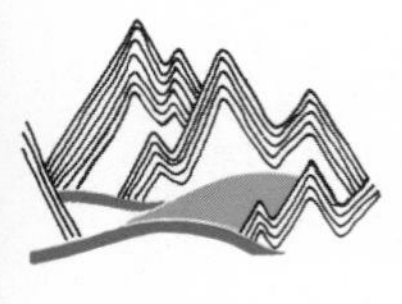

Family Rosaceae.
Description The specific name is derived from the Greek *oxys,* a thorn. A very branched and spiny shrub, it can reach a height of about 33 feet (10m). The white flowers, with their red anthers, are grouped in corymbs at the apex of small branches. The dark red, false fruits are oval and contain a small kernel which is the true fruit. The hawthorn grows wild throughout Europe but is often cultivated as hedge. It is a native of Great Britain and common everywhere except the far north of Scotland. Its medically useful parts are gathered in spring, summer or winter, depending on the geographical area.
Parts used Flowers, leaves and bark.
Chemical compounds Quercetin, quercitrin, amines, tannin, ethereal oil, histamine, vitamin C, a glucoside.
Properties Hypotensive, cardioregulating, cardiotonic, anti-arteriosclerotic, tranquillizer.
Forms of use Infusion, decoction, tincture, fluid extract, dry extract, semi-aqueous extract, syrup, distilled water.
Notes The bark is known to have been used to good effect in cases of malarial and other fevers. The fruits are not very appetizing as the pulp has an insipid flavour but they are otherwise perfectly edible. A variety has, however, been cultivated in southern Europe specifically for its edible fruit; this is *Crataegus azarolus* (azerole or Neapolitan medlar). Its timber is greatly in demand for wood-turning as it is very hard, has a good grain and takes a fine polish. An alcoholic drink, rather like cider, can be made from the fermented fruit.

100 CRITHMUM MARITIMUM L.
Rock samphire

Family Umbelliferae.
Description A herbaceous plant with a creeping rhizome and a slightly branched, undulating striate, glaucous green stem. The alternate leaves are fleshy and bitripinnatisect with linear-ololanceolate segments. Its apical leaves are pinnate. The inflorescences consist of an umbel of ray florets which, in turn, bear smaller umbels. The involucre is composed of bracts and bracteoles. The greenish flowers are 5-petalled. The fruit consists of resiniferous, ellipsoidal, green cremocarps, ribbed lengthways. Samphire can reach a height of over 20 inches (50cm) and prefers dry, sandy soil. A native to Britain, it is rare except in Cornwall and the south coast of England. It is gathered in May.
Parts used Young, growing tips.
Chemical compounds Essence, pectin, vitamins, sulphates, acetic acid.
Properties Carminative, depurative, digestive.
Forms of use Infusion, juice, tincture, essence, syrup, medicinal wine.
Notes Samphire leaves are pickled, after boiling, with salt, vinegar and spices. The essence has a strong fragrance and has pharmaceutical and culinary uses as well as being used in the perfume industry; it contains pinene, eugenol, carvacrol and dilapiol. A few drops of the essence on food is an aid to digestion.

---

101 CROCUS SATIVUS L.
Saffron

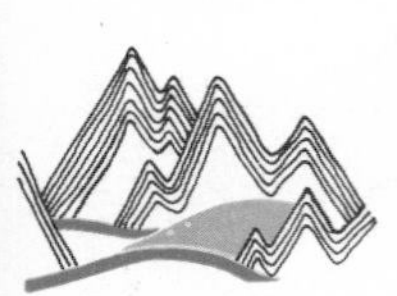

Family Iridaceae.
Description The generic name derives from the Greek *krokos,* a thread, alluding to the stigmas. A small, herbaceous plant arising from a bulb covered by a fibrous, reticulate tunic. It has a short stem encased in overlapping sheaths which continue upwards to envelop the floral stems. The leaves are linear with somewhat revolute margins and marked lengthways by a white line on the upper surface. The venation protrudes on the underside. The flowers grow singly; they consist of a long tube that broadens out at the top into 6 oval, pointed, violet lobes. The tripartite stigma in the centre is reddish-orange. The fruit is a pointed, oblong, dehiscent, trilocular capsule containing round seeds. In Britain the plant, which is autumn-flowering, is generally cultivated, but may be found growing wild as a relic of cultivation. It is gathered in September.
Parts used Stigmas.
Chemical compounds Lycopine, oil, starch, safranine, polychroite, crocin, crocosium, picrocrocin.
Properties Stimulant, antispasmodic, emmenagogic, eupeptic.
Forms of use Powder, tincture, infusion, syrup.
Notes It is included in the composition of several galenic preparations such as laudanum and the elixir of Garus, tincture of aloes being the main ingredient. It is also used in cookery for certain dishes. A dental analgesic is obtained from the stigmas. In view of the high cost of this drug, it is often adulterated with plants that resemble it.

102 CUCUMIS CITRULLUS Ser.

Citrullus lanatus (Thumb.) Mansf.

Water melon

Familu Cucurbitaceae.

Description A herbaceous plant with long, prostrate stems and simple tendrils. The greenish, delicate leaves are lobed, deeply incised, undulate and petiolate. The flowers are monoecious; the male flowers have a yellowish-green corolla with 3 stamens and the female have a simple, monolocular ovary. The fruits are oval or spherical melons, with a smooth, striate, light green rind. The pulp is a translucent red or pink with a crisp, spongy texture and a sugary flavour; a great many black seeds are embedded inside. It is grown in southern Europe on open, flat plains, on river banks and even in some desert areas but it is not a wild plant. It is gathered when it ripens in summer.

Parts used Fruit.

Chemical compounds Water, salts, vitamins, nitrogenous compounds.

Properties Endermic, diuretic.

Forms of use Juice, pulp.

Notes Because its calorie content is extremely low, it is often eaten by overweight people as part of a diet. The biological water it contains has a strong diuretic effect which is useful in cases of dropsy and renal stones. An oil obtained from the seeds has a hypotensive action. Face-masks of the pulp are widely used on delicate skins.

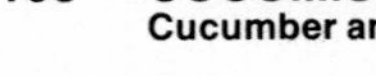

103 CUCUMIS SATIVUS L.

Cucumber and gherkin

Family Cucurbitaceae.

Description An annual herbaceous plant with creeping circular stems that cling to the ground, with regularly spaced, prominent nodes. The alternate leaves are palmate-lobate with a long petiole; they have rough leaf blades covered with rigid hairs. Tendrils spring from the base of the petioles and these enable the plant to climb any structure provided for it. There are plants with either male or female flowers. The calyx is pilose with slender, pointed, divaricate sepals and a corolla with 5-lobed, pointed, yellow petals. The fruit is cylindrical, irregular and curved with an enlarged apex and ribs running lengthways; it has oval seeds inside. This plant is widely grown throughout Europe as a salad vegetable and for pickling, although in Britain it is generally cultivated under glass. It is gathered in summer, before it is fully ripe.

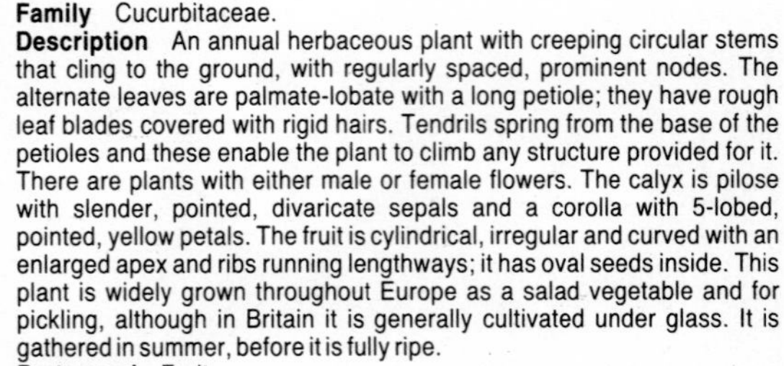

Parts used Fruit.

Chemical compounds Essence, vitamin C, carotene, amino-acids, cellulose.

Properties Emollient, anticatarrhal, depurative.

Forms of use Juice.

Notes This fruit is extensively used in cosmetic preparations to whiten the skin, the pulp in face-masks and the juice in creams and lotions. It is excellent in salads although inclined to be indigestible; it is not acceptable to everyone because of its high cellulose content. There is great demand for commercially prepared pickled cucumbers and gherkins. The seeds, as with all members of the Cucurbitaceae family, have a vermifuge effect (expelling worms from the intestine) as well as containing a little oil.

104 CUCURBITA MAXIMA Duch.
Pumpkin

Family Cucurbitaceae.
Description A creeping plant with twining stems which may grow to over 16 feet (5 m) in length. Its cordate, rounded leaves have ill-defined, rounded lobes. The long, hollow petioles are covered with leathery, but not prickly, hairs. The flower has a 5-lobed, campanulate, yellow corolla and is borne on a cylindrical pedicel. The fruit is pulpy with a greenish skin; it contains somewhat irregular, rather flat, whitish seeds. Originally from Central America, it is now extensively grown almost everywhere. It is gathered in August.
Parts used Seeds.
Chemical compounds Cucurbitin, peponoside, cucurbic acid, leucine, tyrosine, vitamins.
Properties Vermifuge.
Forms of use The pulp of the seeds in emulsion.
Notes When the emulsion has been taken to expel tapeworm or other parasitic worms, a purge must be given; this may be oily, unlike that given after taking a fern-based remedy. There are many uses for the pulp of this fruit in the kitchen, patisserie and preserving industry. Nourishing face-masks are also made from it for dry skins. Pumpkin can be dried and rehydrated as required. The flowers are also edible and are considered a great delicacy by gourmets. The seeds contain an edible oil which may one day be regarded as commercially viable in view of the high percentage yield.

---

105 CUPRESSUS SEMPERVIRENS L.
Italian cypress

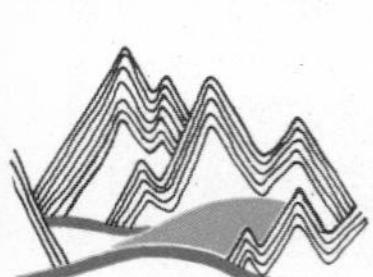

Family Cupressaceae.
Description There are 2 types of this tall tree: one has spreading branches, the other has branches held close to the trunk. The branchlets bear small, decussate, scale-like leaves with resiniferous glands. The flowers are grouped in male and female catkin-like structures. The fruit, known as a 'cone', is a woody transformation of the bracts of the female flowers. On ripening, the scales split to allow the single-winged seeds to fall. Originally from Asia Minor, this tree is now quite common in the Mediterranean area and on the Aegean coast. The medicinally useful parts are gathered from January-April.
Parts used Cones and young branches.
Chemical compounds Essential oil with a variable yield of from 0.2 to 0.6% containing mainly pinene, camphene, silvestrone; pectic substances and, in the cones, tannin.
Properties Astringent, antidiarrhoeic, antiseptic, antipyretic, balsamic, toxifuge, antihaemorrhoidal, vasoconstrictive, antirheumatic.
Forms of use Decoction, fluid extract, semi-fluid extract, dry extract, essential oil, tincture, distilled water, syrup.
Notes The timber has the great advantage of being impervious to woodworm and is, therefore, much sought after for works of art that will stand the test of time. The plant also retains its fragrance, similarly to sandalwood. The resin is obtained either by making incisions in the bark or by tapping it as it oozes out naturally. With its strong, aromatic perfume it encourages whitlows to come to a head and has a vulnerary effect on slow-healing wounds. A decoction of the wood is used in foot-baths to combat perspiration of the feet.

106 CUSCUTA EPITHYMUM (L.) L.
Lesser dodder

Family Cuscutaceae.
Description A small, annual, leafless parasitical plant, it is yellowish-orange in colour. With no roots or chlorophyll, it has a thread-like stem equipped with haustoria which penetrate the cambium of the host plant. The sessile flowers are white or pink and grouped in glomerules. The calyx is 5-parted and campanulate. The gynaecium has a superior ovary. The fruit is globose with a 3-locular capsule. Its numerous seeds are smooth and yellow. In Europe it grows almost anywhere, from coastal plains to mountainous terrain, on specific plants which it covers with a carpet-like growth. It is native to Britain, usually found in the south of England on heather or gorse. It is gathered from June-September.
Parts used Whole plant, freed from the plants to which it attaches itself.
Chemical compounds Cuscutin, tannin, resin.
Properties Cholagogic, mild laxative, carminative.
Forms of use Fluid, semi-fluid and dry extracts, infusion.
Notes It is inadvisable for anyone suffering from haemorrhoids to use any preparation containing this plant as it contains anthracenosides which cause blood to converge in the abdominal region. The plant is used in homoeopathy. Genera that are particularly prone to infestation by the lesser dodder are *Medicago* (lucerne), *Calluna* (ling or heather) and *Thymus* (thyme).

---

107 CYNARA SCOLYMUS L.
Globe artichoke

Family Compositae.
Description A herbaceous plant with a cylindrical rhizome, it produces stems of 40 inches (1 m) or more. The basal, lobate-bipinnatisect leaves are very large; their lower surface is pubescent but much less so above. The stem leaves may be pinnatisect or entire. The inflorescence is formed of purplish-blue flowers grouped in heads which have an involucre of several long bracts which, in some cases, are spiny. The fruit is an oval achene with a plumed pappus. It is never found wild in Britain, preferring warm sunny climates. It is gathered in April-May.
Parts used Leaves.
Chemical compounds A non-definite, acid substance called cinarin as well as inulin, enzymes, tannin and sugars.
Properties Cholagogic, anticholesterolic, biliary fluidifying, diuretic, antirheumatic, digestive, bio-activating, lithontriptic biliary, hypoglycaemiant and hepatoprotective.
Forms of use Decoction, tincture, distilled water, medicinal wine, fluid and dry extracts.
Notes The globe artichoke should be cooked quickly, as it is more digestible this way. It should be avoided by pregnant women or women who are breast-feeding as it contains a substance that curdles milk. The leaves provide a dark grey fabric dye.

108 CYNOGLOSSUM OFFICINALE L.

Hound's tongue

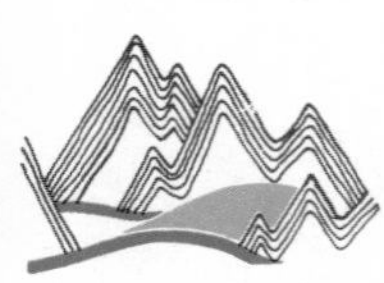

Family Boraginaceae.
Description A biennial herb with basal leaves in rosette form from which, in its second year, the stem grows to a height of about 40 inches (1 m). The rather black root is spindle-shaped. The stem is erect, branched and pilose. The basal leaves are oblong and lanceolate while the stem leaves are sessile, entire and amplexicaul. All the leaves are downy. The inflorescence consists of red or violet-coloured funnel-shaped flowers and the calyx of each flower is 5-sepalled. The fruit is composed of 4 slightly spiny achenes. When the plant blooms, the basal leaves become dry. It grows throughout Europe in grassy areas where the soil is dry and is often seen near the sea. Hound's tongue is native to Britain and most common in central and south west England. It is gathered at the end of the spring of its second year.
Parts used Root-bark.
Chemical compounds Cynoglossin, cynoglossine, inulin, allantoin, choline, alkannin, resin, tannin, gum.
Properties Antispasmodic, cicatrizer, emollient, slightly narcotic.
Forms of use Decoction, fluid extract, tincture, juice.
Notes A plant known since antiquity for its medicinal qualities, it is, nevertheless, to be used with caution because of the narcotic effects that may result from large doses. It is normally used externally as a poultice on chaps and haemorrhoids. Homoeopathic preparations based on this drug are very effective in the treatment of insomnia.

---

109 CYTISUS ALPINUS Mill.

Var. of *Cytisus laburnum*
Laburnum

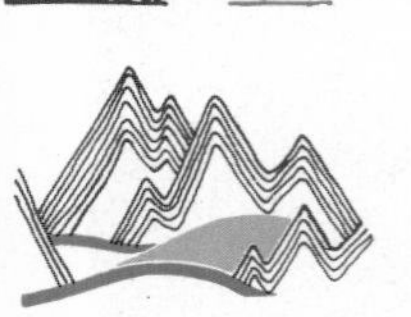

Family Leguminosae.
Description A smooth-barked tree or shrub, its young branches are covered with down. The trifoliate, fasciculate leaves are positioned alternately on the branches and are equipped with pilosect stipules. The dark green leaflets are oval and pointed. The flowers are grouped in long, pendulous racemes with a pilose flowering stem; the base of the calyx is rounded into 2 lips. The brilliant golden-yellow corolla is papilionaceous. The oblong fruit consists of a pod, borne on a short pedicel, with a flat wing on the upper suture; inside are its dark, kidney-shaped seeds. It grows extensively in the mountain woodlands of continental Europe and elsewhere, as well as being cultivated. The medicinally useful parts are gathered in May.
Parts used Leaves.
Chemical compounds Cytisine, choline, essence, tannin, sugars, wax, mucilage, urease.
Properties Cholagogic, purgative.
Forms of use Infusion, powder, tincture.
Notes Cytisine is particularly poisonous, having an effect similar to strychnine. Any preparations containing laburnum should be given, therefore, only under strict medical supervision. The leaves have a similar effect to tobacco and have thus been used in treating nicotinism. The timber is highly esteemed by wood-turners because of its hardness.

110 DAPHNE MEZEREUM L.
Mezereon

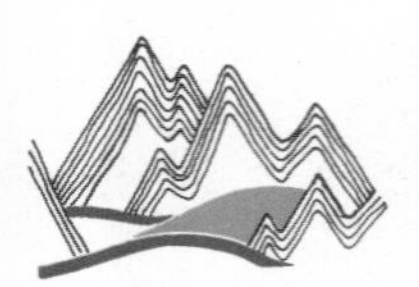

Family Thymeleaceae.
Description The stem of this hardy shrub is contorted and woody with smooth, grey, speckled bark. The root is also woody. The green, ovate-lanceolate leaves are arranged spirally on a short petiole; they are deciduous and, when young, ciliate, emerging after the plant has bloomed. The red or pink, sessile flowers are grouped in clusters of 2-4 beneath an apical cluster of leaves. The androecium consists of 8 stamens and the gynaecium has a short style. The fruit consists of red, ovoid drupes. The mezereon grows freely in the damp mountain woodlands of Europe, almost down to the plains and although a native it is rarely found growing wild in the British Isles. The bark is collected in autumn.
Parts used Bark.
Chemical compounds Daphnin, mezerein, mezerinic aldehyde, mucilage, oil, wax.
Properties Rubefacient, vesicant, drastic.
Forms of use Decoction, tincture, ointment.
Notes This plant is very poisonous if taken internally and must never be ingested. It is quite frequently used for external application in anti-rheumatic creams or poultices which, in view of the heightened activity, often give rise to an erythemal condition (patches of inflammaion on the skin) and blisters; such treatments should, therefore, only be administe-red under expert guidance. Although ignored by allopathic medicine, it is used in homoeopathy to relieve various skin complains and inflammation in the form of tincture and dynamization. There are several species of birds that eat the fruit without suffering any ill effect.

---

111 DATURA STRAMONIUM L
Thornapple

Family Solanaceae.
Description An annual, wild plant growing to a height of about 40 inches (1 m), it has a dichotomous, branched, cylindrical stem. The alternate leaves are ovate-triangular and acute with a margin incised into several lobes; they are borne on sturdy petioles. The underside of the leaves is ridged by numerous, very pronounced veins. The single flowers, which have a tubular calyx, are white with violet venation; they usually emerge from the bifurcation of the branches. The corolla has 5 acuminate lobes. The fruit is a very spiny oval capsule, rather similar to the pericarp of the fruit of the horse chestnut; it is 4-valved and contains numerous rough, black seeds. The plant, which has an unpleasant odour, grows freely in Europe on dry, waste ground and among rubble or the ruins of old buildings. It was introduced into England and Wales where it is uncommon. It is gathered throughout the summer.
Parts used Leaves and seeds.
Chemical compounds Daturine, hyoscyamine, atropine, scopolamine, salts, essence.
Properties Antispasmodic, narcotic, neurosedative, anti-asthmatic.
Forms of use Fluid extract, tincture, powder, anti-asthma cigarettes.
Notes This plant is contra-indicated in conditions of nervous erethism and cardiovascular diseases. In view of the presence of alkaloids similar to belladonna and henbane, this can be regarded as a poisonous plant and, therefore, not to be used in the home. A symptomatic but effective result is obtained when the titrated fluid extract is used in cases of Parkinson's disease. The tincture is used in cases of laryngitis.

112 DAUCUS CAROTA L.
Carrot

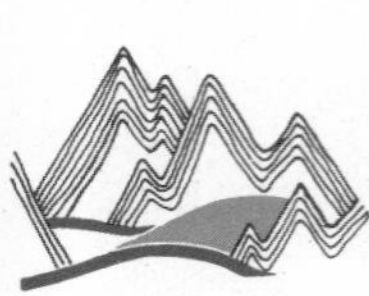

Family Umbelliferae.
Description A biennial plant with a fleshy taproot and an erect, branched stem which may grow as high as 40 inches (1 m). The alternate, pinnately veined, bitripinnatisect leaves are well sheathed and borne on a short petiole. The white flowers are grouped in a terminal umbel, the peripherals being sterile. The fruit consists of an ellipsoidal, spiny cremocarp splitting into 2 single-seeded portions. The seeds are flat and green. The plant, a native of the British Isles, is common in fields and on grassy or waste places. Although seldom found in its wild state, the carrot is extensively grown as a root vegetable. It is dug up from August-October.
Parts used Seeds and root.
Chemical compounds Root: contains glucose, sucrose, protein, salts, pectin, carotene, vitamins, asparagine. Seeds: essence containing pinene, limonene, carotol, daucol, isobutyric acid, asarone. It gives a yield of about 1.2% and the density is about 0.9. It is released in 90% vol. alcohol.
Properties Root: diuretic, ophthalmic and a source of minerals. Seeds: carminative, lithontriptic, galactagogic.
Forms of use Decoction, juice, essence, tincture.
Notes Carrot flour is sometimes used to make a kind of bread. The root is rich in the colouring matter known as carotene which, when consumed, is transformed into vitamin A; this is particularly good for the eyes and the eyesight. Its distinctive essence make an excellent basis for modern perfumes. Carrot leaves contain a vitamin-E rich oil and, in some areas, are used in the making of soup. Fermentation of the root-flesh enables the alcohol to be extracted.

---

113 DICTAMNUS ALBUS L.
Burning bush

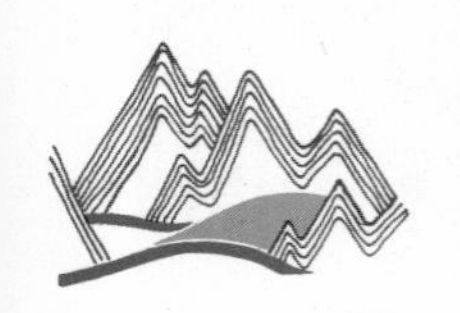

Family Rutaceae.
Description A fragrant herbaceous or subshrubby plant. it has an erect, simple stem, smooth at the base and slightly pilose towards the top. The leaves are arranged alternately, the upper ones being sessile, simple and obovate; the rest are compound, imparipinnate and petiolate with elliptical, glandular leaflets whose margins are denticulate. The upper surface is covered with silky hairs and the underside is glabrous. The flowers, which are yellowish-white, veined in dark red, are grouped in simple racemes and have a 5-sepalled calyx and a 5-petalled corolla. Each flower has 10 very long stamens. The fruit is a capsule that splits open lengthways when ripe into 5 sections, each containing 2 oval seeds. It grows wild in southern and central Europe in mountainous regions and on the lower slopes as well as being cultivated. It is gathered from June-August.
Parts used Tops of the flowering stems, root.
Chemical compounds Essence, gum, wax.
Properties Aromatic, stimulant, digestive, antispasmodic, galactagogic.
Forms of use Infusion, essence, powder, medicinal wine.
Notes The essence which is extracted from this plant, which has a distinctive aromatic odour, has not yet been analyzed. It is used a great deal in liquor-distilleries and perfumeries. A digestive infusion can be made from its leaves as an alternative to tea.

114 DIGITALIS LUTEA L.

Digitalis parviflora All.
Yellow foxglove

Family Scrophulariaceae.
Description A perennial, herbaceous plant with a spindle-shaped root and a glabrous, simple or slightly branched stem, often achieving a height of more than 40 inches (1 m). The ovate-lanceolate leaves are denticulate, semi-sheathed and have short petioles. The flowers, borne in a raceme, are held horizontally and close together and have a multi-lobed, yellow corolla. This plant is frequently found growing wild in Europe in woodland areas, hedgerows and uncultivated fields, on siliceous soil in south west Europe. It is gathered in summer.
Parts used Second-year leaves.
Chemical compounds A-acetildigitoxin, acetildigitoxin, lanatoside, acids, salts.
Properties Cardiotonic.
Forms of use Powder, infusion, fluid extract, tincture.
Notes A poisonous plant, although less dangerous than the better known *Digitalis purpurea* (as its effects are not cumulative), it is a drug not to be used with impunity in the home but only under medical supervision. Its use has a very strong diuretic effect because of the digitoxin content. It is incompatible with Peruvian bark, tannin and iodine.

---

115 DIOSPYROS KAKI L. fil.

Japanese persimmon

Family Ebenaceae.
Description A tree of up to about 33 feet (10 m) in height, it has an erect trunk which branches into a rounded crown with a network of slender branches. The leaves are ovate, oblong and briefly acuminate with prominent venation; the upper surface is glossy and the lower is pubescent. The flowers grow singly, their calyx being larger than their yellowish corolla. The male flowers have up to 24 stamens and the female only 8. The fruit is a globose berry with 8 loculi and 8 hard, semi-oval, acuminate, flattened seeds and sweet, viscous, orange-yellow pulp. Originally from Japan, the persimmon is now cultivated quite extensively in Mediterranean countries, where its fruit is popular. The fruit is gathered in winter.
Parts used Fruit.
Chemical compounds Glucose, fructose, protein, tannin, carotene, vitamin C, pectin.
Properties Astringent, laxative, nutrient.
Forms of use The pulp when under- or over-ripe.
Notes When the fruit has become over-ripe, delicious and nourishing jams can be made from it. The pulp of unripe fruit is used in the cosmetic industry as the basis for face-packs because of its firming qualities. The ripe pulp has a laxative effect on children.

116 DIPSACUS FULLONUM L.
Common teasel

Family Dipsacaceae.
Description The generic name derives from the Greek *dipsao*, to be thirsty, because of the characteristic cups formed by the leaves which hold water. The plant is a herbaceous biennial, growing to a height of about 6½ feet (2 m), with a thick, contorted, branched root. The stem is erect, ridged, spiny and branched at the apex. The basal leaves are lanceolate and up to 12 inches (30 cm) long with a short petiole; they are arranged in rosette form and their leafy blades are armed with spines, especially along the venation. The stem leaves are sessile, amplexicaul and more pointed than the basals. The lilac-coloured flowers are arranged in ovoid heads positioned at the top of each stem. Every flower is equipped with spiny bracts. The fruit consists of achenes. The common teasel grows freely in the Mediterranean area and throughout Europe, including the British Isles, and is both wild and cultivated. It is gathered in September.
Parts used Root.
Chemical compounds Inulin, a scabioside glucoside, bitter, salts.
Properties Diuretic, stomachic, diaphoretic.
Forms of use Infusion, tincture, medicinal wine.
Notes This plant is grown for its heads which are still used for carding (also known as 'fleecing' or 'teasing') some types of woollen cloth, such as the green baize used on billiard tables. It is also used in the making of slightly bitter home-made spirituous liquors, producing an anti-uricaemic effect. The stems which bear the flowering heads are keenly collected by flower arrangers as they retain their natural colour, when dried, indefinitely. A tincture made from the flowering plant is used in homoeopathic medicine in the treatment of skin diseases in general.

---

117 DROSERA ROTUNDIFOLIA L.
Rossolis rotundifolia Moench
Sundew

Family Droseraceae.
Description A plant which grows from a small rhizome, it has fasciculate rootlets and leaves which emerge directly from it in rosette form. The leaves are spoon-shaped and rounded with a very long petiole, their upper surface being covered with red, glandular hairs which secrete a sweetish fluid. This secretion is attractive to insects which become smeared with it and unable to escape; the plant then exudes a digestive fluid which enables most of the creature to be absorbed into its system. It is not surprising, therefore, that the sundew is referred to as 'carnivorous'. The tiny, 5-petalled flowers, with their white corolla, are grouped on one side only of the flowering stem to form a simple raceme. The fruit is an ellipsoidal capsule containing numerous rough-textured seeds. This grows in damp, peaty conditions on the banks of ponds and in bogs and marshes and is common throughout Britain, where it is native. It is gathered in summer.
Parts used Whole plant.
Chemical compounds Naphthoquinone, glucose, droserin, plombagol, tannic acid, propionic acid, resin.
Properties Antispasmodic, anticonvulsive, expectorant.
Forms of use Infusion, fluid extract, tincture, syrup.
Notes This small plant digests insects by means of enzymes similar to those in the human stomach, and milk will, in fact, curdle if the two are heated together. It is widely used in homoeopathic products for treating whooping-cough, for which it is a specific remedy as it reacts on the nerve-ends of the larynx. This plant also contains substances with an antibiotic action.

118 DRYOPTERIS FILIX-MAS (L.) Schott

Polystichum filix-mas Roth., *Nephrodium filix-mas* Rich., *Aspidium filix-mas* Sw., *Polypodium filix-mas* L.

Male fern

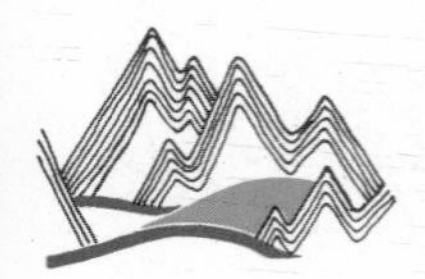

Family Polypodiaceae.

Description A fern with a large nodose, scaly rhizome which is reddish on the outside and greenish-white on the inside; it has a great many rootlets. The compound fronds, which may be between 2-4 feet (60-120 cm) in length, are oblong, lanceolate, bipinnate and petiolate with leaflets that are opposite, obtuse and crenate. The venation on the underside of the fronds is covered with sori which are rich with sporangia. It thrives, in a wild state, in the damp undergrowth of hilly and mountainous areas throughout Britain and continental Europe. It is dug up in autumn.

Parts used Rhizome.

Chemical compounds Filicin, aspidinole, albaspidin, flavaspidic acid, oil, fat, sugar.

Properties Taenifuge, anthelminthic.

Forms of use Powder, ethereal tincture.

Notes No preparation containing any form of this plant should ever be used by those who suffer from heart trouble or by pregnant women. Its unsupervised use can cause lesions of the optic nerve. It is the most effective remedy known for treating tapeworm infestations. Immediately after the drug has been taken, a completely non-oily purgative should be ingested. Antirheumatic cushions and mattresses can be made from the fronds which may have a slightly radioactive effect.

---

119 ECBALLIUM ELATERIUM (L.) A. Rich.

Momordica elaterium L., *Elaterium cordifolium* Moench, *Ecballium agreste* Rchb.

Squirting cucumber

Family Cucurbitaceae.

Description The generic name derives from the Greek *ecbállo*, to squirt out, alluding the plant's means of dissemination. It is a prostrate, herbaceous plant with a white, fleshy root and a succulent stem with small branches. The petiolate leaves are rough-textured, hispid, hastate, cordate or truncate at the base, dentate, or crispate at the margin and tuberculate; the upper surface is grey-green and the lower is whitish. The yellowish male flowers are campanulate with a 5-lobed corolla arising from the leaf axils. The female flowers are similar to the male. The green fruit, to be more exact, the 'pepo', is rather large, hispid and fleshy. The accumulation of fluid increases the pressure inside the fruit which, when it eventually bursts, shoots out the smooth, flattened seeds for quite a distance. It grows freely around the shores of the Mediterranean and extends a little way inland. It is gathered in summer.

Parts used Dried flakes of the juice.

Chemical compounds Elaterin, elaterases; linoleic, stearic and palmitic acids; sugars, starch, alcohol, resin.

Properties Drastic, biliary deobstruent, anti-icteric.

Forms of use Elaterium, tincture.

Notes A plant which, if swallowed in any form, can cause serious prostration, gastroenteritis with the passing of blood and, where excessive doses have been taken, even death. In pregnancy the plant is abortive, and, therefore, a factor in legal medicine. Elaterium, in correct amounts, has been used to treat constipation and obesity, usually in conjunction with sedatives or mucilaginous substances to alleviate its drastic action.

120 ECHIUM VULGARE L.
Viper's bugloss

Family Boraginaceae.
Description The generic name derives from the Greek *ekios*, a viper, referring to the resemblance the fruit bears to the head of such a creature. It is a biennial or perennial plant with a spindle-shaped root and erect, simple stems which are bristly, hispid and spotted with dark red; these can grow to a height of 40 inches (1 m). The lower leaves are lanceolate, entire, pilose and hispid; the upper ones are sessile and narrow at the base. The flowers, which are grouped in branched scorpioid clusters, are at first reddish-pink, turning to a brilliant blue, although occasionally they are white. The corolla is funnel-shaped with 5 lobes and 5 stamens. The rough, angular fruit (nutlet) consists of 4 achenes. The plant is frequently found growing in uncultivated fields and by the roadside in the plains and lower-lying areas of Europe, including the British Isles. It is common in south east England and favours dry soils and sea cliffs. It is gathered in July.
Parts used Flowering tops.
Chemical compounds Mucilage, cynoglossin, consolicin, nitrates, tannin.
Properties Antitussive, diuretic, vulnerary.
Forms of use Infusion, juice, powder, tincture, medicinal wine.
Notes The young leaves contain similar properties to borage and can be eaten in the same way, in salads, before they become hispid. At one time, a red colouring substance for dyeing fabrics was extracted from the root. The juice is used cosmetically as an effective emollient for reddened and delicate skins. The fresh flowering tips can be chopped up to make poultices for treating whitlows and boils.

---

121 EPILOBIUM ANGUSTIFOLIUM L.
Epilobium spicatum Lam.
Rosebay willow-herb

Family Onagraceae.
Description A herbaceous plant with an oblique rhizome covered in rootlets. The stem, which grows to about 40 inches (1 m) high, is erect, simple and slightly branched. The lanceolate leaves are pinnately veined and have an entire margin; they are either verticillate or alternate on the stems. The pink inflorescence consists of an apical raceme which bears flowers with a 4-lobed calyx; the corolla is 4-petalled with 2 petals larger than the others. The capsule is long and contains elongated, oval seeds. The plant grows freely in rocky areas, on scree and waste ground, wood edges and in gardens and is extremely common throughout most of Europe, including Britain. It is gathered in summer.
Parts used Rhizome and flowers.
Chemical compounds Tannic acid, mucilage, pectin, salts.
Properties Astringent, emollient.
Forms of use Decoction (rhizome), infusion (flowers), tincture, powder, fluid extract.
Notes The willow-herb is a favourite plant with bees and is, therefore, liked by apiarists. The leaves are known to have been used as a substitute for tea or to adulterate it. Mountain-dwellers in some parts of central Europe have been known to use the plant as an antidiarrhoeic or as a healer on recent wounds. The flowers are used cosmetically on reddened and delicate skins. For the treatment of enteritis and colitis, the tenderest leaves can be mixed into salads.

122 EQUISETUM ARVENSE L.

Horsetail

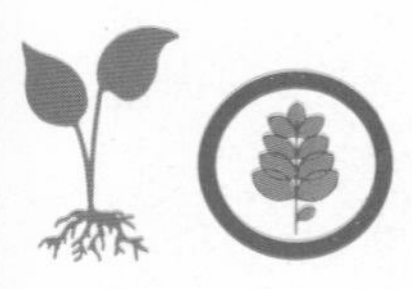

Family Equisetaceae.
Description The generic name derives from the Latin *equi-setum*, a horse's mane. A perennial plant that is cryptogamic and thus without true leaves or flowers. Growing to a height of 8-20 inches (20-50 cm), it has a branched rhizome from which arise the brownish-yellow, fertile stems. These stems have membranous toothed sheaths with segmented branchlets in green verticels. The spores ripen in sporangia held in an ovoid spike about 1¼-1½ inches (3-4 cm) long. Horsetail is found growing wild throughout Europe, including Britain, preferring moist, loamy or sandy soil.
Parts used Sterile stems.
Chemical compounds Silicic acid, equisetin, equisetrin, ferrous oxide; potassium and aluminium chlorides; vitamin C, tannin, resin.
Properties Minerals, diuretic, haemostatic, lithontriptic.
Forms of use Juice, fluid extract, powder, decoction.
Notes In view of its high silica content (10%), this plant was, at one time, used as an abrasive on articles made by cabinet-makers and to clean copper objects. Its juice is known to have a particularly good effect on nasal polyps. It has a very effective coagulant action on nosebleeds and haemorrhages. The fertile branches, without sporangia, can be eaten as a substitute for asparagus. Some people believe that the silicic acid content could be usefully applied to the re-knitting of bone fractures. According to research carried out by Tichy in 1923, the use of horsetail would encourage the slowing down of tumoral degeneration. A tincture of the fresh plant is used in homoeopathy to treat cystitis and other urinary complaints.

---

123 ERIGERON CANADENSIS L.

Canadian Fleabane

Family Compositae.
Description A herbaceous plant with a branched root, its many-leaved stem is hirsute and may grow to a height of over 40 inches (1 m) to terminate in a branched panicle. The leaves are ciliate, the lower ones being lanceolate and occasionally incised while the upper ones are lanceolate or linear. The heads are scaly and consist of small white or pink flowers. The fruits are achenes and have a large, white pappus. This plant originated in North America and has become naturalized throughout Europe, growing on waste ground, by roadsides and in fields. In Britain it is most common in southern and eastern England. The medicinally useful parts are gathered in early autumn.
Parts used Tops.
Chemical compounds Resins, tannins, flavonoids, essential oil containing citronellol, menthone and terpenes.
Properties Balsamic, antirheumatic, diuretic.
Forms of use Decoction, juice, fluid extract, tincture.
Notes The very low yield of essence obtained from this plant is balanced by easy availability. The smell is similar to that of cumin but it has a special quality that would make it suitable in the making of perfumes with unusual nuances. A decoction of Canadian fleabane is known to have given excellent results in cases of bleeding piles by relieving the congestion and pain.

124 ERYNGIUM CAMPESTRE L.
Field eryngo

Family Umbelliferae.
Description A low, herbaceous plant of about 2 feet (60 cm), it has a thick, yellowish root. The leathery leaves are tripinnate-parted with sharply angled triangular lobes which are pointed like thorns; the lower leaves have a long, almost triangular petiole but the upper ones have a decreasingly short petiole until, nearing the apex of the stem, they become sessile and sometimes amplexicaul. The flowers are grouped in heads in umbellate clusters. Each head has 5 thorns at its base. The calyx consists of 5 long, pointed lobes while the white corolla is 5-lobed. The fruits are sub-ovate, rhomboidal and divided into 2 aculeate achenes. The plant, which is rare in Britain, is frequently found in central and southern Europe on dry ground, from the sea inland to the lower slopes of the mountains. It is dug up in autumn.
Parts used Root.
Chemical compounds Saponin, tannins, sucrose, inulin, resin, gum, cinesin.
Properties Diuretic, sudorific, antispasmodic, galactofuge.
Forms of use Decoction, tincture, powder, medicinal wine.
Notes The field eryngo is often cut and used in dried-flower arrangements as it retains its colour for a long time. The root, being edible, can be boiled and eaten; it is easy to digest.

---

125 EUCALYPTUS GLOBULUS Labill.
Eucalyptus

Family Myrtaceae.
Description A large tree with a smooth trunk and bark that peels off easily. The young, blue-grey leaves are very different from the adult ones; they are sessile and grow in opposite pairs. The adult leaves, which grow on the older branches, are alternate with a sturdy petiole; they are sickle-shaped with an asymmetrical leaf base. The flower, which has numerous stamens, is apetalous with a cup-like calyx; this broadens out into 4 ribs and is enclosed by a membrane that falls off like a lid as the flower expands. The fruit is a distinctively shaped leathery capsule that releases a tremendous number of seeds. Originally from Tasmania, this tree has acclimatized well in other parts of the world and is frequently cultivated in southern Europe. It grows best in a damp, marshy site. The parts for medicinal use are gathered from June-October.
Parts used Adult leaves without their petiole.
Chemical compounds Essential oil (up to 80% eucalyptol), aldehydes, hydrocarbons, pinene, camphene, azulene, tannin, resin.
Properties Balsamic, hypoglycaemic, antiseptic.
Forms of use Infusion, inhalants, fluid extract, cigarettes, tincture, powder, essence.
Notes For quick growth, this tree needs a great deal of water. In the past, it was grown extensively in malarial areas in the belief that it could combat the debilitating and recurring fever. It is used a great deal nowadays in both pharmacy and liquor-distillery. The flowers are a favourite with bees and the eucalyptus honey retains the properties of the plant. The wood is used to obtain cellulose but is not suitable for carpentry work.

126 EUGENIA CARYOPHYLLATA Thunb.

Syzygium aromaticum (L.) Merrill & Perry

Tropical myrtle

Family Myrtaceae.
Description An evergreen tree with brownish-yellow bark which grows to a height of about 33 feet (10 m). The leaves are oval, pointed at base and apex, and borne on a petiole that is half the length of the leaf. The bright green blade has a prominent central venation and a great many transparent glands that are rich in essential oil. The inflorescence on the terminal branches consists of a cluster of about 20 flowers each with a long, cylindrical receptacle and 4 sepals. The corolla is 4-petalled, its petals being so tightly packed as to give the bloom the appearance of a gracefully falling, upright half-sphere. The fruit consists of an ellipsoidal berry with two small, opposite loculi which contain numerous seeds. The calices are gathered just before the seeds ripen, and these are the fruits that are generally known as 'cloves'. This tree grows in the warmer parts of Europe and in the milder regions of Brazil.
Parts used Calices.
Chemical compounds Eugenol, caryophyllin, tannin, resin, mucilage, gum.
Properties Eupeptic, carminative, antifermentative, analgesic, antiseptic.
Forms of use Infusion, essence.
Notes The essence is extracted to give an average yield of 18%, the greater part being eugenol. It is used in a number of odontalgic preparations because of its powerful antiseptic quality. It is also used in liquor distilleries and perfumeries as well as in the making of inks. Anaesthetics based on extracts of cloves are currently being produced.

---

127 EUPATORIUM CANNABINUM L.

Hemp agrimony

Family Compositae.
Description This perennial, herbaceous plant derives its name from the king of Pontus, Eupator, a connoisseur of poisons. Its straight, reddish stem is branched and slightly angular, reaching a height of over 5 feet (1.5 m). The spindle-shaped root is white with numerous rootlets. The palmate leaves are opposite and petiolate with lanceolate and dentate segments. The flowers are grouped in numerous heads to form a reddish apical corymb with slightly fragrant glands. The fruit is a black achene with 5 ribs and a white pappus. Commonly found growing wild throughout Europe, including Britain, by ditches, streams and in low-lying damp sites generally, it is gathered in summer.
Parts used Leaves, root and flowering tops.
Chemical compounds Eupatorin, inulin, tannin, resin, salts, essence, valerianate of methyl.
Properties Leaves and flowering tops: cholagogic, depurative, tonic, diuretic. Root: laxative, diaphoretic, tonic.
Forms of use Infusion, decoction, powder, distilled water, tincture, fluid extract, medicinal wine.
Notes A plant that has been used since antiquity for its laxative properties which do not provoke irritation. It was also used in cases of malarial fever, with doubtful results. In some rural areas of continental Europe, one of the current uses of hemp agrimony juice is in the form of a friction which is rubbed into the coats of animals as an insect repellent. Distilled hemp agrimony water was at one time used to treat eye-rheum.

128 EUPHORBIA LATHYRUS L.
Caper spurge

Family Euphorbiaceae.
Description A biennial, herbaceous plant, about 40 inches (1 m) high, with a taproot. The erect stem is hollow, bearing branches only at the apex. The leaves are opposite, decussate and lanceolate with a broad base and smooth margin. The inflorescence is comprised of an umbel-like cluster of 3-5 ray-flowers and lanceolate, oval or cordiform bracts. The flowers are both male and female: the male are distinguished by their long stamens and the female by the ovary above the male flowers; both are surrounded by a cup-shaped involucre. The fruit is a smooth, trilocular capsule containing dark-coloured, oval, rough seeds. The caper spurge, possibly a native of Britain, is commonly found growing throughout Europe anywhere from the coast to the lower slopes of mountains. It flowers in summer and is gathered when ripe.
Parts used Seeds and latex.
Chemical compounds Seeds: resin, fixed oil of palmitic, stearic and oleic acids. Latex: gallic, malic and acetic acids, euphorbone, resin.
Properties Revulsive, purgative, corn-remover.
Forms of use Powder, oil.
Notes Oil of euphorbia can be extracted from the seeds; it is a drastic purgative and no longer used. 'Euphorbius' resin has not yet been fully researched but it is thought that it may be used as a substitute for curare. The latex has, in some instances, been used as a depilatory but the results have been negative due to its revulsive effect.

---

129 EUPHRASIA OFFICINALIS Lagg
Eyebright

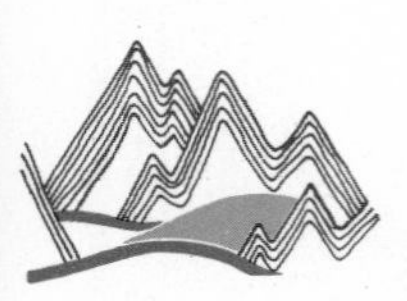

Family Scrophulariaceae.
Description An annual plant with a small, creeping, woody root and an erect, slender, branched stem averaging about 6 inches (15 cm) high. It is parasitic, 'preying' on the roots of grasses. The sessile leaves are oval, dentate and slightly pubescent. The flowers grow in small clusters from the upper leaf axils with bracts almost equal to the leaves. The calyx is campanulate and tubular and the labiate corolla is white with purple veining and a yellow patch on the central lobe. The androecium has 4 stamens while the gynaecium is bilocular and has a slender style with a bilobate stigma. The fruit is an oblong, flattened capsule with ovoid, rough seeds. Eyebright thrives in the moist grasslands of lower- to middle-mountain slopes of Europe and is a native of the British Isles. It is gathered in summer.

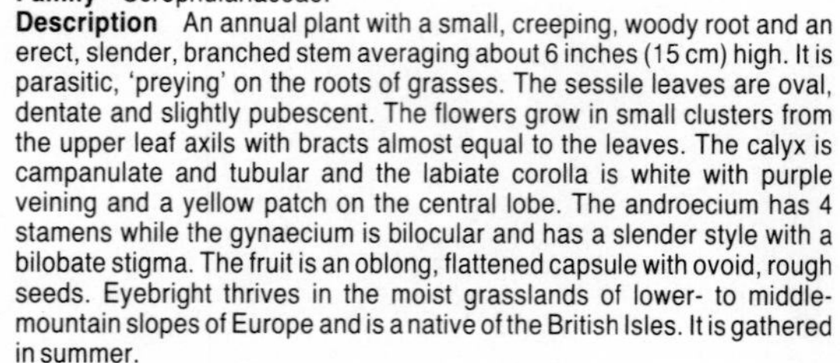

Parts used Whole plant.
Chemical compounds Rhynantine, tannin, essence, colourant, salt.
Properties Tonic, digestive, ophthalmic.
Forms of use Infusion, distilled water, powder, tincture.
Notes This herb has been recognized for centuries as an effective remedy for a number of eye diseases and is still used in this field, although it is not yet known whether its curative properties are in the resin or the tannin. Eyebright is also used in homoeopathic medicine to treat colds. Some people use it, too, in salads for its slightly bitter flavour.

130 FAGUS SYLVATICA L.

Fagus sylvestris Gaertn.

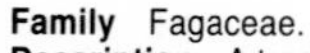

Beech

Family Fagaceae.

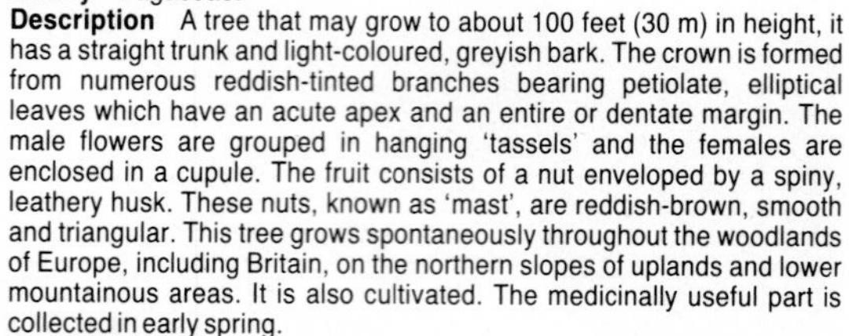

Description A tree that may grow to about 100 feet (30 m) in height, it has a straight trunk and light-coloured, greyish bark. The crown is formed from numerous reddish-tinted branches bearing petiolate, elliptical leaves which have an acute apex and an entire or dentate margin. The male flowers are grouped in hanging 'tassels' and the females are enclosed in a cupule. The fruit consists of a nut enveloped by a spiny, leathery husk. These nuts, known as 'mast', are reddish-brown, smooth and triangular. This tree grows spontaneously throughout the woodlands of Europe, including Britain, on the northern slopes of uplands and lower mountainous areas. It is also cultivated. The medicinally useful part is collected in early spring.

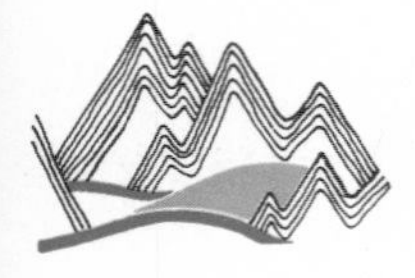

Parts used Bark.

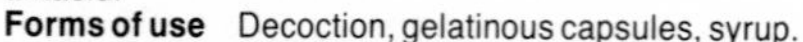

Chemical compounds Guaiacol, creosol, cresolin, tannin, phlorol.

Properties Expectorant, antitussive, antiseptic, odontalgic, antipyretic, antacid.

Forms of use Decoction, gelatinous capsules, syrup.

Notes An oily fluid, with a distinctive smell, is obtained from the dry distillation of beech branches. This is known as creosote, not to be confused with creosote oil, distilled from coal tar. Pure creosote, which should not be used in the home, was at one time often included in remedies to give temporary relief from toothache. Beech-mast is quite nutritious; it contains about 20% of odourless oil which is highly regarded as a substitute for olive oil. Its roasted fruit can be used as an alternative to coffee. The ash from beech branches is used as a dye for blond hair. Creosote should not be prescribed for arthritic patients or kidney sufferers.

---

131 FERULA ASAFOETIDA Regel

Asafoetida

Family Umbelliferae.

Description A native herbaceous plant of Afghanistan and Iran, found only in cultivation in Europe, it grows to a height of about 40 inches (1 m) and has a thick, fleshy taproot. The stem is hollowed and branched. The leaves are compound-pinnate with lobed segments. The flowers are arranged in compound apical umbels bearing up to 50 ray florets each flower having entire, ovate petals with acute, retroflexed tips; sometimes involucres of bracts or bracteoles are present. The fruit is flat and almost circular or ellipsoidal with a membraneous, winged margin. It is gathered in summer.

Parts used The gummy oleoresin content is obtained by cutting the roots.

Chemical compounds Asaresinotannol, ferulic acid, essence of exenile, exenile disulphide, vanillin.

Properties Antispasmodic, cardiotonic.

Forms of use Tincture, fluid extract, enema.

Notes Asafoetida, as its name implies, has an unpleasant garlicky smell; it is so nauseating that it used to be called *Stercus diabuli* (dung of the devil). Nevertheless, it is used locally as a seasoning for food. Drugs with which it has a synergic effect are: camphor, valerian and *Nux vomica*. It is contra-indicated with acids. Nowadays it is used in tincture form as a mild cardiotonic.

132 FICUS CARICA L.
Common fig

Family Moraceae.
Description A bush or small tree with a cylindrical stem, it grows to a height of about 13 feet (4 m) and has an abundance of latex-producing ducts. The rich green leaves are scabrous with a pubescent lower surface; they are 3-5 lobed with a cordate base and are borne on a long petiole. The flowers are monoecious, being enclosed in a fleshy receptacle known as a syconium which changes from green to deep purple as it ripens. The fruits are achenes which are contained in the pulp of the syconium which, mistakenly, is generally regarded as the fruit of the fig. Originally from Asia Minor, it is now often cultivated, being propagated either from side-shoots or by grafting on to the wild fig (caprifig). It is occasionally found in Britain as an ornamental plant, but rarely ripens the fruit.

Parts used Syconium.
Chemical compounds Sugars, protein, salts, vitamins A and B, gum.
Properties Pectoral, laxative, emollient, energy-giving, anti-boil.
Forms of use Its main use is as an edible fruit given the nutritive principles it contains; its secondary uses are as a decoction and as a poultice.

Notes A fig is high in calories and is easy to digest and assimilate. The latex that oozes out of the freshly-cut leaves contains chymase (a milky fluid with a coagulant action), lipase, amylase and protease; it also contains a diastasic enzyme which accounts for the custom in some rural areas of Europe of brushing it over freshly-killed meat to aid the maturation process. It also has an analgesic effect against insect stings and bites. The leaves of the variety that has dark syconia can be used in decoction form as a dye to darken the hair, while a decoction of the young branches is an excellent pectoral.

---

133 FOENICULUM VULGARE Mill.
Foeniculum officinale All., *Foeniculum capillaceum* Gilib., *Meum foeniculum* Spreng., *Anethum foeniculum* L.
Fennel

Family Umbelliferae.
Description The generic name derives from the Latin *foenum*, hay, referring to the foliar structure. The plant is a biennial growing to a height of about 6½ feet (2 m), with a large, spindle-shaped root that is nearly always bifid. The leaves have a thick, amplexicaul, fleshy sheath which is edible. The flowers are grouped in small umbels which, in turn, are grouped into larger umbels; their corollas have 5 yellow petals. The fruit consists of 2 prominently-ribbed ovoid achenes. Although seldom seen growing wild, except around the shores of the Mediterranean and up into the hills, it is now widely cultivated throughout the world. In Britain, where it is possibly native, it is quite common, growing wild around the English and Welsh coasts. It is gathered from August-November.

Parts used Root and fruit.
Chemical compounds Essence: anethole, pinene, camphene, limonene, phellandrene, pectin, fats, sugars, calcium oxalate, starch. Distillation of the fruit gives a yield of 3.7%; the essence, which is greenish, has a distinctive smell and an average density of 0.97.

Properties Carminative, galactagogic, diuretic, emmenagogic, expectorant, antispasmodic.
Forms of use Infusion, fluid extract, tincture, essence, medicinal wine.
Notes The fruit is much used in liquor-distilleries and perfumeries as well as in everyday items of food, acting as a preservative. Taken in large doses, the essence can cause convulsions and animals happening to swallow it become very timid. A yellow colouring substance is also extracted from this plant.

134 FRAGARIA VESCA L.
Wild strawberry

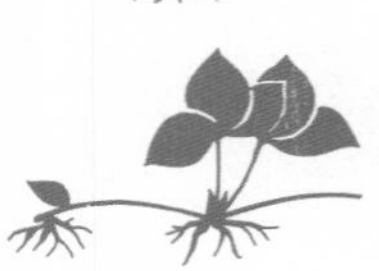
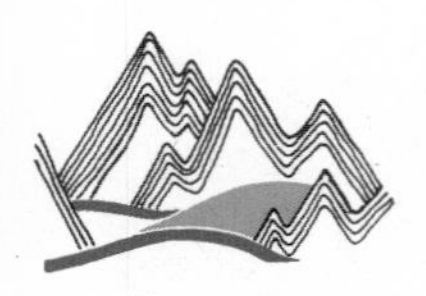

Family Rosaceae.
Description The generic name is a distortion of the Latin *fragrans*, fragrant. A herbaceous, perennial plant with a cylindrical rhizome and stoloniferous stems with nodes (stolons) from which new plants develop; unlike the cultivated hybrids, it has no runners. The leaves emerge from the rhizome, in rosette form, borne on long petioles; they are ternate elliptic, serrate and slightly pubescent. The flower-bearing stalks can reach a height of 8 inches (20 cm). The flowers are white, 5-sepalled and 5-petalled. The false fruit is a fleshy receptacle which bears very small oval achenes. A native of the British Isles, it is also to be found in the woodlands and damp undergrowth throughout Europe; it is gathered in May.
Parts used Rhizome.
Chemical compounds Tannin, alcohols, mucilage, potassium, salts.
Properties Astringent.
Forms of use Decocotion, powder, tincture.
Notes The leaves are used in many areas as a pleasant tea as well as in compresses for delicate skins. The strawberries themselves contain vitamins, proteins, sugars and salts; they are ideal for sufferers from uricaemia and diabetes. They are also preserved commercially in syrup and made into jam. The seeds have a high percentage of oil with drying properties rather like boiled linseed oil and walnut oil. The strawberry is used extensively in the cosmetic industry in skin-care creams.

---

135 FRAXINUS EXCELSIOR L.
Ash

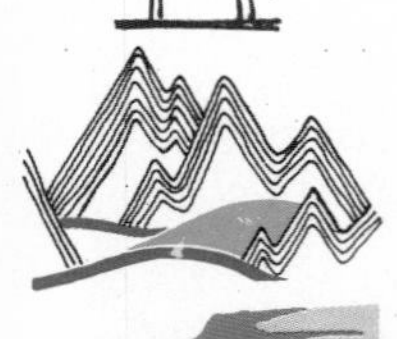

Family Oleaceae.
Description A very tall tree with a short, thick trunk that branches from about 10-20 feet (3-6 m); its bark is smooth in younger trees becoming rougher with time. The opposite leaves are imparipinnatisect and pointed, borne on a short petiole that is dilated at the base; the leaflets have a slightly dentate margin, the teeth being widely spaced and not very prominent. They are light green on the upper surface and slightly downy on the lower. The inflorescence is male and female. The flowers are in panicles and bloom before the leaves unfurl; they emerge from flower-buds on year-old shoots and have neither calyx nor corolla but only pistils and 2 stamens with pollen. The ovary, which becomes the fruit, is positioned between the stamens. The fruits (keys) are elongated, truncate, greenish-brown, winged samaras that remain on the tree until the leaves fall. The ash thrives on alkaline, moist ground and is often cultivated in extensive groves as well as being extremely common wild throughout Britain and Europe. The medicinally useful parts are gathered in spring and summer.
Parts used Bark, leaves and fruit.
Chemical compounds Malic acid, inositol, mannitol, quercitrin, tannin, gum, bitter substance.
Propeties Eupeptic, laxative, diaphoretic, diuretic.
Forms of use Decoction, infusion, tincture, powder, poultice.
Notes Ash-wood is widely used by carpenters for its strength and flexibility. It was, at one time, believed to have an antidotal effect against the venom of vipers. Its seeds contain an edible oil similar to sunflower oil. A green colouring substance is obtained from the leaves. The purgative effect of leaves and fruit is mild but reliable with no side-effects.

136 FUCUS VESICULOSUS L.
Bladderwrack

Family Fucaceae.
Description A seaweed that thrives around the shores of the North Atlantic ocean. Its thallus, which may exceed 8 inches (20 cm) in length, is branched dichotomously, and has a median rib. Elliptic vesicles, filled with air, arise at irregular intervals allowing the strands to float. The reproductive organs are sited at the tips of the thallus in the form of spore-rich tubercules.
Parts used Thallus.
Chemical compounds Algin, alginic acid, fucose, iodine, bromine, potassium, mannite.
Properties Slimming, glandular resolvent.
Forms of use Decoction, fluid extract, dry extract.
Notes Tannin, strophanthus, citric acid, caffeine and *nux vomica* are all contra-indicated in the use of this seaweed. Apart from its pharmacological uses, it is also utilized industrially to extract potassium salts and iodine. Nearly all the slimming extracts on the market contain bladderwrack but its many contra-indicated substances complicate its application. Many cosmetics which have a basis of bladderwrack make use of its local fat-dissolving properties.

---

137 GALEGA OFFICINALIS L.
Goat's rue (French lilac)

Family Leguminosae.
Description A herbaceous plant with erect, striate stems of up to 40 inches (1 m) high. The petiolate leaves are compound and imparipinnate with entire, lanceolate leaflets which are sometimes emarginate. The mauvish-blue or white flowers are arranged in axillary racemes on long peduncles. The bell-shaped calyx has 5 teeth and their corolla, like that of the bean-flower, is keeled. The fruit is a cylindrical pod, narrowing between one seed and the next, and slightly striate; it contains 2-6 brown, kidney-shaped seeds. Although not very common in its wild state, goat's rue is widely cultivated; it thrives best in moist, low-lying submontane regions and by ponds and streams. In Britain it is naturalized in the south. It is gathered in summer.
Parts used Whole plant.
Chemical compounds Galegin, galateolin, arginine, sugar, fat, saponin.
Properties Galactagogic, hypoglycaemic, diaphoretic.
Forms of use Infusion, tincture, syrup, fluid extract.
Notes The effect of galegin is known to be hypoglycaemic. Although not scientifically tested, the galactagogic effect (increase in milk flow) of goat's rue has been confirmed in practice as it can easily be observed in cattle to which the plant is given as fodder; the yield of milk increases by as much as 50%. Goat's rue is also extremely useful in the agricultural practice of green-manuring as it contains a high percentage of nitrogen which is a valuable plant food when ploughed back into the soil. It is used cosmetically, too, in hand- and foot-baths. Extracts of this plant are incompatible with belladonna and camphor.

138 GALIUM APARINE L.

Galium agreste Wall., *Aparine hispida* Moench

Cleavers (Goosegrass)

Family Rubiaceae.
Description A plant that may reach a length of about 6½ feet (2 m), it has a creeping, rhizomous root and a soft, quadrangular, hooked stem. The narrow, lanceolate, spiny leaves are arranged in whorls. The greenish-white flowers are grouped on peduncles which arise from the leaf axils and the end of the stems. The fruit is an almost spherical hispid capsule with 2 parts. Commonly found in Britain in hedgerows and on the cultivated plains and hilly areas of Europe, it is gathered in early summer.
Parts used Whole plant.
Chemical compounds Asperulin, citric acid, starch, colouring matter, gallic acid.
Properties Dermatopathic, diuretic, antiphlogistic.
Forms of use Infusion, ointment.
Notes As with the other members of the Rubiaceae family, a red dye is obtained from the decoction of the rhizome. The crushed or finely chopped plant has given good results when used in local poultices in treating skin complaints. The young, tender tops of the stems are often used in soups. At one time, this plant was reputed to have anticancerous properties; to date, this claim has not been verified but neither has it been disproved. It also has other uses in homoeopathy.

---

139 GALIUM VERUM L.

Galium luteum Lam.

Lady's bedstraw

Family Rubiaceae.
Description This plant has a cylindrical, creeping rhizome from which emerge the straight, quadrangular stems with small nodes and bearing small branches. The plant can reach a height of 20 inches (50 cm) or more. The linear leaves, which have prominent venation on their lower leaf surfaces, arise from the nodes on small petioles. The leaf margins are parallel right to the base. The flowers are arranged in panicles with a 4-lobed yellow corolla. The fruit consists of a greyish, oval, 2-sectioned cremocarp, which contains rough-textured seeds. Lady's bedstraw, a native of Great Britain, is frequently seen throughout Europe growing wild by the roadside in waste land from the coast to the hills. It is gathered in summer.
Parts used Flowering tops.
Chemical compounds Asperulin, asperulosin, phytochimase, colouring matter.
Properties Antispasmodic, astringent, vulnerary.
Forms of use Infusion, tincture, ointment, poultice.
Notes Lady's bedstraw was, at one time, used in cheese-making because of its coagulent qualities. The Rubiaceae family has long been a source of natural dyes and these are still being used by those who practice the craft, a red colouring substance being obtained from the roots of lady's bedstraw and a yellow dye from its flowering tops. The seeds have been used as a substitute for coffee together with other roasted cereals. A powder made from the fresh plant can soothe reddened skin and reduce inflammation.

140 GENTIANA ACAULIS L.

Gentiana kochiana Perr. et Song.
Trumpet gentian

Family Gentianaceae.
Description A small plant with a spindle-shaped root and almost no stem, which grows to a maximum of 4 inches (10 cm) high. The oblong, lanceolate, nervate, green leaves have a denticulate margin and are in the form of a basal rosette; the stem leaves are very small, ovate and opposite. The apical flower is borne on a short pedicel; it has a 5-toothed, tubular calyx with small, lanceolate teeth. The sky-blue corolla is tubular and 5-lobed. The fruit is a bivalve capsule with numerous seeds. This charming plant is quite commonly found growing in the siliceous soil of the Alps.
Parts used Whole plant.
Chemical compounds Gentiocaulin, tannic acid, gallic acid, sugars.
Properties Antipyretic, digestive, bitter tonic, choleretic.
Forms of use Infusion, tincture, fluid extract, medicinal wine.
Notes This small plant, with similar properties to the better known gentians, is used a great deal in liquor-distilleries for preparing bitters. Used externally, as an infusion, it helps to lighten freckles. It is a protected species.

---

141 GENTIANA LUTEA L.

Great yellow gentian

Family Gentianaceae.
Description A perennial herbaceous plant with a very long and rather thick taproot. It has an erect, smooth stem which may grow to a height of 40 inches (1 m) or more. The pointed, oval leaves, which have 5 prominent veins, are positioned opposite each other, in pairs; the upper ones are sessile but, lower down the plant, the margins at the leaf base narrow into a large petiole. The yellow flowers are arranged in whorls in the upper leaf axils; the calyx is divided into 5 small teeth and the corolla is 5-petalled. The fruits are unilocular, ovoid capsules with flat, brown seeds. The yellow gentian grows wild in the mountainous areas of continental Europe and is gathered in autumn.
Parts used Root.
Chemical compounds Gentiopicrin, gentiin, gentiocaulin, gentiamarin, sugars, essential oil, tannin.
Properties Bitter, cholagogic, antipyretic.
Forms of use Infusion, powder, tincture, fluid extract, medicinal wine.
Notes This is perhaps the bitterest of the roots mentioned, and is contra-indicated for patients suffering from an excessive number of red blood cells as it has a haemopoietic effect. It has been used as a substitute for quinine in cases of malaria. It is one of the ingredients in all bitter liquors. Alcohol can be obtained from the young root after it has been macerated.

142 GERANIUM ROBERTIANUM L.
Herb robert

Family Geraniaceae.
Description The generic name derives from the Greek *gheranos*, a crane, because the fruit resembles the beak of this bird. This annual or biennial plant is pubescent and glandular; it has a small taproot and an erect, red stem, reaching a height of about 1 foot (30 cm). The green leaves, borne on long petioles, are palmatisect with pinnate-parted segments. The pink flowers are pedunculate, emerging from the leaf axils; the calyx is 5-sepalled and the corolla 5-petalled. The fruit consists of 5 independent carpels, each of which contains a cotyledon type of seed. The whole plant is downy and has an unpleasant smell. It is a common native of Britain growing freely in the undergrowth, in hedgerows and almost anywhere that is fairly low-lying, moist and shady. It is gathered in summer.
Parts used Whole plant.
Chemical compounds Geranin, ellagic acid, tannin, resin.
Properties Vulnerary, antidiarrhoeic, antirheumatic.
Forms of use Infusion, tincture, fluid extract, poultice.
Notes The root of this plant can be used as a substitute for golden seal (turmeric root). Tests have shown that the fluid extract has an effective antiglycosuric action. At one time this plant was also used to treat opthalmic complaints because of its gallic acid content. According to the 'Doctrine of Signatures', a 16th-17th century medical doctrine which held that medicinal plants and minerals exhibit in their shape and colour some sign of their therapeutic efficacy, the herb robert plant was believed to be able to regenerate the blood. Poultices applied externally help to relieve rheumatism.

---

143 GLECHOMA HEDERACEA L.
Ground ivy

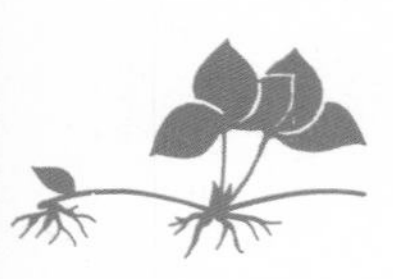

Family Labiatae.
Description One of the commonest and most easily recognizable of the wild perennial, herbaceous plants; it is small, rather pretty and has nothing in common with the common ivy (*Hedera helix*). Some of the unbranched, square, creeping stems send down roots from nodes at intervals while others are erect and bear the flowers. Its leaves are kidney-shaped with long petioles; they have a dark green upper surface and a rather paler lower one; their venation gives them a rough-textured appearance. The leaf margins are characterized by small, closely placed lobes. The flowers, in loose whirls of from 2-5, are bright purplish-blue arising from the upper leaf axils. The calyx is 5-sepalled, tubular and pilose. The anthers are unique in that they are arranged in 2 joined, crossed pairs. The tubular corolla is bilabiate: the upper lip has 2 lobes and the lower has 3 lobes. The fruit consists of 4 smooth, ovoid, rounded achenes which are rather dark in colour. This plant, a common native of Britain, is frequently to be seen growing wild throughout Europe in damp, waste ground, hedgerows and on the outskirts of woods. It is best gathered at the end of June.
Parts used Whole plant above ground.
Chemical compounds Bitter substance, essential oil, tannin, choline.
Properties Antitussive, galactofuge, antineuralgic.
Forms of use Infusion, syrup, fluid extract.
Notes The leaves, dried and mixed with verbena leaves, can be used as a substitute for tea. In some areas the young leaves are mixed into salads to add a slight aromatic tang.

144 GLOBULARIA VULGARIS L.
Globularia

Family Globulariaceae.
Description A low-growing, subshrubby perennial with an erect, woody stem which branches out almost at ground level. The pale green, oblong, pointed, leathery leaves are arranged alternately on short petioles and have an entire margin. The inflorescence at the apex of each stem consists of flowers arranged in a tightly-packed capitulum surrounded by an involucre. The persistent, tubular calyx has 5 toothed lobes. The sky-blue corolla is bilabiate. The fruit is contained in the persistent calyx. This plant is found everywhere in southern Europe and around the Mediterranean area from the mountains to the plains. It thrives in dry, calcareous ground and is gathered in June.
Parts used Leaves.
Chemical compounds Globularin, resin, mucilage, bitter substance, tannic acid, globularic acid.
Properties Purgative, stimulatory, antirheumatic.
Forms of use Decoction, powder, fluid extract.
Notes This is a mild laxative but it also has a stomachic action which makes it doubly effective and, therefore, preferable to other purgatives. The related *Globularia alypum* is much more drastic and so is not recommended for use. The globularia has been used in local compresses to heal wounds but there are other more efficacious plants for this purpose.

---

145 GLYCYRRHIZA GLABRA L.
Liquorice

Family Leguminosae.
Description The generic name derives from the Greek *glykys* and *rhiza*, a sweet root. It is a perennial, herbaceous plant with a thick rhizome of a dark, reddish-brown outside, and yellowish inside, from which its stolons and very long rootlets spring. The leaves are imparipinnatisect, that is, formed by a series of almost opposite leaflets, in pairs, and a central, apical leaflet; they are all oval-elliptic, the base being slightly more rounded than the tip. They contain numerous oil glands which make them sticky. The almost sessile flowers are arranged in a raceme, emerging from the fork of 2 leaves. The calyx is tubular with 5 pointed teeth. The corolla is 5-petalled, of a delicate blue tending towards violet. The fruit is a pod which contains a few dark-coloured, slightly oval seeds. Liquorice thrives particularly well in those areas with a maritime climate, whether growing in the wild or cultivated. It is harvested in autumn.
Parts used Three-year old root.
Chemical compounds Glycyrrhizin, saponin, glucose, gum, sucrose, flavanoids, phytosterols.
Properties Antitussive, anti-ulcerous, laxative, antihistaminic.
Forms of use Infusion, dry extract, fluid extract, powder.
Notes Recent research has shown that liquorice can, with prolonged use, raise the blood-pressure. It also has a hormonal effect similar to the ovarian hormone. It is used in the confectionary industry and as an aromatic element in the curing of tobacco. Its use is incompatible with compounds containing Peruvian bark and calcium.

146 GOSSYPIUM HERBACEUM L.

Cotton root

Family Malvaceae.
Description A branched biennial or perennial shrub of up to about 8 feet (2.50 m) in height, with a long taproot. The stem is glabrous or slightly pubescent and it has alternate, palmate-lobate leaves with unevenly incised lobes. The flowers are borne singly on a long peduncle or emerge in groups of 2-3 from the leaf axils, enveloped in bracts which form an outer calyx. The true calyx is relatively undeveloped and forms a cup with 5 obtuse teeth. The corolla consists of 5 large, white (or sometimes pink or yellowish) petals, fused at the base. The numerous stamens form a central column. The fruit is a capsule with 2-5 loculi, each of which contains a fluffy tuft of cotton-wool in which the seeds rest. Cotton root probably originates in Pakistan but is occasionally cultivated in southern Europe. The medicinally useful part of this shrub is gathered just before flowering time.
Parts used Bark.
Chemical compounds Acetovanillon, phenolic acid, betaine, phytosterol, salicylic acid, ceryl alcohol, oleic acids, sugars.
Properties Emmenagogic, haemostatic, oxytocic.
Forms of use Infusion, tincture.
Notes This plant is grown extensively for its cotton-wool which is used either in its natural state or woven. An edible oil is extracted from the seeds, the residue being made into oilcake for cattle fodder or manure.

---

147 GRINDELIA ROBUSTA Nutt.

Grindelia

Family Compositae.
Description A perennial or biennial plant, less than 40 inches (1 m) high, with a subshrubby appearance, slightly woody at the base but generally herbaceous. The stem leaves are sessile, dentate, triangular and pointed; they are often amplexicaul or narrow in the petiole and are rather stiff. The yellowish-orange heads have outer bracts arranged in several layers. The fruits are achenes with 2-8 coarse bristles at the top. This is an American plant which thrives west of the Mississippi to the Pacific and Mexico in dry areas and salty plains. In Europe it occurs only in cultivation. It is gathered while in flower.
Parts used Flowering tops.
Chemical compounds Resin, cerotic acid, phenolic substances, borneal, various acids, tannin.
Properties Balsamic, antiphlogistic, vascular tonic.
Forms of use Infusion, syrup, fluid extract.
Notes Grindelia is used externally in local compresses on inflamed or irritated areas of the skin. It slows down the heartbeat and reduces the stimulation of the nerve endings in the air passages which causes coughing; it is, therefore, extremely effective as a calming agent in asthmatic crises.

148 HAMAMELIS VIRGINIANA L.
Witch hazel

Family Hamamelidaceae.
Description This shrub or small tree is part of the native flora of North America from Canada to Florida and Nebraska to Texas. In Europe, it is a favourite plant in parks and gardens. The alternate, ovoid, glabrous leaves are borne on short petioles and have stipules; their shape is that of a rounded rhomboid with deep-cut channels marking the venation on the upper surface; the venation protrudes from the lower surface. The flowers are grouped in axillary glomerules of 2 or 3 with short peduncles, each one having 4 sepals, 4 petals, 4 stamens and 2 styles. The fruit is a dehiscent, woody, bilocular capsule containing 2 dark-coloured, glossy seeds. Although it sometimes blooms in autumn, it usually flowers from January-April. The medicinally useful parts of this plant are gathered in spring.
Parts used Leaves.
Chemical compounds Tannin, sesquiterpenes, phenol, choline, saponin.
Properties Vascoconstrictive.
Forms of use Infusion, distilled water, tincture.
Notes This plant was imported into Europe in 1735. Because it is so rich in tannin, it is used in the treatment of varicose veins and any form of roseola. It is also used by the cosmetic industry as a basic ingredient in almost any preparation made to remedy capillary weakness. The European hazel (*Corylus avellana*) has disinfectant and astringent properties similar to witch hazel.

---

149 HEDERA HELIX L.
Common ivy

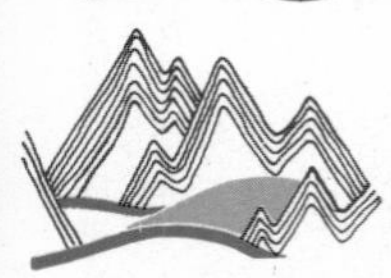

Family Araliaceae.
Description A climbing, subshrubby plant with a woody stem that is capable of growing very large, both in diameter and length; it is equipped with numerous branches from which arise adhesive, non-parasitical, supportive roots. The dark green, glossy, leathery leaves are petiolate, their shape ranging from cordate to elliptic and palmate-lobate with a multi-nervate leaf blade; they have a distinctive, aromatic smell. The greenish-yellow flowers are grouped in dense umbels, each flower having a 5-toothed calyx and a 5-petalled corolla. The black fruit is a globose, spheroidal berry, enclosing seeds which have a corneous endosperm. The common ivy grows wild throughout most of Europe, including Britain, in all types of soil. The medicinally useful parts are gathered in autumn.
Parts used Leaves.
Chemical compounds Saponins, ethereal compound, folliculin, inositol, salts, tannin.
Properties Antineuralgic, antirheumatic, tossifuge, emmenagogic, vasoconstrictive.
Forms of use Decoction, poultice, fluid extract, tincture, ointment.
Notes Taken in large amounts, this plant is poisonous, especially its berries, although birds and some animals eat them without coming to any harm. Its soothing effect on the sensitiviy of the peripheral nerves makes it particularly suitable for external application in cases of rheumatism and neuralgia. Whooping-cough responds in a remarkable way to the tincture. A decoction of the leaves is used to restore faded black fabrics and to dye the hair.

150 HELIANTHUS ANNUUS L.
Sunflower

Family Compositae.
Description The generic name derives from the Greek *helios*, the sun. An annual plant with a taproot and numerous rootlets. The stem, spongy in texture, is usually simple, reaching a height of about 10 feet (3 m). It bears a few very large, petiolate leaves, cordiform or oval in shape, with strongly marked venation; they have wooly leaf blades and dentate margins. The flowers are grouped apically into a large head; they are ligulate and yellow in the outer row but small and brown in the inner disc. The fruit is a blackish, oval achene with no pappus. Rarely known in the wild, this plant is extensively cultivated throughout Europe for ornament and oil. It is gathered in summer.
Parts used Flowering head and seeds.
Chemical compounds Flowers: phytosterol, betaine, quercetin, choline, anthocyanin, faradiol, arnidiol. Seeds: oil containing linoleic, oleic, palmitic, stearic and arachidic acids; lecithin, cholesterin, albumin.
Properties Febrifuge, stomachic, nutrient.
Forms of use Fluid extract, tincture, powder.
Notes Almost the only reason for using this plant is for the anticholesterol action of the oil extracted from it. The seeds, when roasted, are a substitute for coffee and drinking-chocolate. Flour made from sunflower seeds is often mixed with wheat flour by biscuit manufacturers because of its high nutritional value. The petioles of its leaves are boiled and mixed in with various other foodstuffs. Special note: an interesting feature of the flowering head is that it may contain over 1,000 seeds, arranged in concentric, hyperbolic spirals.

---

151 HERACLEUM SPHONDYLIUM L.
Cow parsnip

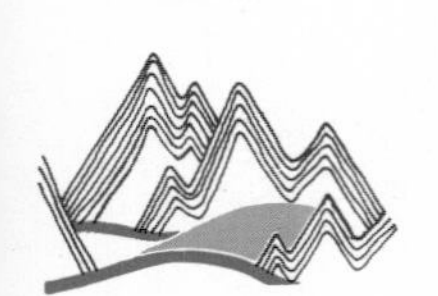

Family Umbelliferae.
Description The generic name derives from the Greek name *Heracles*, Hercules, alluding to the vigorous qualties of this plant. It reaches a height of about 6½ feet (2 m) and has a fasciculate root. The erect stem is branched, hollow, angular and pubescent. The alternate leaves are compound pinnate with serrate, pinnatisect or lobate leaflets. The white flowers are borne in terminal and axillary umbels; the calyx of each flower is 5-toothed and the corolla 5-petalled. The fruit is a cremocarp (or diachaenium) which separates into 2 flattened portions on ripening. This is a very common plant growing wild throughout most of Europe, including Britain, especially in moist, mountainous grasslands and near ditches and waterways. It is gathered in autumn.
Parts used Root and leaves.
Chemical compounds Heraclein, essence, glutamine, resin.
Properties Sedative, anti-hysteric, aphrodisiac, digestive.
Forms of use Decoction, powder, fluid extract, tincture.
Notes The stem exudes a sugary juice which coagulates in the air, and so the whole plant can be used to obtain an alcoholic liquid. The root is edible, when boiled, as are the young shoots and leaves. A tincture made from the aerial parts is used to relieve general debility, although why it should be beneficial is not clear.

152 HIERACIUM PILOSELLA L.
Mouse-ear hawkweed

Family Compositae.
Description A perennial plant with a creeping rhizome from which emerges first a rosette of basal leaves and then stolons that throw out roots at the nodes. The stolons bear alternate leaves which become smaller towards the apex. Leafless flower stems emerge from the basal rosette to a height of about 8 inches (20 cm). The basal leaves are recumbent and spathulate-lanceolate with an entire margin; their upper surface is greenish-grey and hairy while the lower one is hoary. The lemon-yellow flowers, often tinged with dark red underneath, are in solitary heads at the top of the stems; the head is at the centre of a closely packed row of lanceolate bracteoles. The fruit is a striate, cylindrical achene with a pappus of grey bristles. The mouse-ear hawkweed is commonly found in most of Europe, including Britain, growing wild on high ground and in dry, upland pastures. It is gathered in spring and summer.
Parts used Whole plant above ground.
Chemical compounds Pilosellin, bitter, tannin, oxycumarin, umbellifer-one.
Properties Antibiotic, astringent, diuretic.
Forms of use Tincture, fluid extract, powder, infusion.
Notes The antibiotic property is only active if the plant is used when fresh. It is specific in brucellosis (also known as Malta fever and by other names). When dry, the plant is only astringent. An infusion of the fresh plant will more than double the daily amount of urine passed. In rural areas of southern Europe the mouse-ear hawkweed is occasionally used by shepherds as an application to help heal small wounds.

---

153 HIPPOPHAE RHAMNOIDES L.
Sea buckthorn

Family Elaeagnaceae.
Description A thorny shrub, about 6½ feet (2 m) high, with many almost horizontal branches, its roots are long with a large number of suckers which anchor it firmly into the ground as protection against heavy storms off the sea. The lanceolate, pointed, alternate leaves are silvery on the upper surface and light brown underneath; the main central vein is well defined. Bushes have either male or female flowers. The male flower is catkin-like with a 2-sepalled calyx, 4 stamens and no corolla. The fruit is a drupe which emerges from an involucre; this turns a brownish-orange when ripe and contains a seed enclosed in a woody case. The sea buckthorn grows wild in much of Europe, including Britain, and is found mainly by the sea among sand dunes and on chalky cliffs. It is gathered in autumn.
Parts used Fruit.
Chemical compounds Flavonic glycosides, vitamin C, organic acids.
Properties Astringent, vitamin.
Forms of use Pulp, electuary.
Notes This plant has a very high vitamin-C content and its fruit is sometimes used in conjunction with rose hips which are also rich in this vitamin. As the berries are edible, they can be made into excellent, rather sharp, home-made jam or jelly. At one time, the fruits of sea buckthorn were believed to be poisonous and this belief still persists in many places. The berries can be crushed and used on open wounds, as an emergency measure to stop bleeding.

154 HORDEUM VULGARE L.

Hordeum sativum Jes.
Barley

Family Gramineae.
Description An annual plant with an erect stem of about 40 inches (1 m). The leaves are linear lanceolate and sheathed at the base where they encircle the stem; they are green on both sides and their lengthways venation is well defined. The flower consists of 2 acute, simple glumes enclosing 2 large, unequal glumellae (palea) which represent the corolla. The fruit is an oval, ridged caryopsis with rounded ends. The spike may be long or short, according to the plant type, but it always has several glumes with filiform awns that may diverge. Barley can be cultivated throughout Europe wherever the soil is calcareous. It is harvested, when ripe, in summer.
Parts used Caryopsis.
Chemical compounds Ordenin, maltine, starch, sugars, fats, proteins.
Properties Nutritive, emollient, anticatarrhal.
Forms of use Decoction, fluid extract.
Notes Pearl barley is the decorticated caryopsis, while barley that is allowed to germinate and is then dehydrated is called malt. A very nourishing drink made from the latter can be used as a substitute for coffee. Barley is also used commercially in the making of beer and whisky. There are many varieties of this cereal plant.

---

155 HUMULUS LUPULUS L.

Hop

Family Cannabaceae.
Description A herbaceous, perennial liana with a thick, fleshy root from which arise long, herbaceous stems which often support themselves by twisting around one another; they are quadrangular in cross-section. The palmate-lobate leaves are opposite or alternate with a pilosect petiole; they have 5 well-defined lobes edged with broad, pointed teeth. The male flowers are grouped in panicles at the end of the branches; they are without sepals but have 5 tepals and 5 stamens. The female flowers are gathered together into catkins, rather like small cones; these nearly always grow singly or in small groups. The fruits, containing the seeds, are rounded, grey achenes enclosed in large bracts which are plentifully equipped with resiniferous glands that secrete a yellow substance. This plant can be found growing wild throughout Europe, including Britain, in hedgerows and on sunny waste ground. It is also extensively cultivated in northern Europe, especially in south east England, for use in beer-making. It is picked at the end of summer.
Parts used Female inflorescences.
Chemical compounds Ethereal oil (myrcene and humulene), myrcenol, linalool, tannin, resin.
Properties Sedative, eupeptic, antipyretic.
Forms of use Fluid extract, tincture, infusion, syrup, pills.
Notes The young shoots can be boiled and eaten, like asparagus. Lupulin resin can be given in tablet form to nursing mothers to improve the flow of milk; recent research has discovered that it contains a related hormone which would account for this beneficial effect. In beer-making the flowers are traditionally used for their distinctive, rather bitter flavour.

156 HYOSCYAMUS NIGER L.
Henbane

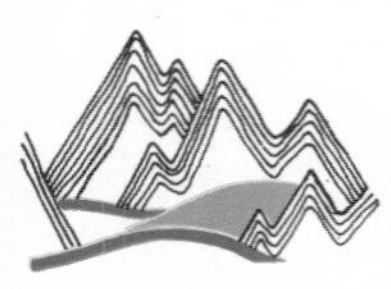

Family Solanaceae.
Description A pilose, herbaceous plant with a spindle-shaped root and simple or branched, erect stem which may grow to a height of more than 40 inches (1 m). The alternate, delicate leaves are pilose, ovate, slightly lobed and sessile. The flowers, borne on terminal spikes, are campanulate, 5-lobed and yellow with deep purple veining. The corolla is infundibuliform. The capsule contains a great many small kidney-shaped seeds. The plant, which has an unpleasant smell, is not very common but may be found growing wild throughout Europe, including Britain, by the walls of fields, on waste ground, near buildings and in stony places from low-lying ground to lower mountain slopes. It is gathered in summer.
Parts used Whole plant.
Chemical compounds Hyoscyamine, scopolamine, atropine, oil, starch, stearin, salts, gum.
Properties Analgesic, narcotic, mydriatic.
Forms of use Powder, tincture, fluid extact, syrup, infusion, ointment, oily solution.
Notes A very poisonous plant and yet, at the same time, recommended for external use in analgesic preparations to relieve rheumatism and arthritis. It is a helpful toothache remedy. The leaves can be smoked to give relief in asthmatic crises. The syrup has a sedative effect in cases of Parkinson's disease.

---

157 HYPERICUM PERFORATUM L.
Perforate St. John's wort

Family Guttiferae.
Description A herbaceous plant with a short rhizome which grows to a height of about 40 inches (1 m). The stem is erect with a woody base; the branches are opposite and paired and immediately under the fork of each pair there are 2 opposite, sessile leaves. The leaves on the branches are also positioned in pairs, opposite each other. All the leaves, which are oval and elliptic, are generously furnished with oil glands which are seen as translucent dots. The flowers, which are often in groups of 3, are nearly always at the top of the herbaceous branches. In the centre, at the end of each stem, these clusters open out with several branchlets and flowers. Each flower has 5 green sepals and 5 golden-yellow, lanceolate petals with many stamens protruding. The fruit is a trilobate capsule which contains dark-coloured seeds. This plant grows freely, in most of Europe, including Britain, especially in dry, sunny positions. The medicinally useful parts are gathered in early summer.
Parts used Fresh flowering tips.
Chemical compounds Essential oil, tannin, hypericine, hyperoside.
Properties Vulnerary, emollient, anti-enuretic, pectoral, vermifuge.
Forms of use Infusion, fluid extract, syrup, oil, medicinal wine.
Notes The generic name of this plant derives from a Greek word meaning to overcome an apparition and, in olden days, many homes would have had a branch of it hanging over the door to ward off evil spirits. St. John's wort releases a yellow colourant in water and a red one in oil and alcohol. It is used in liquor distilleries for its aromatic qualities. The leaves are used as an alternative to tea.

158 HYSSOPUS OFFICINALIS L.
Hyssop

Family Labiatae.
Description A perennial, subshrubby plant which grows to a height of about 23-28 inches (60-70 cm); it is mainly cultivated but also grows wild in some areas. It has a short, fibrous rhizome and a stalk dividing into many woody stems which become herbaceous towards the top. The leaves are entire and lanceolate, arranged in whorls, the basal ones being petiolate and the upper sessile. The flowers are grouped in leafy whorled spikes towards the top. The little 5-sepalled calyx is tubular and the light-blue or purplish corolla is also tubular. The fruit is an ovoid, 4-sectioned cremocarp. Hyssop grows wild in southern and eastern Europe. The medicinally useful parts are gathered in early summer.
Parts used Flowering tops.
Chemical compounds Essential oil, ethereal compound, tannin, saponin, phytosterol.
Properties Antitussive, sedative, tonic, emmenagogic.
Forms of use Infusion, syrup, distilled water.
Notes No form of hyssop should be taken during pregnancy. An essence in the form of a yellowish liquid is produced from this plant which exudes a resinous aroma. An average yield of 0.6% is obtained. This oil should not be used in aromatherapy by highly-strung patients as it can cause epileptic symptoms. Hyssop is used commercially both in liquor distilleries and in the cosmetic industry. The flower tops are used as an ingredient in various aromatic infusions.

---

159 ILEX AQUIFOLIUM L.
Holly

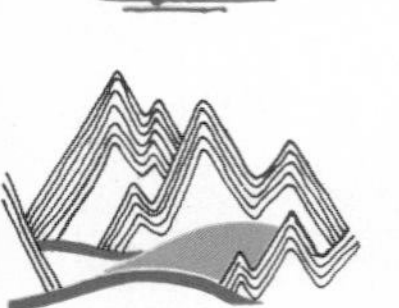

Family Aquifoliaceae.
Description A bush or tree, usually cultivated but also found growing wild throughout Europe, including Britain, it can reach a height of over 30 feet (10 m). It has many green branches and leathery, alternate leaves; they are ovate-lanceolate and undulate with a spiny margin and a short petiole. The flowers arise in dense clusters in the leaf axils and have such a small peduncle as to appear sessile. The calyx is 4-lobed and the white corolla consists of 4 petals joined at the base. The ovary has 4 loculi and the fruit is a fleshy, red berry, containing 3-5 seeds. Holly commonly grows in most well-drained soils. The medicinally useful parts are gathered in spring.
Parts used Leaves, fruit.
Chemical compounds Ilicin, tannin, gum, wax, acids.
Properties Antipyretic, bitter, antidiarrhoeic.
Forms of used Infusion, powder, tincture.
Notes The berries can be used, in small doses, as a purgative although it is better to avoid them as they can easily have an emetic effect. The fruit can be roasted and used as a substitute for coffee. The wood of holly is well regarded by cabinet-makers. The root was, at one time, used as a diuretic but, in order not to endanger the species, it is better to resort to other commoner and more effective plants.

160 INULA HELENIUM L.

Aster officinalis All., *Aster helenium* Scop.
Elecampane

Family Compositae.
Description A very sturdy, showy, perennial plant with a thick, fleshy, rhizomous root, it grows to a height of about 5 feet (1.5 m). The basal, slightly denticulate leaves, which can be as wide as 6-8 inches (15-20 cm), are borne on a long petiole and arranged in rosette form. The light green stem leaves are smaller, somewhat cordiform, sessile, almost amplexicaul, very thick and rough on the upper surface but delicately hoary on the lower. The flowers are arranged in large, yellow heads, about 3 inches (8 cm) in diameter, with an outer ray of slender ligules. The receptacle bears numerous layers of small, overlapping bracts which are so pointed as to look like leaves. The fruit is a small, smooth, oval achene with a long-haired pappus. The plant is found in south eastern Europe in moist, grassy sites, and is naturalized in Britain. The plants are harvested in spring or autumn, when they are at least 3 years old.
Parts used Rhizome.
Chemical compounds Essential oil, azulene, inulin, resin, mucilage, salts.
Properties Bitter, stomachic, antitussive, dechlorinating.
Forms of use Decoction, fluid extract, tincture, syrup, powder, medicinal wine.
Notes Elecampane is used in liquor distilling and as an ornamental plant. It is rarely seen in the wild, being mainly found under cultivation for its appearance or as a medicinal plant. It can be used as a compress to relieve pruritus. It yields up to 2% of semi-fluid essence in distillation. It is easy to obtain alcohol from elecampane. At one time the root was candied and eaten as a sweetmeat but this practice now only continues in Germany.

---

161 IRIS GERMANICA L.

Purple flag

Family Iridaceae.
Description A perennial, herbaceous plant with a thick rhizome and a large number of rootlets. The stem grows to a height of 20-40 inches (50 cm-1 m). The bluish-green sword-shaped leaves are long and pointed. Each plant bears only a few flowers; these are deep purple, almost sessile, with 2 bracts, 3 recurved petals having yellow beards, 3 erect petals, 3 stamens and 3 stigmas. The fruits are dark-coloured, ovoid capsules that open into 3 portions to release a few very dark seeds. The iris thrives in a temperate climate. It is seldom found in the wild but is widely cultivated and naturalized in Europe, including Britain, and there are many varieties of it. Plants that are 2-3 years old are dug up in summer, after flowering.
Parts used Rhizome (known pharmaceutically as orris-root).
Chemical compounds Essential oil, irone, iridin, mucilage, starches, calcium oxalate.
Properties Expectorant, diuretic.
Forms of use Decoction, powder.
Notes Iris rhizomes are ground down into a type of flour, known as orris-powder, which is the raw material used in steam distillation and in the manufacture of face-powders. Oil of orris is a buttery substance obtained by distillation and known commercially as 'orris butter'; it smells strongly of violets and is much used in the perfume industry.

162 IRIS PSEUDACORUS L.

Iris palustris Moench, *Iris lutea* Lam.
Yellow flag

Family Iridaceae.
Description This plant has a thick, horizontal rhizome from which many rootlets descend, The stems emerge, erect and smooth, directly from the rhizome, reaching a height of over 40 inches (1 m), and the erect, smooth, sword-shaped, parallel-veined leaves arise from the same source. The flowers are yellow with a variable perianth; the tepals are oval, the internal segments being narrower than the outer. The capsule contains pointed, trigonal, brownish seeds. The plant, which is wild throughout most of Europe, including Britain grows in damp marshy areas. It is gathered in spring.
Parts used Rhizome.
Chemical compounds Tannin, irisin, mucilage, resin.
Properties Emetic, astringent
Forms of use Powder, infusion, tincture.
Notes Any preparations containing yellow iris should be treated with great respect as they can cause uncontrollable vomiting and violent diarrhoea. The powdered rhizome has been used to encourage sneezing to relieve head colds. If the seeds are well roasted they can be used as an excellent substitute for coffee.

---

163 JUGLANS REGIA L.

Walnut-tree

Family Juglandaceae.
Description The generic name derives from the Latin *glans Jovis*, the acorn of Jupiter. A very leafy tree which grows to a height of about 40-50 feet (12-15 m), it has a straight, well-branched trunk with a smooth, greyish-white bark when young that develops deep, longitudinal furrows with age and becomes very rough. The dark green leaves are alternate and imparipinnate with elliptical, acuminate, leathery, pinnately-veined leaflets. The female flowers have an oblong ovary and the males form a long, drooping catkin. The perianth is 5-lobed. The male flowers develop from year-old buds while the females are from the current year's shoots. The fruit is a fleshy drupe enclosing a woody endocarp. The seed (walnut) is rough-textured and oleiferous. This tree originates in Asia and now grows wild in south eastern Europe on mountain slopes and plains, and is cultivated in Britain. The medicinal parts are gathered in summer.
Parts used Leaves, bark, fruit.
Chemical compounds Inositol, juglone, tannin, gallic acid, juglandin, carotene, pyrogallic acid.
Properties Antihypoglycaemic, depurative, galactofuge, rubefacient, antiscrophulous.
Forms of used Infusion, fluid extract, tincture, maceration, medicinal wine, oily solution.
Notes A yellow dye can be obtained by boiling the green husks and a brown dye is extracted from the leaves, which gives the human skin a deeply tanned appearance. Walnut oil is edible but goes rancid very quickly; it is used by painters as a drying oil. The timber is very highly esteemed in the making of furniture. Hair dyes are obtained from the leaves and bark.

164 JUNIPERUS COMMUNIS L.
Juniper

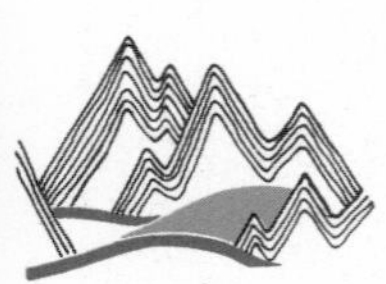

Family Cupressaceae.
Description A shrub or small tree, about 10 feet (3 m) in height. The bluish-green leaves are narrow, leathery and very pungent; there is a pale, concave line running the whole length of the upper surface of each leaf. Male and female flowers are borne on separate trees. The males are grouped in globose catkins each flower having 2 or 3 stamens containing the pollen. The females are borne in the leaf axils; they are scaly and look rather like a small bud at the base of which are situated the ovules. The fruit is a false berry formed by the bracts surrounding the flower; as it grows it hardens to form a bluish-grey ball-like fruit, mistakenly called a berry, which contains 2-8 seeds. The juniper grows wild throughout Europe, including Britain, from coastal areas to the slopes of the Alps and is frequently cultivated. The medicinally useful parts are gathered in the summer and autumn.
Parts used Leaves, ripe fruit (2-3 years old) and bark.
Chemical compounds Essential oil, pinene, camphene, cadinene, terpinol, sugar, resin, organic acids.
Properties Antirheumatic, diuretic, balsamic, digestive, sudorific, antiseptic.
Forms of use Infusion, decoction, fluid extract, essential oil, tincture, syrup.
Notes An average yield of 1% of essence is obtained from the juniper. It is colourless and becomes resinous. It is used in liquor distillation and the residue is either used for animal fodder or for the extraction of alcohol. Another essence, obtained from the branches by dry distillation, is cade oil or juniper tar oil. The well-known *aqua vitae* known as gin is flavoured with the oil made from juniper cones, while juniper leaves are used in aromatic infusions.

---

165 JUNIPERUS SABINA L.
Savin

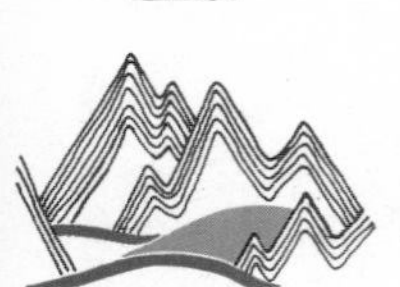

Family Cupressaceae.
Description A low, evergreen shrub, with many branches which end in equally numerous, slender branchlets that appear dark green. This is because they are covered with tiny, decurrent leaves which are of a rather unusual ovate-lanceolate form and the brown of the branchlets does not show through; they are in 4 rows, positioned in opposite, decussate, overlapping pairs. They have an external gland containing an essence that gives the whole plant its characteristically pleasant odour. In the right climate and soil the savin may grow to a height of 26-33 feet (8-10 m). The flowers are unisexual; the males are grouped in oval catkins, each with its own bract, while the females develop in a small, bluish-black false berry, about the size of a kidney bean, which usually contains two rough-textured, oval seeds. This plant is found almost exclusively in the mountainous regions of southern and central Europe but is sometimes grown as a decorative garden shrub. The medicinally useful parts are gathered in spring.
Parts used Branchlets.
Chemical compounds Sabinol, sabinene, pinene, geraniol, citronellol, tannin, wax, resin.
Properties Emmenagogic, emetic, abortive.
Forms of use Infusion, essence, fluid extract, tincture, powder.
Notes A plant to be treated warily, from a legal and medicinal point of view, because of the danger of abortion should any preparation containing it be taken by a pregnant woman. Distillation of the branchlets produces an average yield of 4% toxic essence which, apart from being oxytocic, also has insecticidal properties. Work-tools were, at one time, fashioned from the thicker branches.

166 LACTUCA SATIVA L.

Garden lettuce

Family Compositae.
Description A herbaceous plant generally regarded as an annual but often biennial, it has a taproot with a number of rootlets. The leaves differ in shape, according to variety, but are mostly round or roundish, with an entire margin, and light green in colour; they are often slightly lobate. They overlap one another increasingly towards the centre of the plant to produce a spheroid shape. The internal leaves, near the stem, are sessile and amplexicaul. The inflorescence consists of loose clusters of numerous heads, the flowers of which are small with yellow, strap-shaped florets. The fruits are oval achenes bearing a rostrum and a pappus consisting of numerous little hairs. In Europe this type of lettuce is only found under cultivation. The few plants that may be found growing in the wild are simply rogues that are self-sown. It is gathered in summer.
Parts used Leaves and juice.
Chemical compounds Mineral salts, vitamins, sugars, vegetable proteins.
Properties Tranquillizer, emollient, vitamin-rich.
Forms of use Juice, pulp, fluid extract.
Notes The leaves are eaten voraciously by beetles and other garden pests. Lettuce seeds contain an edible oil. In some places the leaves are dried, cured and smoked like tobacco. By pounding the leaves, thick juice called *thridace* is obtained from the resulting pulp; this, however, is not nearly as effective as the thick milky juice known as *lactucarium* obtained from the poisonous lettuce, *Laetuca virosa*.

---

167 LACTUCA VIROSA L.

Lactuca sylvestris Lmk.
Wild lettuce

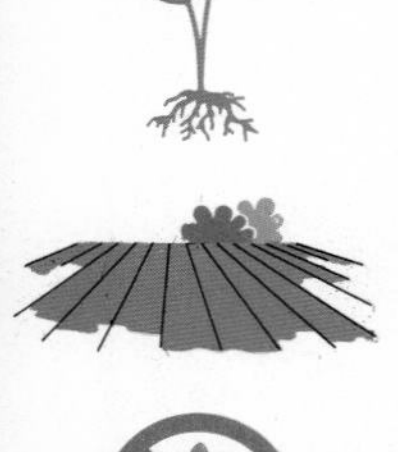

Family Compositae.
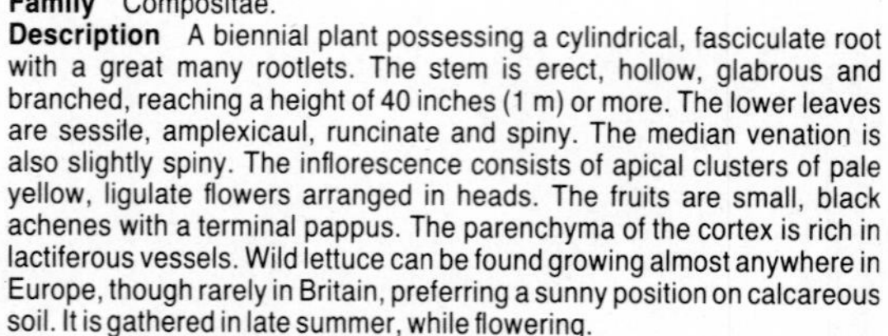
Description A biennial plant possessing a cylindrical, fasciculate root with a great many rootlets. The stem is erect, hollow, glabrous and branched, reaching a height of 40 inches (1 m) or more. The lower leaves are sessile, amplexicaul, runcinate and spiny. The median venation is also slightly spiny. The inflorescence consists of apical clusters of pale yellow, ligulate flowers arranged in heads. The fruits are small, black achenes with a terminal pappus. The parenchyma of the cortex is rich in lactiferous vessels. Wild lettuce can be found growing almost anywhere in Europe, though rarely in Britain, preferring a sunny position on calcareous soil. It is gathered in late summer, while flowering.
Parts used Leaves and latex (lactucarium).
Chemical compounds Undefined alkaloid, organic acids and bitter substances, ester (lactucerol), lactucopicrin and lactucin, alcohol, enzymes.
Properties Sedative and hypnotic.
Forms of use Infusion, fluid extract, juice.
Notes Lactucarium is obtained by tapping the lactiferous vessels in the stem. It produces a similar effect to opium but without becoming addictive. The toxic aspect of this plant must not be underrated, however, as it can cause death through cardiac paralysis.

168 LAMIUM ALBUM L.
White dead-nettle

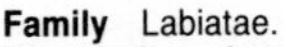

Family Labiatae.
Description A perennial herbaceous plant with a long, rhizomatose root from which spring several stems; these grow to a height of about 20 inches (50 cm) and are square in cross-section with channelled sides. The bright green leaves are opposite, in 2 rows, the lower ones being at a right angle to the upper ones; they are oval, cordate, very rough-textured and pointed, with a dentate margin. Most of the leaves are borne on recurved petioles but the apical ones are almost sessile. The flowers, clustered in the upper leaf axils, have a tubular 5-toothed calyx; the white corolla is bilabiate, the lower lip being recurved and split down the centre while the upper one is somewhat helmet-like. The fruit is a dark, triangular, 4-sectioned cremocarp. This plant grows wild throughout most of Europe, including Britain, in fields, hedgerows and on moist, waste ground. It is gathered in summer.
Parts used Flowering tops.
Chemical compounds Mucilage, tannins, ethereal oil, saponin, potassium.
Properties Vasoconstrictive, haemostatic.
Forms of use Infusion, powder, juice, tincture.
Notes The plant tips are usually boiled and mixed in with salads. They can also be used in compresses and applied to external piles. The distilled water of the flowers and leaves makes an excellent and effective eye-lotion to relieve opthalmic conditions.

---

169 LARIX DECIDUA Mill.
Larix europaea DC., *Pinus larix* L., *Abies larix* Lam.
European larch

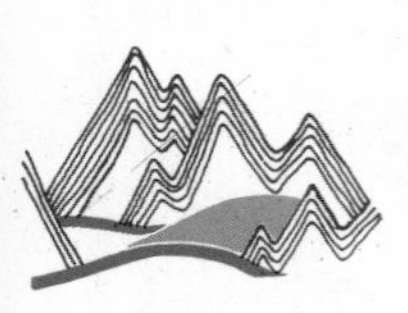

Family Pinaceae.
Description A tall tree with a straight trunk, the bark of which, on mature trees, is covered with reddish fissures. The branches grow almost horizontally, with a slight upward tendency. The pale green leaves are like flattish needles with a ridge running along the whole length of both leaf surfaces. The tree bears both male and female flowers, the males in the form of small catkins and the females in clusters of green, pink or white scales which develop into a cylindrical fruit. This takes the form of a consistent reddish-brown cone made up of overlapping scales. The oval seeds have a type of wing firmly attached to one margin and lightly linked to the other. The natural habitat of the larch is the mountainous terrain of the Alps; it can be found in its wild state at an altitude of up to about 6,500 feet (2,000 m). It is widely planted throughout Europe, including Britain. Tapping takes place in autumn.
Parts used Resin.
Chemical compounds Turpentine, essential oil, larixinic acid, resin, bitter substance.
Properties Balsamic, haemostatic.
Forms of use Syrup, essence, ointment.
Notes The resin is contra-indicated for anyone with a kidney complaint. Oil of turpentine is distilled from it; this has several uses, one of them being as an antidote to phosphorous poisoning. The leaves contain vitamin C and are helpful, therefore, in treating colds. The trunk exudes a sugary manna. This tree is often host to the larch agaric (*Polyporus officinalis*), a white form of fungus.

170 LAURUS NOBILIS L.
Sweet bay

Family Lauraceae.
Description A perennial plant that can grow to a great size, depending on the type of soil. It is very branched with many leaves which are smooth, leathery, glossy on the upper surface and opaque on the lower; they are deep green in colour and are borne on a very short petiole. The leaves have prominent veins, among which the numerous oleiferous glands are clearly visible against the light. The yellowish flowers are in small clusters, the 2 sexes being separate: the male flowers have 8-12 stamens while the females have a monolocular ovary, a style and a stigma. The fruit consists of a dark, almost black, drupe which contains one seed. This plant is quite commonly seen growing wild in the woods of warm-temperate areas and is cultivated throughout Europe, including Britain, both as an indoor and outdoor shrub. It is generally gathered in summer.
Parts used Leaves and fruit.
Chemical compounds Essence: lauric acid, pinene, phellandrene, eugenol, ethers, mucilages, tannin, resin.
Properties Digestive, antiseptic, balsamic, carminative, antitussive.
Forms of use Infusion, tincture, fluid extract, essence.
Notes The leaves are often used in cookery for their aromatic flavour. An essential oil is extracted from the leaves which gives a variable yield of 1 to 3%; it is yellow and has a distinctive aroma. The berries contain fatty oil used in the perfume industry for making toilet soap. At one time this oil was used by pharmacists in the preparation of several ointments. Oil of bay is one of the ingredients in a number of alcoholic drinks. The wood is used for smoking meat and cheese, to which it gives an aromatic tang. A specific remedy for alopecia (baldness) was developed some time ago from the berries.

---

171 LAVANDULA ANGUSTIFOLIA Mill.
Lavandula officinalis Chaix, *Lavandula spica* L., *Lavandula vera* DC., *Lavandula vulgaris* Lam.
Lavender

Family Labiatae.
Description A hardy, herbaceous, bushy plant with straight, woody branches, the lower of which are leafless, putting out numerous herbaceous stems to a height of about 40 inches (1 m); these are quadrangular, greyish and pubescent. The leaves are opposite, long, narrow, lanceolate and light greyish-green with a downy appearance. There is an inflorescence at the end of each slender stem where the densely packed layers of flowers seem to be in whorls; they are, in fact, so closely grouped that there are no leaves in the floral sector and they form, therefore, a compact spike. The long calyx is tubular, pilosect and 5-lobed. The tubular corolla is bilabiate: the upper lip is 2-lobed and the lower one 3-lobed. The whole flower is a mauve to violet shade tinged with light blue. The plant is sometimes found growing wild in the Mediterranean area between the coast and the lower mountain slopes and is extensively cultivated throughout Europe. It is gathered in summer.

Parts used Flowers.
Chemical compounds Linalyl acetate, linalool, coumarin, tannin, saponin, ethereal compound.
Properties Antiseptic, tonic, antispasmodic.
Forms of use Infusion, syrup, tincture, fluid extract, essence, distilled water, oil solution.
Notes Oil of lavender is obtained with a variable yield of 0.8 to 1%. The leaves give an aromatic flavour to salads. It is a favourite plant of bees. The essential oil is reputed to have the power to neutralize a viper's venom. It is an excellent insecticide and an antiseptic.

172 LEONTOPODIUM ALPINUM Cass.

Gnaphalium leontopodium L.
Edelweiss

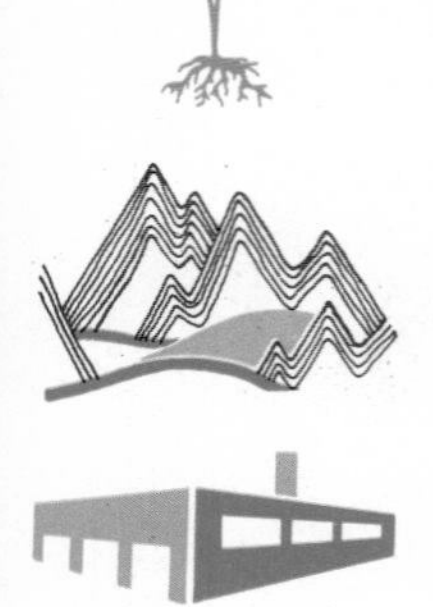

Family Compositae.
Description This small plant has an oblique rhizome and numerous rootlets. The erect stem is downy, as is the whole plant, and grows to a height of 10-12 inches (25-30 cm). The leaves are lanceolate to oblong, the basal ones being in rosette form while the stem leaves, which are wooly and grey-green, are positioned spirally. The flowers are in a terminal head set on spreading, wooly white bracts in a star formation; the peripheral flowers are female and those in the centre are male. The fruit consists of a hairy, truncate-cylindrical achene. Edelweiss grows wild in the mountains of central and southern Europe.
Parts used Whole plant.
Chemical compounds Tannin, gum, salts, bitter.
Properties Astringent, antitussive.
Forms of use Powder, tincture, infusion.
Notes This well-known plant has become a symbol of mountains. It has been avidly collected, over the years, to be kept as a dried flower but this has caused it to become rare in mountain zones and it is now legally protected. Attempts to cultivate it meet with little success.

---

173 LEVISTICUM OFFICINALE Koch

Lovage

Family Umbelliferae.
Description A herbaceous perennial plant with a long taproot. The stem is cylindrical, growing to over 40 inches (1 m) in height, and branched towards the top. The large leaves, 2-3 pinnate, have a roughly diamond-shaped or cuneiform leaf blade with an irregularly dentate margin. The inflorescence consists of umbels of greenish-yellow, fertile flowers, with an involucre of bracts; the calyx and corolla are 5-sepalled and 5-petalled respectively, with an auricle at the apex. The fruit is oblong and smooth and has two 5-ribbed achenes. The plant grows wild in the mountain pastures of continental Europe and in hedgerows near streams; it is also cultivated. It is gathered in either spring or autumn.
Parts used Root, leaves, seeds and young stems.
Chemical compounds Essential oil, terpinol, terpenes, esters, acids, tannin, resins, gum, fats, sugar.
Properties Carminative, digestive, diuretic, emmenagogic.
Forms of use Powder, tincture, infusion, medicinal wine.
Notes Distillation of this plant gives an average yield of 0.5% essence. This is used in perfumeries and in liquor distilleries where it lends its distinctive flavour to several types of fortified wines. It also serves as a digestive. In many mountainous areas the apical leaves are used in the kitchen as aromatic herbs.

174 LIGUSTRUM VULGARE L.

Common privet

Family Oleaceae.
Description A shrub or small tree, with slightly pubescent branches, privet often reaches a height of well over 6½ feet (2 m). The opposite leaves carried on short petioles are oval or elliptic-lanceolate and leathery with well-defined median venation and an entire margin; the upper surface is glossy and the lower one opaque. The flowers are grouped in apical panicles and have short pedicels; each flower has a tubular 4-toothed calyx and a white, tubular, 4-lobed corolla. The fruit consists of a blackish, ovoid berry containing oil seeds. Privet grows wild in western Europe, including Britain, and the medicinally useful parts are gathered in June.
Parts used Leaves.
Chemical compounds Ligustrin, resin, tannin, mannitol.
Properties Vulnerary, detergent.
Forms of use Infusion, poultice.
Notes Internal use of this plant is to be avoided as it can produce allergic symptoms although the bark was, at one time, used as a stomachic. However, privet preparations for external use are extremely effective and completely safe.

---

175 LILIUM CANDIDUM L.

Madonna lily

Family Liliaceae.
Description A bulbous plant, it has an erect stem about 40 inches (1 m) high. The basal leaves emerge from the bulb, which has numerous whitish scales. These leaves are sessile, acute-lanceolate and have an undulate margin. The apical leaves become smaller towards the top of the plant until they are merely bracts. The flowers, borne in a raceme at the apex of the stem, are pedunculate with white tepals, recurved at the tips. They have 6 stamens with yellow anthers. The fruit is a capsule containing round, reddish-brown seeds. Originating in south west Asia, the madonna lily is now cultivated throughout Europe, including Britain, but is rarely found in the wild. The medicinally useful parts are gathered in August.
Parts used Bulb.
Chemical compounds Scilline mucilage, tannin.
Properties Emollient, expectorant, emmenagogic.
Forms of use Decoction, poultice, ointment, oily solution.
Notes This plant is widely grown for the beauty of its flowers. It has an anti-eczematous effect which is obtained by applying the oil solution made by macerating the tepals in oil. The madonna lily is used to treat abscesses and boils by applying the crushed bulb. It was also used, at one time, in powdered form as an analgesic to relieve menstrual pains.

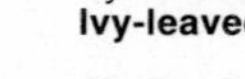

176 LINARIA CYMBALARIA (L.) Mill.

Cymbalaria muralis Gaert., *Antirrhinum cymbalaria* L.
Ivy-leaved toadflax

Family Scrophulariaceae.
Description A delicate, small herbaceous perennial, it has slender, trailing, purplish stems. These have nodes at intervals from which rootlets emerge to cling to dry walls or rocks, its usual habitat. The bright green leaves, which have a variable length petiole, are opposite at the base and then become alternate; they are palminerved, smooth and each leaf blade has 5 or more pointed lobes. The flowers are carried on long pedicles which arise from the leaf bases. The calyx is 5-parted and the tubular corolla is bilabiate, the upper lip being divided into 2 lobes and the lower one into 3. The fruit, which contains the seeds, is a rather long capsule, similar to a clove. The ivy-leaved toadflax is found wild throughout most of Europe; it is naturalized in Britain. It is gathered from April-October, but this has to be done carefully as it is easy to disturb the root.

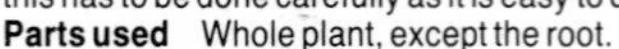

Parts used Whole plant, except the root.
Chemical compounds Mucilage, tannin, gum, acids.
Properties Antihaemorrhoidal, vulnerary.
Forms of use Infusion, poultice.
Notes This plant loses almost all its consistency and is easily pulverized if allowed to become dry. It is of little use in phytotherapy, apart from the folk-remedy of putting its crushed leaves on fresh wounds to stop bleeding.

---

177 LINARIA VULGARIS Mill.

Antirrhinum linaria L.
Common or yellow toadflax

Family Scrophulariaceae.
Description An erect plant with a very small, branching rhizome that throws out a number of rootlets. The stem is cylindrical and may grow to a height of more than 20 inches (50 cm). The leaves resemble those of the *Linum* (flax), from which it derives its generic and English names; they are sessile, linear and alternate on the stem. The sulphur-yellow flowers are grouped in an apical spike; the corolla has a bright orange lower lip, the tube narrowing to a pointed spur at the back. The fruit is an elliptical capsule with flat, membraneous seeds. It is commonly seen growing wild throughout most of Europe, including Britain, by ditches, in hedgerows, on dry banks and roadside verges. It is gathered in summer.
Parts used Whole plant.
Chemical compounds Linarin, phytosterol, mannitol, fat, sugar, tannin, colouring material, mucilage.
Properties Antiphlogistic, antihaemorrhoidal, opthalmic, diuretic.
Forms of use Infusion, tincture, ointment, powder.
Notes This plant provides a yellow colouring substance that was once used for dyeing clothes. In some areas, the young spring shoots are boiled and eaten. An ointment, made from the flowers, was at one time used as an opthalmic remedy to easy eye irritation. Compresses of crushed toadflax are still used in rural areas to heal fresh minor wounds.

178 LINUM USITATISSIMUM L.

Common flax

Family Linaceae.
Description An annual, biennial or perennial plant with a rather weak taproot; the annual has only one stem while the perennial has several. The stems are simple at the base but branched at the top and grow to a height of about 40 inches (1 m). It has rather sparse, alternate, lanceolate leaves, broad at the base of the plant, narrower and pointed at the top; the leaf blade is entire, the lower surface being heavily veined. The sparse sky-blue flowers are arranged in a corymb supported by a long pedicel. The calyx is 5-sepalled and the corolla is 5-petalled with an undulating margin. The fruits are globose, striate capsules held in the persistent calyx and contain about 10 small, smooth, glossy seeds like those of an apple and the same colour. The common flax is rarely found growing wild but is extensively cultivated throughout Europe, including Britain, for flax and oil. It is gathered in autumn.
Parts used Seeds.
Chemical compounds Mucilage, fatty oil, proteins, ethereal compounds and glucoside.
Properties Emollient, laxative, resolvent.
Forms of use Maceration, poultice, infusion, wafer papers made with flax flour.
Notes A fatty drying oil (linseed oil) is obtained from the flax plant which is used in the paint industry. The fibres obtained from its stems are used by the textile industry to make linen. Linolenic acid is effective in cases of thrombosis. The waste materials serve as fattening foods in animal husbandry. Flax flour can be used as a substitute for fenugreek flour.

---

179 LIPPIA TRIPHYLLA (L'Her) O. Kuntze

Lippia citriodora Kunth, *Lippia aloysia* Ort., *Verbena triphylla* Her.

Lemon-scented verbena

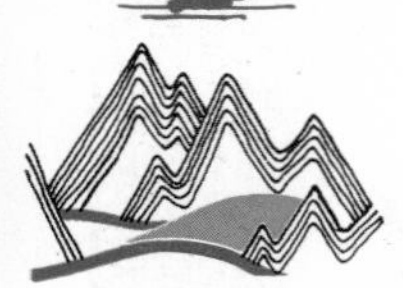

Family Verbenaceae.
Description A shrub that may grow up to about 6½ feet (2 m). The mid-green leaves are arranged in whorls of 3 or 4 and are lanceolate with a pointed apex appearing, in profile, to be hooked with the point reflexed. The margin is rough but entire, with a suggestion of teeth. The main and secondary venations on the lower leaf surfaces are very prominent. The leaves have a strong perfume. The inflorescence is a slim terminal panicle, the flowers consisting of a small, tubular calyx with 4 long narrow teeth and a pale, greenish-mauve corolla divided into 4 acuminate lobes. The fruit consists of two small nutlets each one containing a seed. Originally from Chile, this plant was first imported into Europe in 1784 and is now cultivated for ornament. The vegetative period is closely linked to the climate which should be damp and warm. It flowers later in northern areas and seldom produces seeds; cuttings are, therefore, the best method of reproduction. It is gathered at the end of summer.
Parts used Flowering tops and leaves.
Chemical compounds Essence: citral, limonene, geraniol, verbenaline and verbenine.
Properties Sedative, stomachic, antineuralgic.
Forms of use Infusion, essence, tincture, fluid extract.
Notes A green colouring substance, completely soluble in alcohol, is obtained from its leaves. Distillation of its leaves gives an average yield of 0.5% of essence; this is often adulterated with oil of lemon or by synthesis. Lemon-scented verbena is extensively used in liquor distilleries and perfumeries.

180 LOBELIA INFLATA L.
Lobelia

Family Campanulaceae.
Description An annual plant with an erect, angular, slightly pubescent stem of up to 20 inches (50 cm). The glandular alternate leaves are ovate-lanceolate and acute, with a slightly dentate margin and a pilose leaf surface. The pale blue flowers are either borne in terminal cymes or spring from the leaf axils on long peduncles. The fruit consists of swollen ribbed capsules containing dark brown seeds. Lobelia is native to North America but is widely cultivated in the British Isles for ornament. It is gathered while in flower.
Parts used Flowering tops.
Chemical compounds Lobeline, lobelacrine, inflatin, lobelic acid, essential oil, resin.
Properties Emetic, expectorant, anti-asthmatic, diaphoretic, sedative.
Forms of use Tincture, fluid extract.
Notes This plant is particularly poisonous and is only, therefore, to be used with great care or under medical supervision. Lobelia-based preparations are available which are designed to break the smoking habit. This plant is synergic with deadly nightshade, thornapple and mistletoe.

---

181 LONICERA CAPRIFOLIUM L.
Honeysuckle

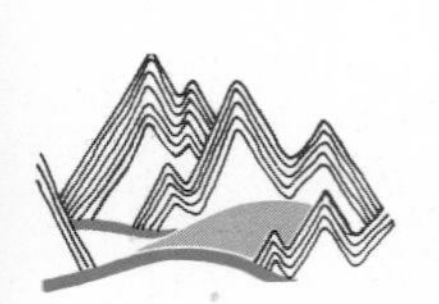

Family Caprifoliaceae.
Description A climbing shrub with a smooth, sarmentose stem of up to about 16-20 feet (5-6 m). The opposite leaves are in pairs, the upper ones being dark green and the lower ones glaucous blue-green. Some are petiolate within the fertile branches; others are joined in such a way as to constitute a single leaf, oval at both ends, in the middle of which there is a stem node from which the branchlets emerge. The central one of these is the peduncle of the flowers. These are in terminal clusters with a tubular, bilabiate, purplish-pink or whitish-yellow corolla. The upper lip is 4-lobed and the lower entire. The fruit is a fleshy berry containing a few seeds. The plant is distributed widely throughout central and southern Europe from coastal plains to mountain slopes with a preference for hilly hedgerows. It is naturalized in Britain and northern Europe as an escape from gardens, where it is cultivated widely. It is gathered in the spring.
Parts used Leaves and flowers.
Chemical compounds Essential oil, glucosides, salicylic acid, tannin.
Properties Emollient, expectorant, antispasmodic.
Forms of use Infusion, decoction, tincture.
Notes The pressed juice of honeysuckle fruit makes a mild purgative. Recent research has proved that this plant has an outstanding curative action in cases of colitis. An infusion of the heavily perfumed flowers can be taken as a substitute for tea. An essential oil was, at one time, extracted from the flowers for making a very sweet perfume but the yield was extremely low.

182 LOTUS CORNICULATUS L.

Bird's-foot trefoil

Family Leguminosae.
Description A small plant with a woody taproot. The trailing stems, up to 12 inches (30 cm)high, are angular, not very branched and glabrous or slightly pilose. The glabrous leaves are pinnate with 5 leaflets, ovate-lanceolate with a cuneiform base. The flowers are grouped in a verticel at the apex of the branches or arising from the leaf axils; the calyx is tubular and 5-toothed while the corolla is 5-petalled and golden yellow with red streaks. The fruit is a brown, cylindrical linear pod containing brownish, oval seeds. Bird's-foot trefoil is commonly found growing wild throughout Europe, including Britain, in pasturelands, by the roadside and on the sunny banks of streams and waterways. It is gathered in July.
Parts used Flowers.
Chemical compounds Hydrocyanic compounds, flavonoids, tannin, colouring material.
Properties Sedative, antispasmodic, sympatholytic, cardiotonic.
Forms of use Infusion, fluid extract, syrup.
Notes Bird's-foot trefoil can also be used externally as a local anti-inflammatory compress in all cases of skin inflammation. It is a newcomer to phytotherapeutic medicine, but research shows results identical to those obtained with the passion flower (*Passiflora*). It is a useful plant for green-manuring as it fixes nitrogen.

---

183 LUPINUS ALBUS L.

Lupinus albo flore Clus.
White lupin

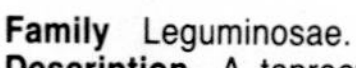

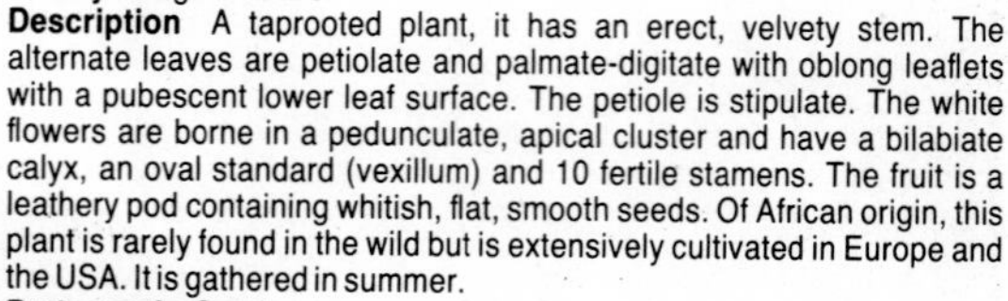

Family Leguminosae.
Description A taprooted plant, it has an erect, velvety stem. The alternate leaves are petiolate and palmate-digitate with oblong leaflets with a pubescent lower leaf surface. The petiole is stipulate. The white flowers are borne in a pedunculate, apical cluster and have a bilabiate calyx, an oval standard (vexillum) and 10 fertile stamens. The fruit is a leathery pod containing whitish, flat, smooth seeds. Of African origin, this plant is rarely found in the wild but is extensively cultivated in Europe and the USA. It is gathered in summer.
Parts used Seeds.
Chemical compounds Lupanine, lupinin, sparteine, proteins, oil, cholesterol, lecithin, salts, inositesaphosphoric acid.
Properties Hypoglycaemic, vermifuge.
Form of use Maceration, infusion, powder, tincture, fluid extract.
Notes The seeds can be eaten when the bitter components have been removed. Roasted, they can make a coffee substitute. Cosmetic face-masks are made from lupin flour and used to invigorate tired skin. An edible oil is extracted from the seeds. Because of the high nitrogenous content, lupins are useful for green-manuring.

184 LYCOPERDON BOVISTA L.

(now known as **Calvatia utriformis** (Bulliard) Jaap).
Puff-ball

Family Lycoperdaceae.
Description A large, white, pyriform fungus, exceeding 4 inches (10 cm) in diameter, with a globose receptacle, it has a delicate, whitish endoperidium which turns into a blackish, powdery substance as it matures. When fully ripe, this powder escapes through the top which opens to release the residual basidia. The greyish spores are small and smooth. The plant is found throughout Britain and Europe in the undergrowth on damp hillsides or among grass under trees. It is gathered before it is ripe.
Parts used Whole fungus.
Chemical compounds Resin, acids, mannitol, salts.
Properties Astringent, haemostatic.
Forms of use Infusion, tincture, powder.
Notes The puff-ball is sometimes used as a very effective veinousconstrictive in treating haemorrhoids, either as an infusion or in powder form. Before puff balls ripen they are excellent to eat, but should never be cooked once the flesh has started to discolour.

---

185 LYCOPERSICUM ESCULENTUM Mill.

Solanum lycopersicum L.
Tomato

Family Solanaceae.
Description A herbaceous plant with a taproot and lateral rootlets, it has a branched stem which grows erect at first and then, unless artificially supported, prostrate. It can grow to a height of about 7 feet (2 m). The large, alternate leaves are pinnate with small, pilose leaflets. The whole plant has a distinctive odour which is noticeable when any part of it is touched or crushed. The flowers, grouped at various levels on the stem and branches, have a 5-lobed calyx, a yellow, 5-petalled corolla and short stamens; they bloom successively from June-October. Once pollinated, the plant will produce fruit of a particular shape, according to its variety: round, oval, grooved or plum-shaped. The pulp contained within the fruit is bright red and has symmetrically arranged seeds. The tomato is cultivated extensively almost everywhere but prefers a mild climate and a neutral or acid soil with plenty of water. In Britain it will rarely ripen the fruit out of doors. The fruit is picked as it ripens.
Parts used Fruit and, ultimately, the whole plant.
Chemical compounds Solanine, saponin, colouring substance, carotene, vitamin C, malic acid, tomatidin.
Properties Eupeptic, nutritive, alkaline rendering.
Forms of use Juice, poultice.
Notes At one time the tomato was regarded as poisonous but became accepted as edible towards the end of the 18th century. It is used as a tincture in homoeopathy to treat rheumatism and severe headaches. The pulp is used cosmetically in face-packs. The powder made from the whole plant is an excellent insecticide, especially against ants. The leaves, dried and cured, can be used in a mixture for pipe-smoking.

186 LYCOPODIUM CLAVATUM L.

Common club moss

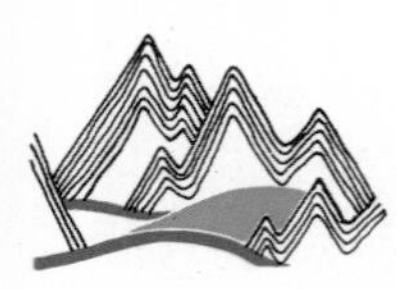

Family Lycopodiaceae.
Description A creeping plant, its adventitious roots emerge from its low-creeping stem. The numerous branchlets are forked and covered with green, slightly toothed, overlapping, linear leaves. The one or two spikelets, at the apex of the branches, which may be 16-20 inches (40-50 cm) or more high, contain kidney-shaped sporangia bearing reticulate, globose spores which appear as yellowish, resinous powder. The plant is commonly found growing wild in northern and central Europe, including Britain, on moorlands, fields and pasturelands. It is gathered in summer.
Parts used Spores.
Chemical compounds Resin, sugar, lycopodine, phytosterol, wax, oil, glycerol.
Properties Decongestant, antipruritic.
Forms of use Powder, infusion.
Notes The spores are used almost exclusively externally as a dusting powder for various skin diseases. The powder is also used cosmetically as a face-powder base and pharmaceutically as a pill-powder (to prevent pills from sticking together in their container and to disguise their flavour). It is also used in fireworks which blaze brightly with a continuous crackling sound.

---

187 LYTHRUM SALICARIA L.

Purple loosestrife

Family Lythraceae.
Description A rhizomatose, herbaceous plant, it has a quadrangular, ramified, slightly pubescent stem. The light green sessile leaves, which are opposite or whorled, are oblong-elliptic and pointed, with an entire margin. The purple flowers spring from the upper leaf axils to form a spike. The cylindrical calyx has 8-12 pointed sepals and a corolla with 4-6 petals. The fruit is a membraneous capsule containing yellowish, elliptical seeds. The plant is frequently found growing wild in Europe, including Britain; its specific habitat is by watercourses, streams, canals and ditches, where it grows particularly well. The medicinally useful parts are gathered when the plant is in full bloom in summer.
Parts used Flowering tops.
Chemical compounds Salicarin, mucilage, starch, iron, pectin, phytosterol, antibiotic.
Properties Antidysenteric, haemostatic, vulnerary, antibiotic.
Forms of use Infusion, powder, fluid extract, tincture, syrup.
Notes This plant has always had the reputation of being an intestinal disinfectant, especially in cases of enteritis. It has an antibiotic effect on the typhus bacilli – both on the *Bacillum coli* as well as on the amoeba. The young branches used to be regarded as gum-stimulators and were given to children for chewing in order to strengthen weak, bleeding gums. The leaves were used in local compresses for their constrictive properties in the treatment of wounds. In some areas a slightly alcoholic liquid is made by fermenting the leaves. The powder is used as a haemostatic in cases of severe nosebleed and, cosmetically, in face-packs to counteract reddened skin.

188 MALUS SYLVESTRIS Mill.

Malus communis Poiret. subsp. *sylvestris* (Mill.) Gams

Wild crab (Crab apple)

Family Rosaceae.

Description A rather small tree, it has a sturdy, erect trunk, that divides into strong branches to create a fine crown. When young, its bark is smooth but it becomes rough with age. The dark green, alternate leaves are oval with a short petiole. The inflorescence consists of clusters of 4-6 flowers emerging from a rosette of leaves. Each flower has a persistent calyx of 5 sepals and a pinkish-white, 5-petalled corolla. The rosy object usually referred to as its fruit is, in fact, a false fruit, as it develops from the entire receptacle. It contains one or two dark, coriaceous seeds in the light-coloured pulp. This cold-resistant tree is to be found wild in most of Europe, including Britain, and will grow almost everywhere, even on the lower mountain slopes. The apples are picked when ripe.

Parts used Fruit.

Chemical compounds Malic acid, citric acid, pectin, galattan, tannin, enzymes, quercetin.

Properties Antacid, anti-uricaemic, antidiarrhoeic, nutritive, tranquillizer.

Forms of use Pulp, juice, infusion.

Notes The leaves can be used to make a very pleasant tisane which may be drunk instead of tea. Both the pulp and juice encourage restful sleep and the powdered peel mixed with lemon balm also makes a good nightcap. Cider can be made by macerating wild apples and allowing them to ferment, although the best type of cider is made from particular varieties of cultivated apple. Crushed apple pulp will heal inflammation or small flesh-wounds by local application.

---

189 MALVA SYLVESTRIS L.

Common mallow

Family Malvaceae.

Description A herbaceous perennial plant, with a rather pulpy taproot, its stem is nearly always erect, growing to a height of 40 inches (1 m) or more, depending on the type of soil. The dark green leaves are 5-lobed with toothed margins; they are borne on petioles which become shorter towards the top of the stem. The flowers range from reddish-purple to crimson, garnet red and sometimes bluish-mauve; they form in small clusters in the leaf axils and have a 5-sepalled calyx with a small outer calyx. The corolla is 5-petalled; the petals are oval with a notched end. The fruit is a capsule containing kidney-shaped seeds. The plant is commonly found on waste ground and along roadsides. It grows wild in many regions of Europe, including the British Isles. The medicinally useful parts are gathered in early spring.

Parts used Leaves without petioles.

Chemical compounds Mucilage, tannin, malvine, malvidine.

Properties Emollient, antiphlogistic, antitussive, laxative, diuretic.

Forms of use Infusion, fluid extract, semi-fluid extract, maceration.

Notes The young, tender tips have various uses in the kitchen. The plant is also an excellent laxative for young children and, at one time, the peeled root was given to them during teething. It is preferable to carry out cold extraction of the mucilage.

190 MARRUBIUM VULGARE L.
White horehound

Family Labiatae.
Description This herbaceous perennial grows to a height of 16-20 inches (40-50 cm) and is scented. It has a woody root and a quadrangular stem with several downy branches. The opposite, petiolate leaves decrease in size towards the apex of the plant and are all slightly dentate with deep veining. The leaves are also covered in wooly hair, the lower ones to a lesser extent. The flowers are grouped in little whorls on the upper leaf nodes, at the axils of which they are situated in varying numbers on a small bract. The calyx is tubular and divided into 10 pointed lobes, which resemble alternately long and short teeth. The corolla is bilabiate and white, the upper lip being erect, bilobate and larger than the lower one. The fruits, enclosed in the leathery calyx, are tetrachene, ovoid and smooth. Common throughout Europe, including Britain, the plant grows wild everywhere from coastal to mountainous areas. It is gathered in spring.
Parts used Flowering, non-woody tops.
Chemical compounds Marrubine, essential oil, choline, tannin, glycoside.
Properties Digestive, colagogic, emmenagogic, diuretic, antiseptic.
Forms of use Infusion, fluid extract, syrup, powder, medicinal wine.
Notes Widely used in the manufacture of spirits. It has a specific use in phytotherapy as a substitute for quinine where the latter is ineffective. Each 100 g contains 30 mg of vitamin C.

---

191 MATRICARIA CHAMOMILLA L.
German camomile

Family Compositae.
Description An annual herbaceous plant with a taproot, it will grow to a height of about 40 inches (1 m) in the right soil. The stem is erect and branches only towards the top. The alternate leaves are mostly sessile, a few having a very short petiole; they are bipinnatisect, delicately lobed and thread-like, ending in a point. The flowers are arranged in small heads arranged in clusters. The flowers consist of several white ligules surrounding the central mound of tiny yellow flowers which are embedded in a hollow, conical receptacle. The light-coloured fruits are very small achenes with no pappus. This plant is found almost anywhere in the wild, throughout Europe, including lower mountain slopes, meadows, fields, hedgerows and rural roadsides. In Britain it has become naturalized. The medicinally useful parts are gathered in summer, with careful avoidance of any flowers in full bloom.
Parts used Flower heads.
Chemical compounds Azulene, alcohols, sesquiterpenes, apigenin, various acids, phytosterol, mucilage, mineral salts, vitamins.
Properties Sedative, emmenagogic, carminative, febrifuge, analgesic.
Forms of use Infusion, fluid extract, tincture, syrup, oil, essence.
Notes An average yield of 0.22-0.23% of essence if obtained; it tends to be slightly blue because of the azulene content; at a temperature of about 32°F (0°C) it becomes buttery. The heads are often adulterated with those of the common daisy (*Bellis perennis*) and the essence is adulterated with cade (juniper-tar) oil. The distilled water is extensively used in the cosmetic industry and the azulene serves as an antiphlogistic in cases of sunburn.

192 MELILOTUS OFFICINALIS (L.) Pallas
Melilot

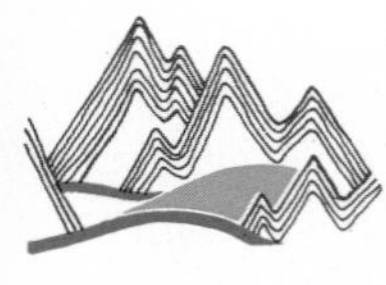

Family Leguminosae.
Description The generic and English names derive from the Greek *méli*, honey, and *lotós,* the lotus. It is an annual or biennial plant, erect and growing to a height of 2-4 feet (60-120 cm), with a partially woody taproot. The stems are simple and often branched. The leaves are borne on a long petiole at the base of which are 2 small bracts; the leaves consists of 3 leaflets, the 2 lateral ones being almost sessile while the central one has a stalk. The 3 leaflets have a smooth margin for half their length and are then finely toothed. The upper leaves are narrower at the base than the lower ones. The flowers are borne in slender racemes which arise from the leaf axils; the tubular calyx is 5-toothed and the corolla consists of 2 fused petals which form a carina. The fruits are small, dark-coloured pods with greenish, ovoidal seeds. The melilot is frequently seen throughout most of Europe, growing wild by the roadside, in neglected fields and on waste ground. It is naturalized in Britain. The medicinally useful parts are gathered in summer.
Parts used Flowering tops.
Chemical compounds Coumarin, glucoside, resin, flavonoids, vitamin C.
Properties Antispasmodic, sedative, anti-inflammatory, diuretic.
Forms of use Infusion, syrup.
Notes Melilot is a great favourite with bees because of its high pollen content. The flowers are used to perfume snuff and pipe-tobacco and to give an aromatic quality to some tisanes. A coumarin-based essence is extracted from the flowers which, if swallowed, can cause considerable discomfort. The distilled water obtained is very effective as an eye-lotion to treat conjunctivitis.

---

193 MELISSA OFFICINALIS L.
Balm

Family Labiatae.
Description A herbaceous, perennial plant with a woody rhizome and square branched stem, it grows to about 40 inches (1 m) high. It is slightly downy and light green with yellowish tinges. The opposite leaves, borne on petioles which become progressively shorter towards the top, are cordate or elongate and pointed. The margin is toothed and the venation on the leaf blade takes the form of large grooves. The flowers are grouped in simple whorls at the leaf axils and begin to bloom in late spring. The calyx is bell-shaped, pilosect and bilabiate, the upper lip being larger than the lower. The pinkish-white corolla is tubular with a convex upper lip while the lower lip has 3 well-defined lobes. The fruit, formed at the base of the calyx, is an oval, 4-sectioned cremocarp with a protruding rib running lengthways; it is dark and glossy. Although native to southern Europe, it is now found elsewhere, including Britain, from coastal plains to mountainous sites, provided the ground is moist. It is gathered from spring to late summer.
Parts used Leaves and flowering tops.
Chemical compounds Aldehydes, mucilages, starch, bitter substance, tannin, saponin.
Properties Antispasmodic, anti-hysteric, tonic, digestive.
Forms of use Infusion, fluid extract, tincture, syrup, elixir.
Notes Extremely attractive to bees and widely used in liquor distillation and perfumery, the yield of essence from this plant is very low and it is, therefore, often adulterated with essence of lippia or by the addition of citrus terpenes. The leaves can be used as an aromatic culinary herb and are the basis of a well-known sauce. They are also used in many sedative tisanes.

194 MENYANTHES TRIFOLIATA L.
Bogbean

Family Menyanthaceae.
Description The generic name derives from the Greek *men*, month, and *anthos*, flower, alluding to the length of its flowering season. An aquatic plant with a creeping rhizome and many rootlets, the stem is fleshy and covered by the leaf sheaths. The leaves are trifoliate and borne on a long petiole that is slightly broader at its base; the 3 segments are oblong, thick and glossy. The flowers are arranged in a raceme at the top of a stem which arises from the leaf axils. The flowers are bell-shaped with a pink or white corolla and a 5-lobed calyx. The fruit is a globose capsule containing numerous yellowish seeds. The plant grows wild in most of Europe, including Britain, in marshy ground, spongy swampland and raised bogs, reaching a height of 20 inches (50 cm) or more. It is gathered in late spring.
Parts used Whole plant.
Chemical compounds Menyanthin, melyanthine, saponin, gum, tannin, oil, menyanthol, choline, carotene.
Properties Stomachic, digestive, emmenagogic, febrifuge, carminative.
Forms of use Infusion, tincture, fluid extract, syrup, powder, medicinal wine.
Notes This little plant is the fundamental ingredient of a number of alcoholic drinks with a bitter base. It has been used commercially as a substitute for hops in beer-making. The prescribed doses should never be exceeded to avoid the emetic effects that may result due to the concentration of menyanthin. In view of the heavy demand for bogbean, it is extensively grown in areas where the land has not been reclaimed, thus enabling it to be economically useful.

---

195 MENTHA x PIPERITA L.
Peppermint

Family Labiatae.
Description A perennial plant about 20 inches (50 cm) high, it has a rhizome and stolons that form after the first year. The nodes on the stolons produce quadrangular stems that grow upwards and roots that grow downwards. The opposite, decussate leaves are lanceolate in shape with a venation that gives them a rough-textured appearance, and they are carried on very short petioles. The leaves are dark green on the upper surface but slightly paler on the lower. The flowers are grouped in a terminal pseudo-spike in the upper foliar axils. The calyx is 5-lobed with pointed lobes; the pinkish-mauve corolla is tubular with 4 lobes, one of which is larger than the others. The fruits are ovoidal, 4-sectioned, dark, glossy cremocarps forming in the leathery calyx. Rarely found growing wild, peppermint is widely cultivated throughout Europe, including Britain. It is gathered during summer.
Parts used Leaves and flowering tops.
Chemical compounds Menthol, menthone, tannin, enzymes, pectin, terpenic derivatives.
Properties Tonic, stomachic, antispasmodic, antitussive, insecticide.
Forms of use Infusion, fluid extract, syrup, powder, essence, juice.
Notes This is regarded as a cross between wild water mint (*Mentha aquatica*) and spearmint (*Mentha spicata*). It has a 0.25-1% content of volatile oil and is used as an aromatic culinary herb as well as in the curing of tobacco. It is extensively used in perfumeries and liquor distilleries. Mint should be avoided by those with anxiety problems and is incompatible with camphor and thymol. Menthol is a powerful antiseptic as well as an insectifuge.

196 MESPILUS GERMANICA L.

Medlar

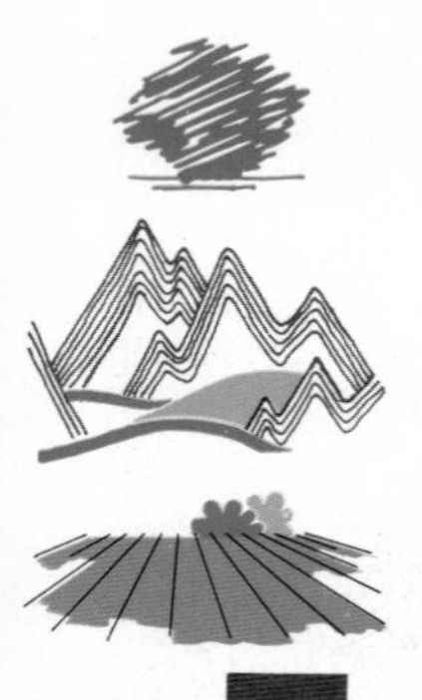

Family Rosaceae.

Description A small tree, about 10-30 feet (3-9 m) high, with a dark, twisted trunk and pilose, spiny branches. The leaves are large, lanceolate and pointed. The margin is entire for the first half of the leaf and then becomes toothed; the upper surface is opaque and smooth while the lower one is pubescent due to the presence of small hairs. The white flowers grow singly; they are subsessile at the apex of the branchlets and surrounded by large leaves. The calyx is 5-sepalled and the white corolla is 5-petalled with numerous prominent, dark stamens. The fruit, or to be more exact, the false fruit (in that the receptacle and calyx are persistent and grow to enclose the true fruit) contains 5 rust-coloured pips and retains the remains of the 5 sepals on the top. The plant thrives in woods and hedgerows in southern Europe and has become naturalized elsewhere, including Britain. It is also cultivated. The medicinally useful parts are gathered in May and in autumn.

Parts used Leaves, fruit and seeds.

Chemical compounds Tannin, citric acid, malic acid, peptic substances, sugars, vitamins.

Properties Pulp: laxative; leaves: astringent; nutlets: lithontriptic.

Forms of use Electuary, decoction, maceration.

Notes The fruit of the medlar is only edible when over-ripe. It makes excellent jelly but does not keep well. Alcohol is obtained from maceration, before distillation. The bark was, at one time, used as a substitute for quinine but with uncertain results. The powdered nutlets should only be taken as a lithontriptic under medical supervision and the dose prescribed not exceeded because of the hydrocyanic acid content.

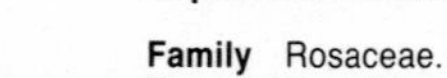

197 MESPILUS JAPONICA Thunb.

(now known as **Eriobotrya japonica** Lindl.)

Japanese medlar

Family Rosaceae.

Description A small tree, it grows to about 13-16 feet (4-5 m) high and has a straight trunk; it is branched, with wooly-haired branches. The glossy green leaves are ovate or lanceolate, leathery, rough-textured, pinnately veined and serrate. The flowers are arranged in tomentose panicles with a 5-toothed calyx and obovate, whitish petals. The pulpy, yellow fruit is ellipsoidal and smooth, containing large, light brown seeds. This plant originates in Japan and is only found in Europe in cultivation. The medicinally useful parts are gathered in summer.

Parts used Fruit and leaves.

Chemical compounds Sugars, tannin, citric acid, malic acid, salts.

Properties Astringent, nutrient, expectorant.

Forms of use Pulp, decoction.

Notes Jellies and jams made from the fruit are easy to digest and have a slight expectorant effect. A slightly alcoholic drink can also be made from the fruit by fermenting it. The leaves are used in decoction form as an intestinal astringent and as a mouthwash in cases of thrush. A decoction made from the twigs and branchlets has the same effect.

198 MORUS ALBA L.
Chinese white mulberry

Family Moraceae.
Description A tree that grows to about 50 feet (15 m) in height; the bark on its branched trunk is rough and cracked, with a yellowish tinge, and the branches form a dense, rounded crown. The leaves are cordate-oval, toothed and often trilobate; the lower surface is pilose along the veins. The plant bears male and female flowers in separate catkins: in the male the perianth is 4-parted and in the female it is 4-5-parted. The fruity spike consists of a fleshy collection of small, whitish drupes. Originally a native of China, this tree has now been established in Europe for several centuries. It was once grown extensively and a number of old examples still exist. It is rarely found in Britain. The medicinally useful parts are gathered in summer.
Parts used Leaves.
Chemical compounds Adenine, protein, salts, glucose.
Properties Astringent, hypoglycaemic, odontalgic.
Forms of use Infusion, tincture.
Notes The mulberry is a vitally important element for feeding silkworms but has become less common since the decline of the silk industry. The fruit has an attractively sweet flavour, juices, jams and jellies being made from it as well as alcohol after fermentation. Fibres obtained from the processed bark are used in weaving. The leaves can be mixed in with normal animal fodder. As with the black mulberry, a tincture can be made from the bark which relieves toothache.

---

199 MORUS NIGRA L.
Black mulberry

Family Moraceae.
Description A tree which grows to a height of about 50 feet (15 m), it has a dense, rounded crown. The alternate leaves are somewhat leathery, the upper surface being dark green and the lower somewhat lighter; they are cordate and toothed with small, saw-like teeth around the margin. The inflorescence is an elongated catkin, both male and female flowers having a 4-parted perianth. The fruiting structure is spherical and dark in colour; when pressed, a deep red juice seeps out from the enlarged tepals that enclose the fruit, which is a small achene. A native of parts of Asia Minor, Armenia and the southern Caucasus, this tree is only found under cultivation in rural areas of Europe, including Britain, preferably in moist, rather sheltered sites. The medicinally useful parts are gathered in summer.
Parts used Fruit, leaves and bark.
Chemical compounds Adenine, glucose, asparagine, calcium carbonate, protein, tannin.
Properties Antidiabetic, astringent, odontalgic.
Forms of use Decoction, fluid extract, juice, powder, tincture.
Notes Excellent home-made jams and jellies can be made from the fruit as well as a pleasant, refreshing juice. The persistent wine-red colouring of the black mulberry is extracted as a dye for use in various products. The root-bark tincture helps to relieved toothache. The fermented mulberries yield a slightly alcoholic liquid, which can be distilled. The bark provides good fibres for weaving.

200 MUSCARI COMOSUM (L.) Mill.

Hyacinthus comosus L.
Tassel hyacinth

Family Liliaceae.
Description This small plant has a bulb, rather like an onion, from which emerges a very dainty, cylindrical stem which may be as tall as 16 inches (35 cm). It has only basal leaves which arise directly from the bulb; the leaves are long, fleshy, linear and have an acute apex. The plant has both sterile and fertile flowers arranged in apical racemes, the fertile ones being borne on stalks. The bell-shaped corolla of the upper flowers is deep violet. The fruit is a capsule containing almost spherical seeds. In North America as well as southern and central Europe the plant grows wild in hedgerows, around the edges of fields and woods, or flanking footpaths. It is gathered in spring.
Parts used Bulb.
Chemical compounds Mucilage, tannin, salts, gum, sugars.
Properties Diuretic, poultice.
Notes The bulbs are edible, after boiling, although somewhat bitter. When crushed, the resulting pulp can be applied externally to reddened skin. In fact, tassel hyacinth bulbs have the same qualities as the onion, especially as a diuretic. The bulb can be pickled in vinegar but much of its bitter principle is lost in this way.

---

201 MYOSOTIS ALPESTRIS Schmidt.

Alpine forget-me-not

Family Boraginaceae.
Description A hardy perennial plant, it has a grey, woody, fibrous creeping root. The plant is erect, delicate and hirsute, with branched stems, about 4 inches (10 cm) high. The basal leaves, which are spatulate and petiolate, are in rosette form while the stem leaves are lanceolate and sessile. The flowers are grouped in small, loose-spiralled clusters and have a campanulate calyx and a sky-blue, tubular corolla with a yellow throat. The fruits are blackish, ovoid achenes. The plant's natural habitat is among the rocks, pastures and woodlands of the Alps, although it is found in mountainous parts of Britain. It is gathered in May.
Parts used Whole plant.
Chemical compounds Tannin, resin, mucilage, salts.
Properties Cicatrizer, opthalmic, astringent.
Forms of use Infusion, juice, distilled water, poultice.
Notes A charming plant that is grown in rockeries for its compact flowering habit and sweet fragrance. It is an excellent remedy for many eye diseases and is used as an eye-lotion. It has good healing properties when ground finely and applied to a wound. At one time, the juice was used to stop nose-bleeds. It is very effective in cases of enteritis in children, especially if used in conjunction with purple loosestrife (*Lythrum salicaria*).

202 MYRTUS COMMUNIS L.
Common myrtle

Family Myrtaceae.
Description A shrub, about 8-10 feet (2.5-3 m) high, its bark is reddish when young, becoming grey and deeply cracked with age. The opposite leaves are sessile or borne on a very short petiole and ovate-lanceolate in shape; the upper surface is dark green and the lower one rather lighter. The leaves are leathery and equipped with a great many glands of essential oil which has a distinctively aromatic perfume. The flowers grow singly from the leaf axils, supported by a long, reddish-brown pedicel. The calyx is divided into 5 triangular sepals. The corolla, which is 5-petalled and scented, is remarkable for its prominent mass of yellow stamens arranged in a half-sphere. The fruit is a purple-black, ovoid, fleshy berry, the remains of the calyx at the top containing the kidney-shaped seeds. This shrub can be seen cultivated in quite extensive groves around the Mediterranean coast where it is also found growing wild. The medicinally useful parts are gathered in spring.
Parts used Leaves.
Chemical compounds Essential oil containing terpenic compounds, myrtenol, myrtol, aldehydes, resins, tannin.
Properties Balsamic, haemostatic.
Forms of use Essence, infusion, fluid extract, tincture, syrup.
Notes An average yield is obtained of ⅓ oz (10 g) of essence per 220 lb (100 kg) of the plant; this essence is yellow, aromatic and has a density of 0.9. The chemical known as myrtol, used as a remedy for gingivitis, is obtained from the essence by fractional distillation. Recent research has revealed a substance in the myrtle plant which has an antibiotic action. In addition, its seeds contain oil. The berries are used as an aromatic culinary herb.

---

203 NASTURTIUM OFFICINALE R. Br.
Nasturtium fontanum Asch., *Sisymbrium cardaminefolium* Gilib, *Sisymbrium nasturtium-aquaticum* L.
Watercress

Family Cruciferae.
Description This herbaceous perennial plant has many rootlets and trailing stalks which grow to a length of about 27-32 inches (70-80 cm). It has bright green imparipinnatisect leaves, the basal ones being petiolate and the upper ones sessile and segmented; the terminal leaf is the largest and is rounded, cordiform and often pointed. The inflorescence starts as a corymb but, as it matures, it takes on the form of terminal racemes in opposition to the last leaves. The flowers are whitish with 4 petals and 4 sepals, the latter being twice as long as the former. The fruits are siliquae and contain a number of seeds arranged in a row on each side of the siliqua. Watercress grows wild in much of Europe, including Britain, in clean, running water that is fairly shallow, most of the plant being immersed. It is widely cultivated but it is very important always to wash it well before eating, as it is often infested with sheep parasites. It is usually gathered in spring.
Parts used Upper part of plant.
Chemical compounds Gluconasturtiin, vitamins A, C and D, sodium, enzymes.
Properties Remineralizing, expectorant, hypoglycaemic, odontalgic.
Forms of use Syrup, infusion, fluid extract, juice.
Notes This plant is a favourite with bees because ot its high pollen content. Watercress juice is a nicotine solvent and is used as such on strong tobaccos. It is a popular ingredient in salads, especially in conjunction with garden rocket (*Eruca sativa*).

204 NEPETA CATARIA L.
Catmint

Family Labiatae.
Description A herbaceous perennial plant, it grows up to 40 inches (1 m) high and has a strong, aromatic smell. It has erect, grey-wooly stems. The opposite leaves, borne on petioles, are cordiform and have a toothed margin; the upper surface is greyish-green and the lower one pilose and paler. The flowers emerge in whorls from the leaf axils, each with 2 little bracts. The calyx is 5-toothed and the tubular corolla is bilobate, the upper lobe being bilobate, too, and the lower one trilobate. Catmint prefers the mountainous areas of Europe but also grows wild in Britain by the roadside and near streams. The medicinally useful parts are gathered in late spring.
Parts used Flowering tops.
Chemical compounds Carvacrol, pulegone, thymol, menthol, nepenattol, tannin, methyl acetate.
Properties Antispasmodic, sedative, emmenagogic, antitussive, stomachic.
Form of use Infusion, syrup, fluid extract, medicinal wine.
Notes This plant has a similar action to valerian and they can be used together in tranquillizing compositions. It can be used, freshly picked, as an aromatic salad ingredient. A greenish essence is extracted from it which has an emmenagogic action (restoring the menstrual flow). The medicinal wine has a soothing effect in the treatment of whooping-cough. This plant is a great favourite with cats; they love to lie on it, perhaps because the smell is reminiscent of the pheromones of cats of the opposite sex. The leaves, if chewed up, help to relieve toothache and, if smoked, will stop hiccups.

---

205 NERIUM OLEANDER L.
Oleander

Family Apocynaceae.
Description The generic name of this shrub derives from the Greek *neros*, damp, because of its preference for the alluvial, stony ground around the shores of the Mediterranean. Reaching a height of about 16½ feet (5 m), it has an erect, grey stem with ascendant branches which diverge as they grow longer. The opposite leaves, borne on a short petiole, are lanceolate-acute with an entire margin and well-marked, central veins; the upper leaf surface is a deeper green than the lower. The pink or white flowers are arranged in corymbs; the calyx is 5-parted and the tubular corolla is 5-lobed. The stamens are fused to the corolla in groups of 5. The ovary is formed from 2 carpels. The fruit consists of 2 follicles; these contain the seeds which have a pappus. The plant is commonly found in the Mediterranean region in the wild and also under cultivation as an ornament. The medicinally useful parts are gathered in summer.
Parts used Leaves.
Chemical compounds Oleandrin, pseudocurarine, resins, sugars, tannins.
Properties Cardiotonic, parasiticide, sternutatory.
Forms of used Infusion, powder, fluid extract, tincture.
Notes This plant is poisonous and the first sign of its effect is vomiting. Restorative medicine should be given immediately and then, once a prognosis has been made, the cardiac rhythm carefully monitored. The powder can be sniffed up the nose to ease a cold in the head. In cases of scabies some relief can be given by bathing the affected areas with a decoction made from the leaves.

206 NYMPHAEA ALBA L.

Nymphaea candida J. & C. Prest, *Castalia alba* (L.) Wood., *Castalia speciosa* Salisb.

White water lily

Family Nymphaeaceae.
Description A perennial, aquatic plant, it has a thick, fleshy, horizontal rhizome, held securely in the mud by long, sturdy roots and scarred where leaves have fallen over the years. The leaves, borne singly, are rotund or oval and cordiform at the base; they are supported on very long, cylindrical petioles. The flowers, also borne singly on a long pedicel, are white tinged with pink; the sepals are oval and lanceolate and the large petals are oblong. The fruit is a submerged capsule containing oval seeds. The plant is frequently seen in Europe, including Britain, growing wild in marshes, ponds, slow-running streams, lakes and canals. The height of this plant varies according to the water depth but is usually between 2-4 feet (60-120 cm). It is gathered in summer and autumn.
Parts used Rhizome and flowers.
Chemical compounds Nymphaline, nympheine, resin, tannin, starch, chlorophyll.
Properties Anaphrodisiac, tranquillizer, parasympathetic.
Forms of use Infusion, tincture, fluid extract, distilled water.
Notes Rhizomes that are several years old can be eaten for their starch content. The seeds are roasted and used as a substitute for coffee. The flower-buds are preserved in brine. The anaphrodisiac properties of this plant have now been proven.

---

207 OCIMUM BASILICUM L.

Sweet basil

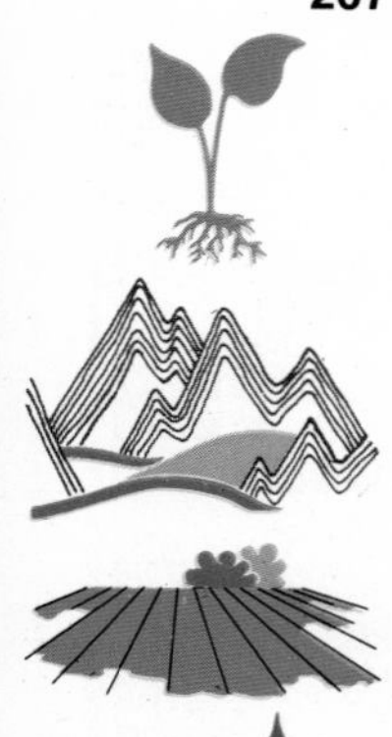

Family Labiatae.
Description A taprooted annual with a square stem, up to 20 inches (50 cm) high, with branchlets on the upper part of the plant. The bright, shiny leaves are opposite, oval or almost lanceolate and pointed with an entire or slightly dentate margin; they are petiolate and fragrant. The flowers are arranged in whorls on long spikes. Each bloom has a tubular calyx, the upper lip being proportionally larger than the lower and divided into 4 slightly lobed teeth. The upper lobe of the tubular corolla is divided into 4 indistinct lobes. The fruits are very dark, 4-sectioned nutlets contained in the persistent leathery calyx. In Europe sweet basil is seldom found in the wild unless it has escaped from a nearby herb or kitchen garden. The medicinally useful parts are gathered when it is fully in flower.
Parts used Leaves and flowering tops.
Chemical compounds Essential oil, tannin, saponin.
Properties Stomachic, carminative, galactagogic, slightly stupefacient.
Forms of used Infusion, powder, essence, juice, poultice, medicinal wine.
Notes It is extensively used in the kitchen, in perfumery and liquor distillery. An average yield of 1.5% of essence is obtained from the flowering tops. It congeals if allowed to cool due to the presence of a compound called camphor of basil. If used externally on the skin, it is a mosquito repellent. It is a specific remedy for emeralopia.

208 OENOTHERA BIENNIS L.
Evening primrose

Family Onagraceae.
Description This biennial plant has a thick, fleshy taproot. The erect stem, which may reach a height of 40 inches (1 m), is simple and angular with leaves emerging along its whole length; these are entire and lanceolate or ovate-lanceolate. The flowers grow singly from the leaf axils to form an apical spike; the 4 sepals are joined in pairs and the 4 petals are sulphur yellow. The fruit consists of a 4-sectioned capsule containing rounded seeds. It is commonly seen in most areas of Europe, including Britain, growing wild by the roadside, in fields, on waste ground and among piles of rubble. It is dug up in autumn.

Parts used Root.
Chemical compounds Mucilage, phytosterol, ceryl alcohol.
Properties Antiphlogistic, antivagal.
Forms of use Decoction, fluid extract, tincture.

Notes This plant still finds a place in many gardens because of its decorativeness, especially the large-flowered varieties. A yellow colouring substance can be obtained from the flowers. The seeds contain a high percentage of fatty oil. A syrup, made from the flowers, has been found to be beneficial in cases of whooping-cough. The flowering tops, finely ground, are used cosmetically in face-masks to counteract reddened skin as well as in poultices to relieve slight rheumatic conditions.

---

209 OLEA EUROPAEA L.
Olive

Family Oleaceae.

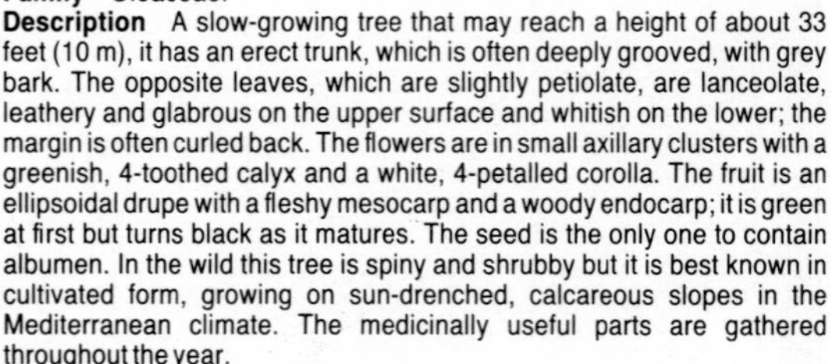

Description A slow-growing tree that may reach a height of about 33 feet (10 m), it has an erect trunk, which is often deeply grooved, with grey bark. The opposite leaves, which are slightly petiolate, are lanceolate, leathery and glabrous on the upper surface and whitish on the lower; the margin is often curled back. The flowers are in small axillary clusters with a greenish, 4-toothed calyx and a white, 4-petalled corolla. The fruit is an ellipsoidal drupe with a fleshy mesocarp and a woody endocarp; it is green at first but turns black as it matures. The seed is the only one to contain albumen. In the wild this tree is spiny and shrubby but it is best known in cultivated form, growing on sun-drenched, calcareous slopes in the Mediterranean climate. The medicinally useful parts are gathered throughout the year.

Parts used Leaves.
Chemical compounds Oleoropine, oleasterol, oleine, olestranol, mannite, glucose, olivine, resin.
Properties Hypotensive, antisclerotic, emollient, vasodilatory, febrifuge, tonic.

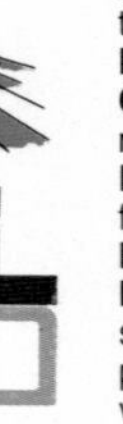

Forms of use Infusion, tincture, fluid extract.
Notes Olive oil has a slightly laxative action; it is the basis of oily solutions. The trunk wood is very highly regarded by wood-workers as it is particularly close-grained and hard. The odorous resin is used as a vaporous inhalant for bronchitis. The leaves can, in an emergency, be used as animal fodder. The glycolic acid content of the olive not only accounts for its hypotensive action but also for its diuretic effect.

210 ONONIS SPINOSA L.
Prickly restharrow

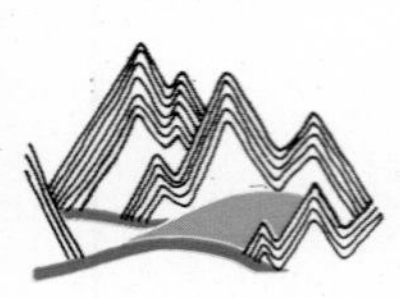

Family Leguminosae.
Description The generic name derives from the Greek *onos*, a donkey, as this plant is one of its favourite foods. The stem of this shrub is woody at the base, very branched and spiny. The leaves consist ot 3 small leaflets on short petioles, at the base of which is a dentate stipule. The flowers are sometimes isolated or in groups of 2 or 3 in the higher leaf axils. The calyx is tubular with 5 long, pointed, pilose teeth. The corolla, which is twice the size of the calyx, has 5 pink petals, of which 2 are fused to the carina. The fruits are small pods slightly longer than the calices, containing 3-4 round, dark-coloured seeds. The plant is commonly found is most regions of Britain and Europe, growing from coastal areas to the lower mountain slopes, mainly on dry, stony ground. It is gathered from September-November.
Parts used Roots, leaves and flowers.
Chemical compounds Onocerin, spirosin, ethereal compound, fatty oil, tannin.
Properties Diuretic, lithontriptic.
Forms of use Powder, infusion, fluid extract, tincture, syrup.
Notes The flowers of this plant are sometimes used to decorate salads. The restharrow is grown in cottage and informal gardens as a decorative border plant. Applied externally, it delays the healing of wounds.

---

211 OPUNTIA FICUS-INDICA (L.) Mill.
Prickly-pear

Family Cactaceae.
Description This shrub reaches a height of up to 10 feet (3 m). The basal part is woody by the transformation of the spathulate stems which appear as branches; the narrowest part is cordate and the upper part rounded. Their surfaces are covered with protruberances, known as areoles, from which sprouts a tuft of yellow barbed bristles. The plant has tiny leaves which are situated for a very short time in the areoles. The flowers are borne on the upper edge of the stems or 'cladodes'; they consist of numerous fat sepals and many brilliant yellow, oval, pointed petals. The fruits, which also have areoles, are fleshy and seed-rich. Originating in South America, this cactus is now commonly found in almost all warmer areas, especially around the Mediterranean. The flowers are gathered in spring and the cladodes are picked throughout the year.
Parts used Flowers and cladodes.
Chemical compounds Mucilage, sugar, vitamin C; glutamic, citric, malic and oxalic acids.
Properties Nutritive, diuretic, antispasmodic, emollient.
Forms of use Infusion, poultice.
Notes This is a very good, nutritious fruit that can be dried and preserved; it makes excellent jam and jelly. In some areas the cladodes are used as pig-food. A distillable fluid alcohol can be obtained by allowing the fruit to ferment.

212 ORIGANUM MAJORANA L.
Sweet marjoram

Family Labiatae.
Description This subshrubby, perennial, herbaceous plant with a woody base grows to a height of about 20 inches (50 cm) or more. The square stems are branched, the lower parts being wooly-haired and the upper glabrous. The opposite leaves are oval with a rounded apex carried on a short petiole. The pinkish-white flowers are in branched clusters, the peduncles of which emerge from the upper leaf axils. The flowers are practically sessile and have a tubular calyx. The corolla is bilabiate and tubular, the upper lip being entire and the lower trilobate. The fruit consists of a dark, 4-sectioned nutlet. Sweet marjoram is now cultivated almost everywhere and also grows wild in southern Europe. It is gathered in summer.
Parts used Whole plant.
Chemical compounds Essential oil, tannin, bitter substance, mineral salts.
Properties Antispasmodic, digestive, bitter-tonic, expectorant, diuretic.
Forms of use Infusion, powder.
Notes A favourite culinary aromatic herb that blends in well with many dishes. Its essence is used in liquor distilleries and perfumeries to lend warmth and strongly aromatic nuances. Sweet marjoram is sometimes used to disinfect beehives. The powder acts as a sternutatory (inducing sneezing) if inhaled and is, therefore, effective against head-colds.

---

213 ORIGANUM VULGARE L.
Marjoram

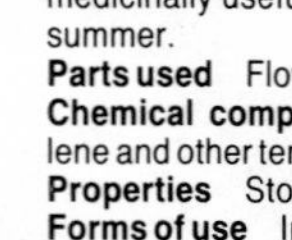

Family Labiatae.
Description A herbaceous plant, it grows to about 32 inches (80 cm) high and has creeping roots that send up stems which bear the semi-spherical inflorescences at their apexes. The stems are square in cross-section, reddish and downy, with projecting spikes. The aromatic leaves are elongate-cordate and pointed, with an entire margin; the petiole is only just discernible. The flowers are clustered at the tips of the branches. The calyx has 5 pointed lobes and is pilose at the throat. The 4-petalled, tubular corolla has a smooth upper lip and a trilobate lower one; it is twice the size of the 5-toothed calyx. The fruit consists of 4 smooth, dark, cylindrical, unattached achenes retained in the calyx which, at this stage, has become leathery. The plant grows wild throughout most of Europe, including Britain, but grows particularly well in the Mediterranean countries; those growing near the sea have the most fragrance. The medicinally useful parts are gathered when the plants are in full flower in summer.
Parts used Flowering tops.
Chemical compounds Thymol, carvacrol, linalool, cymene, terpinolene and other terpenes.
Properties Stomachic, carminative, antineuralgic, anti-asthmatic.
Forms of use Infusion, decoction, syrup, medicinal wine.
Notes It is processed 2 or 3 times to give an average yield of 0.3% of essence. This is rarely employed in the making of perfumes but it is used a great deal in dental preparations. A reddish dye can be obtained from the flowering tops. This plant is one of the best antiseptics because of its high thymol content. It is used a great deal as a culinary herb.

214 OROBANCHE FLAVA C.F.P. Mart. ex F. Schultz
Lesser broomrape

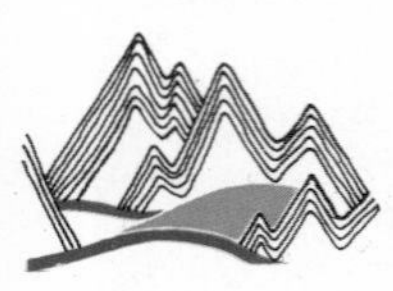

Family Orobanchaceae.
Description The generic name derives from the Greek *orobos*, a legume, and *ankein*, to strangle, referring to the parasitical habit of this plant which can grow to a height of 2 feet (60 cm). It has a rhizomatose root from which numerous rootlets emerge, engaging with the roots of the host plant and penetrating them by means of suckers known as 'haustorii' in order to absorb nutrients and water. The erect, rigid stems are woody and covered in scales (residual rudimentary leaves). This plant is totally lacking in chlorophyll which accounts for its overall yellow-ochre colouring. The flowers form a fairly dense, spiky inflorescence. The calyx is in 5 sections. The fruit is a capsule containing extremely small seeds. Lesser broomrape grows wild in central and eastern Europe. It is gathered in late spring.
Parts used Stems.
Chemical compounds Bitter substances, tannin, salts, carotene.
Properties Astringent bitter.
Forms of used Powder, infusion.
Notes This plant has completely fallen into disuse in modern phytotherapy. It can be invasive and very destructive of other plants. Many varieties of it are to be found throughout the world.

---

215 ORYZA SATIVA L.
Rice

Family Gramineae.
Description A herbaceous, perennial plant with an erect, hollow stem or 'culm' which grows to a height of about 32 inches (80 cm). The very long, lanceolate, dark green leaves are amplexicaul for some distance up from the base; the leaf blade is flat with parallel-line venation. The inflorescence is a branched panicle with spikes of bisexual flowers with glumes or glumellae; the latter adhere tightly to the oblong grain and have 5 veins ending in bristly tips. Each spikelet bears only one flower. Rice has 6 stamens instead of the usual 3 of other members of the Gramineae family. It is grown in paddy-fields, usually in the Far East and sometimes in southern Europe, where a special form of cultivation has to be carried out as the plants must be grown in slowly running water. It is harvested in mid-summer.
Parts used Seeds.
Chemical compounds Starch, vitamins, proteins, fats, glutin, cellulose.
Properties Nutrient, remineralizing, antidiarrhoeic, emollient.
Forms of use Decoction, powder.
Notes An edible oil is extracted from the rice-germ. Another type of oil known as 'rice-oil' is extracted from the husks but this is not edible due to its high content of free acids. 'Furfurol' is also obtained from the same source. A drink rather like beer can be made from fermented rice but by distilling the latter, alcohol is produced. Rice-flour is extensively used in the cosmetic industry as a basis for face-powder.

216 OSMUNDA REGALIS L.
Royal fern

Family Osmundaceae.
Description A fern with a very proud bearing, its rhizome is set obliquely on the ground and fronds emerge from it which can reach a height of about 7 feet (2 m); the leaflets are triangular with the apex of the triangle at the top. They are pinkish-brown when young but become dull green as they mature. The sporangia are borne on the fertile fronds and when these are ripe their 2 valves open to disperse the spores so that the plant may reproduce itself. The young green fronds are shaped like a shepherd's crook, borne on long, sturdy petioles; they consist of pairs of sessile leaflets, almost opposite. The plant grows wild in western Europe, including Britain, and thrives on damp, peaty ground in a shady position on a river bank or by a canal. It is gathered in autumn.
Parts used Rhizome.
Chemical compounds Tannin, osmundine, filicic acid, mucilage.
Properties Diuretic, astringent, vulnerary.
Forms of use Powder, decoction, tincture, medicinal wine.
Notes Cushions and mattresses are filled with royal fern fronds in the belief that they give some relief to rheumatism. The fronds are also used to make compresses for external application to wounds and areas of the body affected by rheumatism, for which purposes they are fairly effective.

---

217 OXALIS ACETOSELLA L.
Wood sorrel

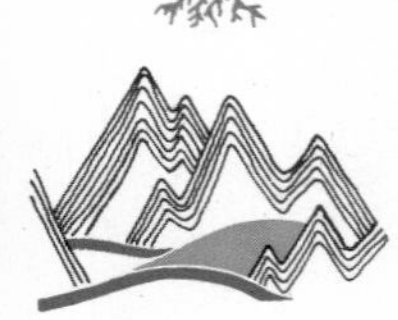

Family Oxalidaceae.
Description The plant has a scaly, creeping rhizome from which the leaves emerge directly; these are stipulate, trifoliate, obcordate and carried on long petioles. The plant averages a height of 4 inches (10 cm). The pink or white flowers are borne singly on a long pedicel. The calyx is 5-sepalled and the corolla 5-petalled, with 10 stamens. The fruit consists of an ovoid capsule containing fleshy seeds which are protected until they are ripe, after the flower has faded, by the stalk bending so that they are hidden under the leaves. The plant, which grows wild in most of Europe, including Britain, is found in cool, shady woods. It is gathered in spring.
Parts used Leaves.
Chemical compounds Potassium binoxalate, ascorbic acid, mucilage.
Properties Astringent, expectorant, diuretic, thirst-quencher.
Forms of use Juice, infusion, poultice, syrup.
Notes This plant is contra-indicated for anyone suffering from gastritis or a calculous condition. It is important not to exceed the dose prescribed as otherwise a toxic condition and poisoning will be induced. For external use, it can be crushed and applied locally to dispel boils and abscesses; it also has an astringent effect on wounds. Wood sorrel is sometimes introduced into salads, lending them a pleasantly acidulous tang. A special salt known as wood-sorrel salt is obtained from the plant and used as a stain-remover.

218 PAEONIA OFFICINALIS L.
Peony

Family Ranunculaceae.
Description A herbaceous, perennial plant with a root and tubers; it grows to a height of about 28 inches (70 cm). The erect stem is smooth and hairless. The large, mid-green leaves are also smooth and sometimes pilose underneath; they are carried on a short petiole. The lower leaves are opposite and trilobate at the top; the upper ones are almost overlapping. The flowers are large and single with 6 sepals, several crimson petals and numerous stamens. The fruit is surrounded by a hardened calyx. It only has a few rather misshapen, slightly rounded lustrous seeds which are reddish at first but ripen to purplish-black. The plant grows wild in southern Europe, in the rocky terrain of mountain woodlands. It is widely cultivated in many varieties and colours. The medicinally useful parts are gathered in autumn.
Parts used Petals, seeds and roots.
Chemical compounds Paeonine, glucoside, oil, tannin, resin, sugars, organic acids.
Properties Antispasmodic, sedative.
Forms of use Infusion, tincture, juice.
Notes If taken in large doses, preparations containing peony products may become toxic. Used moderately they have a soothing effect on whooping-cough and any irritation of the nervous system. Suppositories are also made to ease anal and intestinal spasms. The seeds contain a high percentage of oil.

---

219 PAPAVER RHOEAS L.
Common poppy

Family Papaveraceae.
Description An annual, herbaceous plant, it grows to 16-28 inches (40-70 cm) high, and has a taproot and numerous rootlets. The cylindrical stem is pilose with milky-sap-producing channels; it emerges from the centre of a basal rosette of lanceolate leaves, which are bipinnatisect with irregular incisions, varying in colour from pale to mid-green. The upper leaves are sessile, the base of the petiole being very broad but not amplexicaul. Like the stems, the leaves are pilose. The flowers are borne singly at the top of long pedicels that arise from the leaf axils. They each have 2 caducous sepals and 4 petals which are very broad in relation to their depth; their brilliant red colouring is very distinctive, the petals shading almost to black at their base to blend in with the numerous blackish stamens. The fruit is an ovoid capsule covered by a bell-shaped involucre containing a great many tiny black seeds. The plant will grow wild almost anywhere, including Britain, with a preference for cornfields where it is regarded as a weed. The medicinally useful parts are gathered in summer.
Parts used Petals, which should be dried quickly in the shade.
Chemical compounds Rhoeadine, mucilage colouring substance.
Properties Antitussive, soporific, sedative, emollient.
Forms of use Infusion, fluid extract, tincture, syrup.
Notes Before the flower-buds have formed, the young growth can be used to make salads, either alone or with other edible wild plants. A red colouring material can be obtained from the petals for use as a water-based dye. The fruit must be treated with caution because of its alkaloid content, although it can be used in very small amounts as a sleep-inducing drug under medical supervision.

220 PAPAVER SOMNIFERUM L.

Opium poppy

Family Papaveraceae.
Description A herbaceous plant, growing to a height of 5 feet (1.5 m) or more, it has a spindle-shaped root and a straight, glaucous, hollow stem with few branches. The large, alternate leaves are oblong, toothed and wavy-edged, the stem leaves being amplexicaul. The plant has large solitary flowers with (generally) 4 rounded, delicate petals in colours ranging from white to pale lilac, pink or reddish-purple, 2 or 3 caducous sepals and a number of stamens. The fruit is a globose capsule, with pores at the top, which holds numerous white, kidney-shaped seeds in separate compartments. The white or opium poppy originates in Asia Minor but is also found in the Mediterranean area. In the rest of Europe, it has been extensively cultivated and is naturalized throughout Britain. It is gathered in summer.
Parts used Capsules and thickened latex (opium).
Chemical compounds Morphine, codeine, thebaine, papaverine, noscapine, narcotaline, acids, wax, enzymes.
Properties Narcotic, sedative, euphoric, hypnotic.
Forms of use Powder, syrup, tincture, extract, decoction.
Notes A highly poisonous plant which should not be used, except under strict medical supervision, in order to avoid dependence on it. Cultivation of the opium poppy has to be authorized and this law is strictly enforced in most countries. It is contra-indicated in many infectious illnesses and in constipation.

---

221 PARIETARIA OFFICINALIS L.

Pellitory of the wall

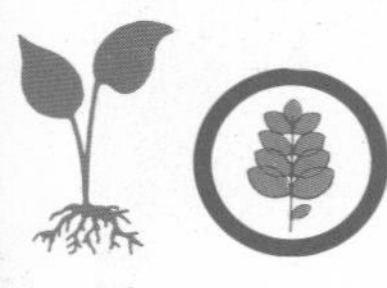
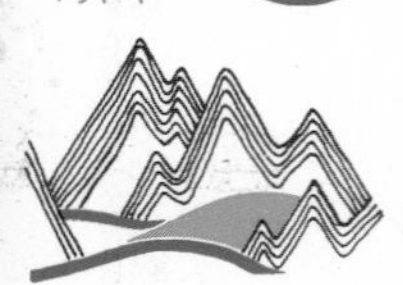

Family Urticaceae.
Description An annual, herbaceous plant, 20-28 inches (50-70 cm) high, it has an elongate rhizome from which arise a number of rather brittle, herbaceous stems. The petiolate leaves are oval or elliptic, tapering to an apical point; they are deep green, with a sheen on the upper surface, while the lower one is almost white with a wooly-haired covering. The flowers are arranged in whorls in small, compact, spherical, subsessile heads containing male and female flowers. The fruits are achenes that become oval and dark as they ripen. This plant is to be found throughout central and southern Europe, growing anywhere between the sea and the mountains, in the driest sites and along walls, which is its main habitat (from which both the generic and English names derive). The plant is usually gathered throughout the summer although its growing period may continue into the autumn.
Parts used Whole plant.
Chemical compounds Potassium salts, tannin, bitter substances.
Properties Diuretic, cholagogic, vulnerary.
Forms of use Fluid extract, tincture, syrup, juice, powder, poultices.
Notes At one time, this plant was used for cleaning windows and copper containers. Pellitory pollen is one of the earliest and most active of the hay fever allergens. The young plant can be used as a salad ingredient. A compress of crushed leaves has a soothing effect on simple burns and scalds.

222 PARNASSIA PALUSTRIS L.

Grass of Parnassus

Family Parnassiaceae.
Description This perennial herb, which averages about 4 inches (10 cm) high, has a thick root and rootlets. The petioles of the basal leaves, in rosette form, arise directly from the roots and are cordiform and entire. The floral stem bears one amplexicaul leaf and an apical, solitary flower with a 5-sepalled calyx and a white, 5-petalled corolla with light green veins. The fruit is an ellipsoid capsule containing the seeds. This plant is commonly found throughout Europe, including Britain, on wet moorlands, marshes and raised bogs up to quite a high altitude. It is gathered from summer-autumn.
Parts used Whole plant.
Chemical compounds Tannin, resin, salts, mucilage.
Properties Astringent, vulnerary, tonic.
Forms of use Infusion, powder, tincture, distilled water, poultice.
Notes The distilled water of the Parnassus grass is an excellent astringent eye-lotion. The plant is occasionally used in decoction form as a mouthwash in cases of stomatitis and, in trituration, on wounds. It also has a slightly diuretic action. The powder can be sprinkled over wounds to aid the healing process.

---

223 PASSIFLORA INCARNATA L.

Passion flower

Family Passifloraceae.
Description The generic name of the plant derives from the Latin *flos passionis* because of the similarity of the flower to the instruments used at the crucifixion of Christ and to the Crown of Thorns. It is a herbaceous perennial with a rhizome from which spring several climbing stems equipped with tendrils. The mid-green, glabrous leaves are alternate, petiolate and have a palmate-lobate blade. The flowers are borne singly on a long pedicel arising from the upper leaf axils; each one has 5 light green sepals and 5 white petals. The filaments form a violet corona (crown) and the very prominent stamens and stigmas give the impression of a hammer. The fragrant fruit is an oval, yellow berry with a whitish pulp in which are dispersed a number of rough-textured seeds. Rarely found in the wild, the plant is widely cultivated in Europe for its beautiful flowers. Although originally from Virginia, in the United States, it thrives wherever the climate is mild. It is gathered in late summer.
Parts used Whole plant.
Chemical compounds Prussic acid, phytosterols, calcium, sugars, alkaloids.
Properties Sedative, antispasmodic, hypnotic.
Forms of use Infusion, tincture, fluid extract, syrup, pills.
Notes This plant is incompatible with hydrogen peroxide. The fruit is edible and can be served as a refreshing soft drink. Passion flower preparations can be used from the earliest age without causing any depressive effects. Externally, the plant can be used locally in compress-form to treat burns and skin irritations.

224 PETASITES ALBUS (L.) Gaertn.

Butterbur

Family Compositae.
Description A rhizomatose herbaceous plant with a rotund stem covered with leafy scales, it grows to a height of at least 20 inches (50 cm). The round or heart-shaped leaves have irregular teeth, the lower surface being wooly-haired with a whitish, cobwebby appearance; the stem leaves have an amplexicaul sheath. The yellowish-white flowers of the heads are carried in dense rounded clusters. The fruit is a pappose achene. The plant is commonly seen growing wild from Norway to as far south as Italy, in marshlands, on river banks and by ponds on the plains and lower mountain slopes. In Britain it has become naturalized. It is gathered in March.
Parts used Rhizome.
Chemical compounds Tannin, bitter substance, inulin, choline, salts, phenol.
Properties Emmenagogic, vulnerary, sedative, hypnotic.
Forms of use Decoction, tincture, fluid extract, powder.
Notes The leaves of this plant were, at one time, used by peasants as a head-covering, hence the generic name; this derives from the Greek *petasos* (Latin *petasus*), referring to the broad-brimmed felt hat worn by travellers, familiar to us as the headgear of Hermes. Like those of the coltsfoot (*Tussilago farfara*), the leaves can be used in infusion as a specific remedy for a cough. The small, fleshy petioles are very palatable when cooked and eaten like asparagus. The rhizome, ground or finely chopped, has a healing effect when applied to slow-healing or weak ulcers or to suppurating wounds. It is often prescribed in homoeopathic remedies in dilution.

---

225 PETROSELINUM CRISPUM (Mill.) A.N. Hill

Petroselinum hortense Suct.
Parsley

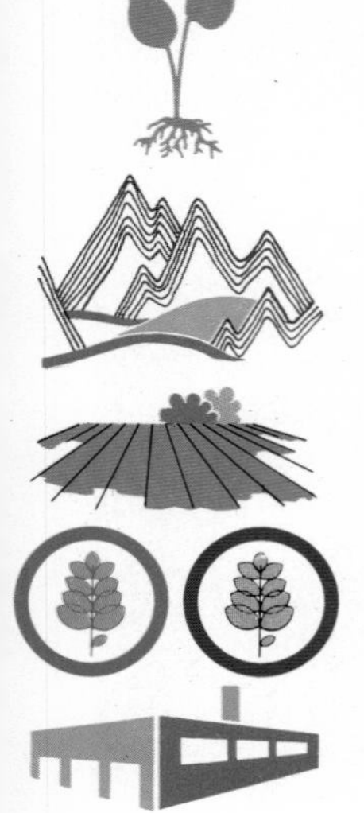

Family Umbelliferae.
Description A fragile plant with a white taproot and a branched, striated, cylindrical stem that grows to at least 8 inches (20 cm). The leaves are 3-pinnate with oval lobes, the basal ones being narrower than the apical, and with a dentate or incised margin. The flowers are grouped in compound umbels of ray-florets; the calyx is entire and the white corolla is 5-petalled with the apex of each petal curved inwards. The fruit is a ribbed diachenium. Although rarely found in the wild, it is grown in kitchen- and herb-gardens throughout Europe, and as a result of extensive cultivation is widely naturalized. It is gathered from spring-autumn.
Parts used Whole plant and root.
Chemical compounds Essence, apiine, mucilage, vitamins.
Properties Diuretic, eupeptic, galactofuge, stomachic.
Forms of use Infusion, juice, distilled water, syrup, poultice.
Notes This plant contains essence which gives an average yield of 0.1% from the leaves and 6% from the fruit; it is greenish, with a density of 0.95, made up of pinene and apiole. The leaves are extensively used for their aromatic quality in cooking. They have a soothing effect when rubbed on to insect bites. If kept close to the breasts of nursing mothers for a few days, the milk flow will cease; this plant should not be used by pregnant women as it can provoke abortion. Parsley juice is an effective mosquito repellent. Care must be taken, when picking parsley, not to confuse it with any of the highly poisonous hemlocks as the young plants are almost the same in appearance.

226 PEUCEDANUM OSTRUTHIUM (L.) Koch

Imperatoria ostruthium L.
Masterwort

Family Umbelliferae.
Description A smooth, perennial plant, it has a thick, blackish rhizome and a simple or branched, erect stem which is closely grooved, hollow and pubescent. It is at least 40 inches (1 m) high. The alternate, petiolate leaves are composed of 3 oblong and sometimes dentate leaflets which are often divided into further entire leaflets. The stem leaves have an inflated amplexicaul petiole. The flowers are grouped in umbels of 30-40 ray-florets; the calices are 5-toothed and the white or pink, 5-petalled corolla is lobed. The fruit is an oval diachenium with a ribbed, winged surface. The plant is frequently to be seen in woodlands, damp fields, on river banks and by mountain streams, throughout Europe, including Britain. It is gathered in spring.
Parts used Rhizome.

Chemical compounds Imperatorine, ostruthine, ostrol, emetine, ostruthol, essence, tannin, starch.
Properties Aromatic, bitter, stomachic, expectorant, diaphoretic, digestive.
Forms of use Decoction, tincture, medicinal wine, essence, powder, fluid extract.

Notes An essence composed of pinene, limonene, phellandrene and ethers used to be obtained from this plant. Its aromatic qualities are used in the preparation of a number of alcoholic liquors. A particularly popular drink is made from the fermented roots. The essence has a euphoric and odontalgic effect. Used externally, it relieves skin irritation. It is very useful in cases of loss of appetite and flatulent colic. An infusion of masterwort helps to relieve migraine.

---

227 PHASEOLUS VULGARIS L.

French bean

Family Leguminosae
Description This annual plant has a spindle-shaped root with radical tubercles. Its slender stem is prostrate for most of its length but rises towards the end (procumbent). The mid-green leaves, borne on long, green petioles, consist of 3 leaflets which are also petiolate: the 2 lateral leaflets are oval and pointed while the central one is larger. The inflorescence is a raceme of a few flowers with a tubular 5-toothed calyx. The 5-petalled corolla is white or lilac and has a keel with a spirally coiled beak. The fruit is a pod of 2-4 inches (5-10 cm) long containing a few kidney-shaped seeds. Originally from South America, this plant is now widely cultivated throughout the world. It is rarely found in the wild. The medicinally useful parts are gathered in midsummer.
Parts used Seeds (beans).

Chemical compounds Allontoine, sugars, leucine, tyrosine, arginine, inositol.
Properties Hypotensive, vitamin-rich, diuretic, hypoglycaemic.
Forms of use Infusion, powder, poultice.

Notes French beans have a notable antidiabetic action, both in infusion and powder form. They can also be roasted to make a highly nutritious coffee-substitute. The flour made from ground beans has been used as a dusting-powder on weeping eczema. In the treatment of ulcers, very good results are obtained by soaking a piece of lint in the water in which beans have been boiled and then covering the ulcers with it. French-bean water is also very effective in reviving woolen fabrics.

228 PHYSALIS ALKEKENGI L.

Cape gooseberry

Family Solanaceae.
Description This herbaceous plant has a creeping rhizome and a great many rootlets. The simple, erect stem is cylindrical and spiky, reaching a height of about 32 inches (80 cm). The petiolate leaves are alternate, oval or diamond-shaped and irregularly sinuate with an acute apex; the leaf blade is glabrous. The flowers, carried on long pedicels, arise from the leaf axils; the calyx is 5-lobed, as is the white corolla, and swells out into an orange-red, papery bladder enclosing the fruit. This consists of a globular red berry containing numerous yellow seeds in an aqueous liquid. The plant grows wild in China and southern and central Europe where it may be seen in hedgerows and by damp paths from plains to lower mountain slopes. It is gathered at the end of summer.
Parts used Fruit.
Chemical compounds Physalin, tannin, citric acid, malic acid, cryptoxanthin, vitamin C.
Properties Diuretic, lithontriptic, anti-uricaemic.
Forms of use Juice, infusion, fluid extract, tincture, syrup, medicinal wine.
Notes Besides their medicinal use, the berries add a delicious flavour to salads; they can also be bottled in vinegar. There is a less acid, yellow-berried variety which is used in the making of sweetmeats when the berries are coated with chocolate. This plant is widely grown in gardens and kitchen-gardens. No part of it, other than the berries, should be used as there is a risk of serious toxic poisoning.

---

229 PHYTOLACCA AMERICANA L.

Phytolacca decandra L.
Poke root

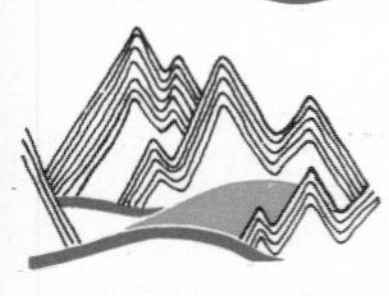

Family Phytolaccaceae.
Description A herbaceous perennial plant of up to about 10 feet (3 m) high, it has a thick, taprooted rhizome. The stem is smooth and simple at the base and then divides dichotomously. The alternate, mature leaves, borne on a very short petiole, are acute at base and apex; their upper surface is mid-green and the lower one opaque with reddish venation. The flowers, carried on short pedicels, have a bract or bracteole and no petals but 5 greenish-white, ovaloid tepals. The fruit consists of dark, fleshy berries with 8-10 raised ribs on the surface which correspond to the carpel divisions. The plant is of North American origin but has now become naturalized among ruined buildings and on untended land in Mediterranean countries and is in general cultivation throughout Europe. It is gathered in late spring.

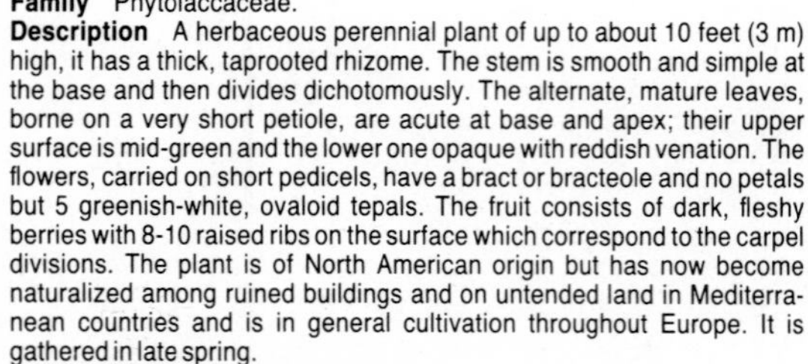

Parts used Whole plant above ground.
Chemical compounds Saponin, rhamnoside, phytolaccin, resin, mucilage, pectin.
Properties Emetic, purgative, depurative.
Forms of use Infusion.
Notes The young shoots can be eated like asparagus. When the juice from the berries has been depurated, it is used as a colouring substance in some wines and liquors. The young leaves are edible and a source of minerals. No preparation made from this plant should be taken internally for any length of time without proper medical supervision, as its saponin content can cause poisoning accompanied by diarrhoea.

230 PIMPINELLA SAXIFRAGA L.
Burnet saxifrage

Family Umbelliferae.
Description This plant has a fibrous taproot and an erect, delicate striate stem reaching a height of about 40 inches (1 m). The leaves are pinnate, obtuse, dentate or finely lobed. The flowers are gathered into apical umbels with at least 10 ray-florets with 5-petalled flowers and stamens protruding above the corolla. The oval fruit is striate and flattened. The plant, which grows wild throughout Europe, including Britain, is generally found in fields, hedgerows and on waste ground from low-lying to hilly areas. It is gathered in autumn.
Parts used Root.
Chemical compounds Pimpinellin, salts, essence, pectin, tannin.
Properties Emmenagogic, cholagogic, diuretic.
Forms of use Decoction, powder, tincture, fluid extract, syrup.
Notes The specific name of this plant derives from the observation that its root manages to penetrate into cracks in stones which led to the belief that it was able to break down carbonates (Latin *saxa frango* – I break stones). Because of this supposed quality, it was at one time used as a lithontriptic. It is still employed in cases of hepatic insufficiency and, externally, in lotions to help regenerate the skin of older people. The tincture, when taken consistently, aids in the restoration of appetite. The distilled water is used as an eye-lotion. The young leaves can be mixed into salads to add an aromatic, parsley-like tang.

---

231 PINGUICULA VULGARIS L.
Butterwort

Family Lentibulariaceae.
Description This small herb has a short, fibrous root. The basal, sessile leaves, arranged in rosette form, are ovate-oblong and fleshy with an incurved edge; they are sticky and able to digest small insects. The 2-lipped and spurred bluish-violet flowers are borne singly on a slender pedicel averaging about 4 inches (10 cm) in height. The fruit consists of an ellipsoid capsule containing many rough-textured elliptic seeds. This plant which grows wild in most of western Europe, including Britain, is quite commonly found in damp sites such as peat-bogs, marshlands and wet rocks. The medicinally useful parts are gathered in June.
Parts used Leaves.
Chemical compounds Mucilage, tannin, benzoic acid, valeric acid, gum, enzyme.
Properties Tossifuge, antispasmodic, broncho-sedative.
Forms of use Juice, fluid extract, infusion.
Notes Butterwort is just as effective against whooping-cough as sundew (*Drosera rotundifolia*) and can be used as a substitute. The enzyme contained in the plant attacks and destroys proteins. Externally, a poultice made with the crushed leaves has a healing effect. A colouring substance can be obtained from the leaves as well as a vegetable rennet for curdling milk to make junket and cheese.

232 PINUS MUGO Turra

Pinus mughus Scop., *Pinus pumilio* Haenke, *Pinus montana* Mill.
Mountain pine

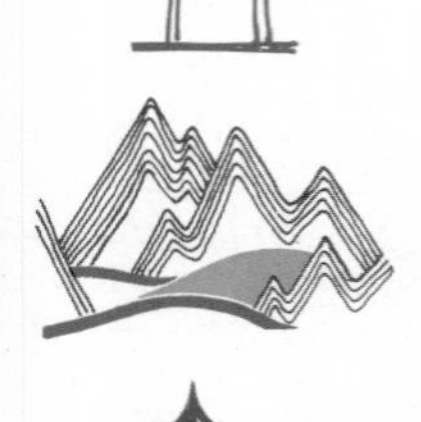

Family Pinaceae.
Description This shrub, which sometimes becomes a tree, has numerous branches which are prostrate at first and then erect. The main stem is contorted and grows to a height of about 10 feet (3 m). The evergreen leaves (needles) are linear, rigid and set in pairs. The male flowers are amenta (catkins) which produce the pollen; the females are brown, often resinous, sessile cones. The seeds are oval with a membranous wing. The mountain pine is frequently seen in the mountains of central Europe growing wild at an altitude of over 3,200 feet (1,000 m).
Parts used Apical branchlets.
Chemical compounds Essential oil, gallic acid, resin, tannic acid.
Properties Balsamic, expectorant, broncho-sedative, anti-asthmatic. cardiotonic.
Forms of use Infusion, syrup, essence, medicinal wine.
Notes Distilling the leaves of this shrub gives an excellent yield of essence, composed of pinene, phellandrene, bornyl acetate, dipentene, etc. This oil (mugo pine oil) is in nearly all pharmaceutical balsamic compositions because of its antiseptic and expectorant qualities. The same essence is used in some perfumes. It is also credited with attributes similar to the foxglove but this theory has not yet been researched. Baths consisting of a decoction of young branches have a stimulating and purifying effect. The essence, which is quickly assimilated, also has a noticeably diuretic effect. The half-open cones are used to give an aromatic tang to *eau-de-vie* and other home-made liquors.

---

233 PINUS SYLVESTRIS L.

Scots pine

Family Pinaceae.
Description This tree, which reaches a height of over 130 feet (40 m), has evergreen leaves (needles), a straight trunk with a rather spreading, irregular crown and bark that is scaly and cracked. The leaves, set in pairs on the branchlets, are aromatic, needle-like, sheathed and glaucous. There are male and female flowers. The males, united in leafy cones on the lower part of the branches, shed a great deal of pollen and then wither; the females, which develop into woody cones, are situated terminally either singly or in small groups. The fruit is a strobilus or cone which takes 2 years to ripen and then releases its seeds the following spring. The Scots pine is frequently found growing wild in the mountains of central Europe and Scotland and is now quite extensively cultivated. The medicinally useful parts are gathered in summer.
Parts used Branchlets, shoots, resin.
Chemical compounds Tannin, resin, primaric acid, primarinic acid, pinipicrine, terpenes.
Properties Diuretic, balsamic, expectorant, antiseptic,
Forms of use Infusion, decoction, fluid extract, essence, tar.
Notes Turpentine, with an external revulsive effect, was once obtained from the resin. 'Wood-wool', formerly widely used for stuffing cushions and as packing material, is obtained by stripping out the fibrous material from the needles. Although Scottish-grown pine is rather soft, European pine is extensively used for many kinds of carpentry. Essential oils are obtained by dry distillation of the wood. The vegetable tar, obtained by destructive distillation from the roots, has many uses, one of which is in preparations to stimulate hair growth.

234 PIPER NIGRUM L.

Pepper

Family Piperaceae.
Description A shrubby liana, its stem grows to a length of about 33 feet (10 m). Indigenous to the East Indies, the plant is now extensively cultivated in the tropics. The stem is slender and slightly woody with petiolate, oval leaves which have an acute apex and prominent venation; the joint at the petiole is sub-rotund. It has a pendulous, tubular spike of small, white, sessile flowers which emerges opposite the leaves; these spikes may be as long as 4 inches (10 cm). The sessile fruit consists of almost spherical berries with a thin casing which are green at first but ripen to red and which contain one seed. The fruits are gathered when ripe.
Parts used Fruit.
Chemical compounds Fatty substances, resin, piperine, starch, salts, cellulose and an essence containing phellandrene and a terpene.
Properties Sialagogic, tonic stimulant.
Forms of use Powder.
Notes This plant was regarded as 'black gold' in the Middle Ages and many battles were fought over its possession. Apart from its culinary use, pepper has a specific action on ringworm, for which it can be used in ointment form, over a period of time.

---

235 PISTACIA LENTISCUS L.

Mastic tree

Family Anacardiaceae.
Description A very branched shrub which grows to a height of about 10 feet (3 m), and has perennial, evenly pinnate leaves and sessile, oval or elliptic, leathery, glossy leaflets with an entire margin. The upper leaf surface is mid-green and the lower one paler and opaque. The petiole is flattened and winged. The flowers are grouped in small clusters in the leaf axils; they are reddish and have a 5-lobed calyx and 5 stamens. The fruit consists of an almost round drupe, red at first ripening to black, which contains one white seed. The plant exudes an aromatic odour. It is frequently found among the scrubby growth of the Mediterranean shores but is rarely seen growing inland. It is gathered in spring.
Parts used Resin.
Chemical compounds Essence, tannin, masticin, mastic acid.
Properties Expectorant, antidiarrhoeic.
Forms of use Powder.
Notes The resin that oozes spontaneously, or when the tree is tapped, is known as mastic and smells rather like turpentine. It is widely employed in dentistry as a cement for filling decayed teeth and is also used in varnishes. In the East, chewable sweetmeats are made from it, as well as breath-sweeteners. Mastic is also used by restorers of antiques and in the photographic industry. At one time, oil was obtained from the mastic tree; this gave a good yield and was used for lamps, soap-making and to sweeten cosmetic preparations.

236 PISUM SATIVUM L.
Pea

Family Leguminosae.
Description There are many varieties of this annual, rather shallow-rooted plant. Some have an upright stem and others a prostrate one. The leaves are pinnate, composed of 2 or 3 leaflets and a tendril; there are 2 prominent, slighty rotundate stipules at the leaf base. The butterfly-like flowers have a stalk and are axillary, growing singly or united in small groups. The fruit is a legume known as a 'pod'; this is curved with 2 symmetrical, swelling sides which contain the round green seeds in a single row. Peas, which grow wild throughout southern Europe and are extensively cultivated elsewhere, including Britain, require well-worked, irrigated and well-drained soil. The fruit is picked in summer.
Parts used Seeds.
Chemical compounds Proteins, lecithins, carbohydrates, fats, salts.
Properties Nutritive, antidermatosis.
Forms of use Flour, poultice, ointment.
Notes Disregarding the nutritive value of peas, they have an appreciable effect on many types of skin complaint. Face-masks made from the crushed fresh fruits are used in cases of acne and on faded, wrinkled skins. Cosmetic creams, based on concentrated pea juices, are also available for the same purpose.

---

237 PLANTAGO MAJOR L.
Greater plantain

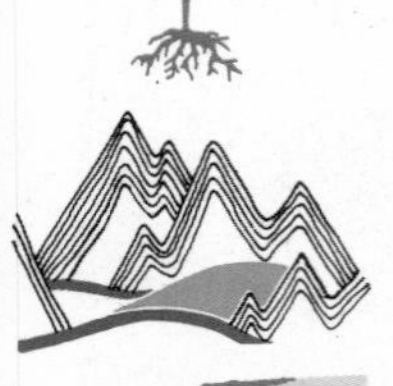

Family Plantaginaceae.
Description A herbaceous perennial plant, which may reach a height of over 8 inches (20 cm), it has a short rhizomous root and rootlets. Its basal, mid-green leaves are arranged in rosette form; they are broad, ovate-elliptic, parallel-veined, sheathed and smooth or slightly pubescent with the blade narrowing gradually into the petiole. The stems bear an inflorescence at the top in the form of a spike with numerous flowers. These have a 4-lobed calyx with oval lobes; the tubular corolla is divided at the top into 4 acute lobes. The fruit consists of a capsule containing dark seeds. A very common wild plant, it may be found throughout most of Europe, including Britain. The medicinally useful parts are gathered from spring onwards.
Parts used Leaves.
Chemical compounds Aucubin, saponin, citric acid, oxalic acid, mucilage.
Properties Depurative, diuretic, haemostatic, vulnerary.
Forms of use Infusion, poultices, juice, tincture, distilled water.
Notes The aqueous extracts are used a great deal in cosmetics. Crushed plantain has always been regarded as an easily available haemostatic to use in an emergency on wounds. The stem and seeds are used as cage-bird food. The distilled water has long been recognized as an excellent eye-lotion while the tincture is still used in home-ma[illegible] remedies.

238 PLANTAGO MEDIA L.

Hoary plantain

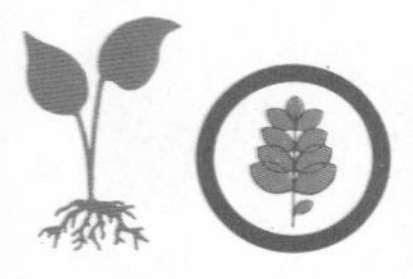
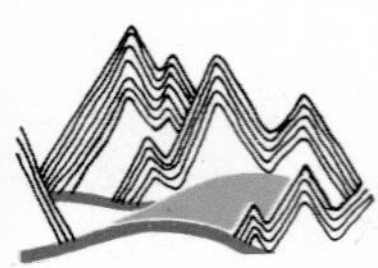

Family Plantaginaceae.
Description A small herbaceous plant, it has a spindle-shaped root and many rootlets. The leaves are all basal and in rosette form, oval-elliptic and entire with prominent venation. The stem, which may reach a height of 4 inches (10 cm), is delicate and slightly downy, bearing its flowers in a blunt spike. The flowers, which are fragrant, have a 4-sepalled calyx and 5-petalled corolla with acute tips to the petals; the anthers are lilac-white. The fruit consists of a 2-loculi capsule, the top half of which comes off like a lid and which contains angular, ellipsoid seeds. It is a very common wild plant in Europe, including Britain, infesting fields and meadows, hills and mountains. The medicinally useful parts are gathered in spring.
Parts used Leaves.
Chemical compounds Aucubin, tannin, pectin, acids, salts, gum, saponin.
Properties Depurative, astringent, vulnerary, opthalmic.
Forms of use Decoction, syrup, distilled water, semi-fluid extract.
Notes The plant is best known for its healing qualities when applied, as a first-aid measure, to wounds. A mouthwash made from it helps to relieve toothache and, as distilled water, it is a good eyewash. An ointment can also be made with it, using an appropriate excipient, to heal grazes and abrasions. The seeds act as a laxative as do those of the psyllium plantain (*Plantago psyllium*). The young leaves can be eaten in salads, before they become leathery.

---

239 PLANTAGO PSYLLIUM L.

Psyllium plantain

Family Plantaginaceae.
Description The specific name derives from the Greek *psylla*, a flea, because the seeds bear a certain resemblance to this insect. The stem of this taprooted, herbaceous plant grows up to 1 foot (30 cm) high and is leafy for its whole length. The opposite leaves are sessile, amplexicaul and lanceolate with an entire or slightly dentate margin. The flowers are borne on a short spike with a long peduncle which arises from the upper leaf axils; they are sessile and have a pointed ovoid bract. The calyx is 4-lobed and the corolla is tubular and 4-lobed. The stamens are very long and prominent. The fruit consists of 2-loculi capsules. The seeds are shaped like a pointed butter-bean, light in colour with a dark median mark. Widely distributed wherever the Mediterranean climate prevails, the plant grows wild on most well-drained soils. It is gathered at the end of summer.
Parts used Seeds.
Chemical compounds Mucilage, aucubine, micronutrients, potassium salts.
Properties Laxative, emollient.
Forms of use Decoction, the whole seed.
Notes It is used cosmetically in face-masks to soften the skin because of its high mucilage content. A type of gum is extracted for making fabric dressings. A mucilage-rich preparation, obtained from the decoction and maceration of the seeds, is helpful in relieving skin irritations and reddened eyelids.

240 PLATANUS ORIENTALIS L.

Oriental plane-tree

Family Platanaceae.
Description The generic name is derived from the Latin *plautus*, flat. This is a tree with a straight, sturdy trunk about 20-30 feet (6.9 m) high with bark that falls off in large flakes. It is branched and has a luxuriant crown. The alternate leaves are palmate with well-defined lobes; they are borne on petioles which broaden out at the base and the leaf blade has prominent nervation. The flowers are grouped into a globose, almost spherical, inflorescence. The fruit consists of an angular nutlet or, occasionally, a follicle. Although often to be seen growing wild in south eastern Europe and Asia Minor, it is now widely cultivated and used to line the streets of many continental European cities. In Britain, the London plane is preferred. The medicinally useful parts are gathered in spring and summer.
Parts used Leaves.
Chemical compounds Quercetin, cellulose, tannin, colouring substance.
Properties Astringent, vulnerary.
Forms of use Decoction, ointment.
Notes The lanugo or downy material which floats from the fruits can cause irritation. Because of the high tannin content, the decoction is used to treat dysentery and the cream to heal wounds and relieve chilblains. The wood is not greatly esteemed for carpentry work although it has certain advantages in cabinet-making and, at one time, coach-building. A fabric dye is extracted from the branches and roots.

---

241 POLYGONATUM ODORATUM (Mill.) Druce

Polygonatum officinale All.
Scented Solomon's seal

Family Liliaceae.
Description A herbaceous, perennial plant, it is about 16 inches (40 cm) high and has a sprawling horizontal rhizome and numerous adventitious roots. The erect stem is angular and basally sheathed. The alternate leaves are sessile, some being amplexicaul, elliptically shaped with an acute apex; they are parallel-veined, the upper lamina being light green and the lower bluish-green. The solitary flowers are borne on a pendulous stalk which arises from the leaf axils; the white perianth is tubular, swelling out towards the base and terminating in 6 ovate, greenish lobes. The fruit is a globose, bluish-black berry. This plant is frequently to be found growing wild in the woods of the lower mountain slopes of northern Europe, Switzerland and Siberia, and sometimes in England, Scotland and Ireland. It is gathered in autumn or spring.
Parts used Rhizome.
Chemical compounds Mucilage, tannin, calcium oxalate, saponin, asparagine.
Properties Resolvent, haemolytic, hypoglycaemic.
Forms of use Infusion, ointment, oily solution, medicinal wine.
Notes The rhizome has the same ecchymotic qualities as tincture of arnica; the effect is achieved by applying a poultice of the bruised rhizome to the affected parts. Ointments made from the bruised roots help heal small wounds. The berries should on no account be used as they are very poisonous.

242 POLYGONUM AVICULARE L.
Knotgrass

Family Polygonaceae.
Description The generic name derives from the Greek *polys gony*, many types. This small plant has a taproot with numerous rootlets from which emerge many prostrate or slightly ascendent stems which can grow to more than 20 inches (50 cm) long. The alternate leaves are oblong-lanceolate or linear and petiolate or sessile. The pink or white flowers, which are set in the leaf axils, are 5-petalled. The fruit is a striate, trigonal nutlet. This is a common, invasive weed which is abundant in any type of ground throughout Britain and Europe from low-lying to hilly areas. It is gathered in summer.
Parts used Whole plant.
Chemical compounds Essence, anthraquinone, resin, silica, mucilage.
Properties Diuretic, lithontriptic, haemostatic, remineralizing.
Forms of use Powder, infusion, tincture, fluid extract, medicinal wine.
Notes It has a slight laxative effect due to the presence of anthraquinone. More specific and well-tested are its haemostatic effect on ulcers and its astringent effect on dysentery. An interesting quality has also been confirmed in treating certain venous conditions with alcohol-based preparations – varicose veins, if of recent development, tend to disappear. In consequence, ointments containing an extract of knotgrass are now available to treat many kinds of roseola. It is also used externally in compresses to correct flabby or dry skin.

---

243 POLYGONUM BISTORTA L.
Bistort

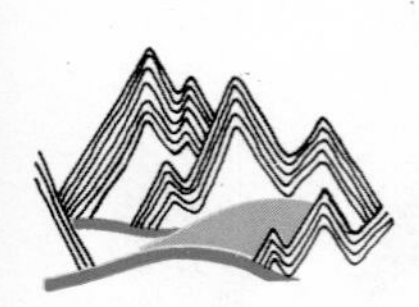

Family Polygonaceae.
Description A herbaceous plant of up to 12 inches (30 cm) high, it has a horizontal, twisted rhizome. The erect stem is nodose. The basal leaves are long, lanceolate and narrow gradually into the long petiole. The apical leaves are narrow, lanceolate, undulate and amplexicaul at the nodes. The pink flowers are grouped in a dense, spiky inflorescence; they have 5 petals and 8 prominent stamens. The fruit is a dark, smooth trigonal nutlet. Quite widely distributed in the cooler regions of the world, it flourishes throughout Europe, including Britain, in moist meadows and by waterways. It is gathered in spring and autumn.
Parts used Leaves and rhizome.
Chemical compounds Starch, gallic acid, oxalic acid, tannin, vitamin C, sugar.
Properties Astringent, antidiarrhoeic, tonic, vulnerary.
Forms of use Decoction, infusion, powder, medicinal wine.
Notes The young, tender leaves can be eaten, as can the root, which is rich in starch. The crushed leaves help to stop wounds bleeding. The antidiarrhoeic action is most effective if the fluid is administered as an enema.

244 POLYPODIUM VULGARE L.
Common polypody

Family Polypodiaceae.
Description This wild fern has a dark brown, creeping, fleshy, cylindrical rhizome with numerous rootlets and is covered with small scales. The flesh of the rhizome is pale yellow and it has a distinctive taste, rather like liquorice. The leathery fronds are petiolate, oblong, lanceolate and pinnate-parted. The linear, obtuse leaflets have a central vein and bear round, rust-coloured sori below, which are arranged in 2 parallel rows. This fern is commonly found growing wild throughout Europe, including Britain, in damp woods and especially in mossy ground and on sheltered trees and rocks. It is gathered in summer.
Parts used Rhizome.
Chemical compounds Sugar, mannitol, glycyrrhizin, malates, tannin, saponin.
Properties Cholagogic, laxative, expectorant.
Forms of use Decoction, powder, fluid extract, syrup.
Notes The rhizome was, at one time, used to adulterate the liquorice root. Normally, it is still used as a sweetener. The leaves have also been found to have therapeutic use as pectorals but they are less effective than the rhizome. Polypody powder is an excellent purgative for children especially if mixed with some convolvulus powder and honey. This fern is often encouraged to grow as a garden plant but does not acclimatize easily.

---

245 PORTULACA OLERACEA L.
Green purslane

Family Portulacaceae.
Description A plant with a taproot and a trailing stem, it may grow to a length of more than 8 inches (20 cm). The sessile leaves are opposite at first, then alternate and finally almost whorled; they are obovate and bright green. The yellowish flowers are set in the bark of the branches; the calyx is bilobate and the corolla 4-5-petalled, with 12 stamens. The fruit is an oval capsule containing a great many minute, dark, circular seeds. A very common, invasive wild plant in southern and central Europe, it has been introduced to Britain and is found in fields, vegetable plots, on roadside verges and by the sea. It is gathered in summer.
Parts used Whole plant above ground.
Chemical compounds Mucilage, saponin, vitamin C, salts, proteins.
Properties Choleretic, depurative, antiscorbutic, diuretic.
Forms of use Infusion, syrup, juice, poultice.
Notes The young growing tops are usually mixed into salads because of their very pleasant flavour; they can also be pickled and used as appetizers. This little plant, which is easily grown from seed, is a great favourite of rabbits. It is wise not to pull the plants early but to pick the stems and leaves as required, which can be done several times during the year. The juice is particularly effective, both internally and externally, in the treatment of skin diseases.

246 POTENTILLA ANSERINA L.

Potentilla argentina Huds., *Argentina vulgaris* Lam.
Silverweed

Family Rosaceae.
Description The specific name derives from the Latin *anser*, a goose, because this plant is a favourite of geese. It is a perennial, growing to a height of about 20 inches (30 cm), with a short rhizome and trailing stems. The leaves are composed of many oval, dentate, grey-green leaflets. The yellow flowers are borne singly at the end of a long pedicel which grows from the leaf axils; they have 5 obovate petals with a wavy margin. The fruit is a kidney-shaped achene. This plant thrives in Europe, including Britain, by ditches or in calcareous, moist, mountainous sites. It is gathered in July.
Parts used Whole plant.
Chemical compounds Tannin, gallic acid, calcium oxalate.
Properties Antispasmodic, astringent, haemostatic, odontalgic.
Forms of use Decoction, tincture, fluid extract, medicinal wine.
Notes Distilled water made from the plant is used cosmetically as a soothing lotion for reddened skin and for the delicate skin of babies. It has also been used to treat stones in the bladder and intestinal colic. The powder is useful in the treatment of external ulcers. As a mouthwash, excellent results have been achieved in combatting pyorrhoea. When this plant is fresh, it has the unusual attribute, shared only with a few others such as shepherd's purse, avens or herb bennet, cyclamen and horse chestnut, of being slightly radioactive; it has, therefore, a local analgesic effect merely by being placed over the painful area.

247 POTENTILLA REPTANS L.

Creeping cinquefoil

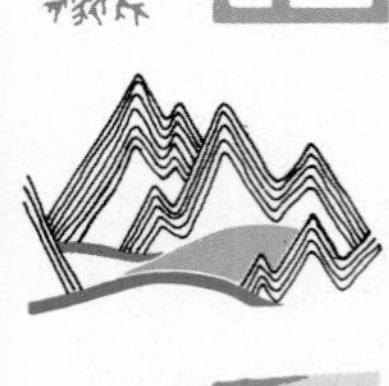

Family Rosaceae.
Description This herbaceous perennial plant has a small rhizome and stolon, bearing pubescent stems. The palmately-lobed leaves are carried at the apex of a long petiole; some of the basal leaves have 2 small, additional, divergent leaflets. All the leaves have a toothed margin. The flowers, which grow singly from the leaf axils, have 5 lanceolate, pointed sepals; the corolla has 5 yellow petals which are oval except for the rounded apex. The fruit is a 5-sectioned cremocarp set in the persistent receptacle of the flower. This plant is frequently to be seen throughout Europe, including Britain, in meadows, hedgerows and by the roadside from low-lying to hilly areas. It is gathered in spring and autumn.
Parts used Leaves and roots.
Chemical compounds Tannin, resin, gum, calcium, oxalate.
Properties Astringent, antidiarrhoeic, febrifuge.
Forms of use Decoction, tincture, syrup.
Notes A concentrated decoction of the root relieves toothache and, applied externally as a compress, helps to tighten up flabby skin. It is one of the ingredients used in many anti-wrinkle cosmetic preparations. The young, tender leaflets are edible and make a useful addition to salads.

248 POTENTILLA TORMENTILLA Nestl.

Potentilla erecta Rausch., *Tormentilla erecta* L.
Common tormentil

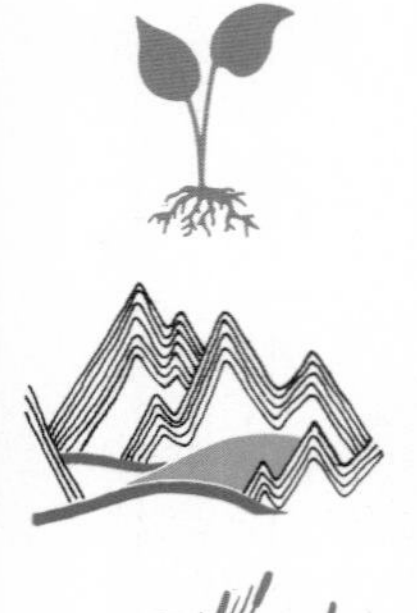

Family Rosaceae.
Description This plant has a thick, cylindrical root from which many branched, delicate stems emerge to a height of about 8-12 inches (20-30 cm). The basal leaves are petiolate and 3-5-lobed; the stem leaves are trifoliate, sessile, dentate, glabrous or very slighly setose, with basal stipules. The flowers, which are carried on a very long pedicel, have a 5-sepalled calyx with acute tips; the yellow corolla is 4-petalled. The fruit is a smooth, ovoid achene. The common tormentil flourishes throughout most of Europe, including Britain, in the undergrowth, in damp upland meadows and mountain bogs and is gathered in summer.
Parts used Root.
Chemical compounds Tormentiltannic acid, catechin, ellagic acid, tormentil-red, tormentilline, resin, gum.
Properties Astringent, antidiarrhoeic, hypoglycaemic, haemostatic.
Forms of use Decoction, powder, tincture, fluid extract, medicinal wine, ointment.
Notes A very astringent plant with antibiotic qualities which, although not yet fully researched, have been observed in treating many diseases. As a gargle, it is effective against gingivitis and pyorrhoea, while its effectiveness as a toothache remedy is undeniable. It is used externally as a compress to tone up flabby skin and as a cream made for the same purpose. Extracts of tormentil are used to relieve chapping of the anus and of cracked nipples as well as in some types of prolapse. Constant use of the plant has also yielded good results in cases of enuresis in children. The medicated wine has a hypoglycaemic effect, while the decoction can be used in the tanning of hides and skins.

---

249 PRIMULA VERIS L.

Primula officinalis (L.) Hill.
Cowslip

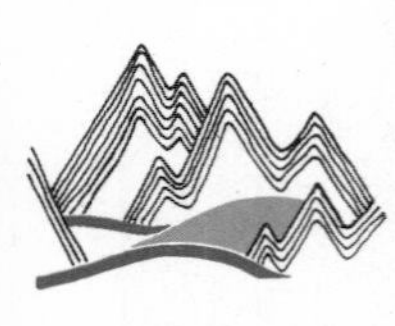

Family Primulaceae.
Description A wild plant but also cultivated in many varieties, it has a small, fibrous rhizome with many rootlets. The leaves, which are united in a basal rosette, are rough-textured, ovate-oblong with a crenate margin and a pubescent lower surface. The yellow flowers are grouped in a terminal, nodding, one-sided umbel-like cluster on a stem of over 4 inches (10 cm) in height; the calyx is campanulate and the corolla 5-lobed. The capsule contains a large number of small flat seeds. The plant is quite common in Europe, including Britain, preferring fields and woods with calcareous soil. It is rare in the Mediterranean region. The medicinal parts are gathered in spring.
Parts used Flowers and leaves.
Chemical compounds Primaverine, primulaverine, chlorophyll, gum.
Properties Antitussive, hypnotic, soothing, diuretic, antirheumatic, anti-arthritic, diaphoretic.
Forms of use Infusion, distilled water, fluid extract, semi-fluid extract, syrup.
Notes The powdered rhizome has been used as a sternutatory while the crushed pulp was used to make sedatory compresses to reduce inflammation. The young, tender leaves are used in depurative salads. It is advisable to look out for any allergic reaction of the skin caused by the stamens, to which some people are prone, although it is easily treated. The cultivated varieties are very popular border plants. At one time, an oil was produced by means of maceration from the flowers; this had an anti-ecchymotic action which was similar in effectiveness to tincture of arnica.

250 PRUNUS AVIUM L.

Cerasus avium (L.) Moench, *Cerasus dulcis* Gaertn.
Gean (Heart cherry)

Family Rosaceae.
Description This tree grows to a height of about 26-32 feet (8-10 m); it has an erect, branched trunk with smooth, reddish-brown bark which flakes off in strips. The petiolate leaves, which are grouped in small whorls, are ovate-elliptic and acute; the leaf blade is glabrous and pinnately veined while the margin is dentate, and there is a gland at the tip of each tooth. The flowers are arranged in apical corymbs on pedicels; they consist of 5 rotund white petals, which are narrowed at the base, and 5 ovaloid sepals. The fruit is an almost spherical, pulpy drupe with a sub-spherical seed. A great many varieties of this tree are grown in mountainous areas and wild examples are not unknown. The medicinally useful parts are gathered in June.
Parts used Cherry stalks.
Chemical compounds Salicyclic acid, potassium salts, phenols, tannin.
Properties Diuretic, anti-uricaemic.
Forms of use Decoction, fluid extract.
Notes The fruit is always in great demand for the table as well as for jam-making, crystallizing and glazing. A special type of alcoholic spirit *(aqua vitae)* can be made from the fermented fruit. If a small cut is made in the trunk, a reddish-brown, aromatic, crystallizable resin seeps out which many people use as an inhalant for a persistent cough. Its leaves, after being left to macerate and ferment, are used in aromatic, pipe-smoking mixtures. Cherry kernels must never be used as they are dangerous, due to the presence of hydrocyanic acid.

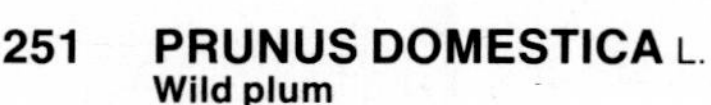

251 PRUNUS DOMESTICA L.

Wild plum

Family Rosaceae.
Description A branched tree, which reaches a height of about 30-40 feet (8-10 m), its dark brown bark is smooth when young, tending to be rough with fissures and cracking when older. The petiolate leaves, which may be alternate or in whorls, are oval-oblong, serrate and narrow at the base; the upper leaf surface is glabrous and the lower pilose. The stalked flowers are united in fascicles; they have a 5-sepalled calyx and a white, 5-petalled corolla rounded at the apex. The fruit consists of an ellipsoid drupe with a surface bloom, which contains one seed. Although indigenous to western Asia, the plum is now widely distributed throughout Europe, including Britain, in its various cultivated forms. The fruit is gathered in summer.

Parts used Fruit.
Chemical compounds Sugar, malic acid, citric acid, proteins, tannin, salts, vitamins.
Properties Laxative, vitamin-rich.
Forms of use Pulp, decoction.

Notes The bark is also used sometimes as a febrifuge. Delicious and nourishing jams can be made with the plums as well as alcoholic drinks. A pleasant, very alcoholic spirit *(aqua vitae)* can be obtained by fermenting the pulp and distilling it. The seeds (kernels) are not used because they contain the very dangerous glucoside, amygdalin. They are, however, used cosmetically in the production of face-masks for dry skin. As with almonds, an edible oil can be extracted from plums. The laxative action of the fruit is due to its fibre and pectin content; plum pulp is often mixed with that of tamarinds which results in a very agreeable purgative electuary.

252 PRUNUS LAUROCERASUS L.

Padus laurocerasus Mill.
Cherry laurel

Family Rosaceae.
Description This prolific, heavily branched shrub varies a great deal in height. The glossy, mid-green leaves are alternate, ovate-elliptic and acute in shape with a dentate margin; the central rib is well defined. There are some glands near the petiole. The small, white flowers are borne in erect, oblong racemes which arise from the leaf axils; they are bisexual, 5-sepalled and 5-petalled. The fruit is a black, oval-shaped drupe containing a spherical kernel. This plant, which originates in Asia Minor, was introduced into Europe in 1676 and is now widely grown for ornament. It is rarely seen growing wild. The medicinally useful parts are gathered in summer.
Parts used Leaves.
Chemical compounds Laurocerasin (now known as Prulaurasin), tannin, sugar.
Properties Antispasmodic, sedative, tossifuge.
Forms of use Cohobated water, inhalations, infusions, syrup, powder.
Notes This is a poisonous plant which transforms the Prulaurasin into hydrocyanic acid. The use of the cherry laurel is incompatible with cocaine, Peruvian bark, caffeine and casein. The fruit is very poisonous in its early stages but can be used, when ripe, to prepare various alcoholic drinks which taste pleasantly of almonds; it is essential, though, to use only the pulp without rupturing the seed. It is used externally for its anti-pruriginous and analgesic effect on local pains. The cohobated water, which is merely concentrated distilled water, is widely used to control fits of coughing, as it has an undeniably soothing effect.

---

253 PRUNUS SPINOSA L.

Sloe

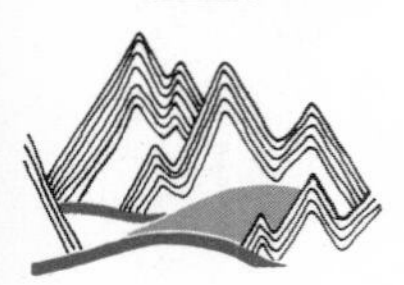

Family Rosaceae.
Description A shrub with a twisted habit and almost black, spiny branches which, in some types of soil, can grow to as high as 10 feet (3 m) and which needs to be controlled as it can become invasive. The alternate leaves are oval and elliptical with a serrate margin and linear stipules. The small, white flowers, which open before the leaves appear, are usually solitary; they are 5-petalled with numerous stamens. The bluish-black fruit has a surface bloom and a spherical drupe containing a small amount of greenish pulp and a large, yellow, hard stony seed. The plant is commonly found throughout Europe, including Britain, growing in the wild in woodland clearings, hedgerows and scrubland almost anywhere. The medicinally useful parts are gathered in May and September.
Parts used Flowers, bark, leaves, drupes.
Chemical compounds Tannin, amygdalin, essential oil, quercetin, gum.
Properties Astringent, depurative, laxative, febrifuge.
Forms of use Decoction, fluid extract, infusion, tincture.
Notes A variety of alcoholic drinks are made with the drupes and a type of rough brandy (*aqua vitae*) can be obtained by allowing them to ferment. A preparation in which the flowers are used is an excellent laxative for children. The main stem was, at one time, used to make walking-sticks of twisted, interesting shapes. Apart from its antipyretic quality, the bark is particularly suitable as a tanning material because of its high tannin content. The leaves have been used as a substitute for tea. The fruits can be made into delicious jams and jellies with a rather sharp but pleasant tang. The pulp of the fruit is used cosmetically in the making of astringent face-masks.

254 PULMONARIA OFFICINALIS L.

Common lungwort

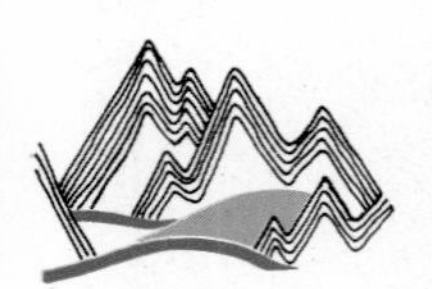

Family Boraginaceae.
Description This herbaceous plant has a fleshy, cylindrical rhizome. The basal leaves, in rosette form, are petiolate, oval-elliptic, rough-textured, pilose and entire with an acute apex; the upper surface is marked with spots of a lighter green than the main area. The upper leaves are sessile. The erect stem, which is about 1 foot (30 cm) high, is pilose and slender with terminal racemes of deep pink to pale bluish-purple flowers; the calyx is tubular and 5-lobed with a regular funnel-shaped corolla. The fruit is an oval, pubescent, 4-sectioned cremocarp. The plant thrives in moist places, its usual habitat being the river banks and mountain grasslands of central Europe. In Britain it has become naturalized. The medicinally useful parts are gathered in spring.
Parts used Leaves.
Chemical compounds Phytosterol, mucilage, silicic acid, carotene, saponin, vitamin C.
Properties Antitussive, diuretic, diaphoretic, resolvent.
Forms of use Infusion, syrup, poultice.
Notes The generic name derives from the 'Doctrine of Signatures', the pale blotches on the surface of the leaves bearing a striking resemblance to lungs (Latin *pulmones.*) Lungwort is used in liquor distilling as an ingredient of vermouth. In spring, the young, tender leaves can be cooked and used as a vegetable in soups. The distilled water is known to have been used as an effective eyewash for tired eyes.

---

255 PUNICA GRANATUM L.

Pomegranate

Family Punicaceae.
Description This small tree or shrub can achieve a height of at least 10 feet (3 m), throwing up a great many suckers. It has a rough, grey main stem with smooth branches. The lanceolate leaves are either opposite or united in whorls. The large, carmine-red flowers are fleshy and arranged in groups of 2 or 3. The fruit is a large, globose berry; its rind, which is leathery and warty, is a deep yellowish-orange streaked with red. It is divided internally into membranous compartments containing numerous rather acid, juicy, red or pink seeds. Originally from western Asia, this plant is hardly ever seen growing in the wild in Europe; it is quite commonly cultivated in sunny orchards in the warmer areas of the Mediterranean; it is not frost-resistant. The fruit is harvested in autumn.
Parts used Rind of the fruit.
Chemical compounds Pelletierine and derivatives of pyridine, pyrogallic acid, granatotannic acid, resins, colouring substance, calcium oxalate, mucilage.
Properties Taenifuge, anthelminthic, antidysenteric.
Forms of use Powder, decoction.
Notes The root-bark can cause serious poisoning. The rind of the fruit has been used as tanning material and as a fabric dye. Delicious, refreshing summer drinks can be made from the seeds. If the flowers are chewed, the saliva in the mouth turns violet. When used to combat parasitic tapeworms, a decoction of the bark should only be taken under medical supervision, as it has a powerful effect and some people may not be able to tolerate it.

256 QUERCUS ROBUR L.
English oak

Family Fagaceae.
Description This is a very long-lived tree which has a greyish bark and a broad, rounded crown. The dark green leaves have a smooth surface; they are leathery and wavy with deep lobes and a short petiole, their general shape being ovate with a lobate apex. The male and female flowers are separate; the males are grouped in yellowish-green, drooping catkins, at the base of the new shoots, with a 5-lobed involucre; the females are in groups of 2-5 on short, erect stalks above the males and have a calyx covered with overlapping scales which eventually enclose the ovary. The fruits are achenes in the form of acorns, the overlapping scales having become the 'cup'. The plant will grow wild in Europe and Britain at almost any level from coastal areas to the lower mountain slopes, together with several other varieties. The oak is seen less frequently nowadays due to extensive deforestation. The medicinally useful parts are gathered in summer.
Parts used Bark and fruit.
Chemical compounds Tannin, gallic acid, resins, bitter substances, ellagic acid, pectin, fluoroglucine.
Properties Astringent, haemostatic, decongestant.
Forms of use Infusion, decoction, tincture, powder, fluid extract, medicinal wine, mellite.
Notes Oak galls or, as they are more familiarly known, oak apples, are spherical excrescences produced on almost any part of the tree by certain insect larvae. They were once used to make excellent inks which would remain legible for centuries without fading. Acorns can be roasted to produce a coffee substitute. Oak bark is widely used for tanning leather and for smoking fish. In central Europe, oak leaves are gathered and used as a basis for litter in cow-sheds and pigsties as well as for cattle fodder.

---

257 RHEUM PALMATUM L.
Turkey rhubarb

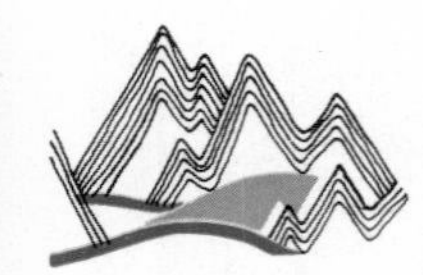

Family Polygonaceae.
Description A herbaceous perennial plant which is about 6½ feet (2 m) high; it has a bulky rhizome with a great many fibrous roots. The leaves are basal with a sturdy petiole that broadens out at the base to encircle the stem. The leaf blade is large and divided into 5 lobes with broad teeth; the venation is prominent. The flowers are arranged in panicles, each flower having 6 pale yellow tepals and 9 stamens. The fruits are pendulous achenes enclosed in a thin membrane. Although originally from western China, it is now cultivated throughout Europe. It is gathered in autumn.
Parts used Rhizome.
Chemical compounds Anthraquinons and anthranolics; rheumemodin, chyrsophanic acid, rhein, calcium oxalate, sugars, pectin, resin.
Properties Laxative, purgative, bitter, cholagogic, choleretic.
Forms of use Powder, infusion, fluid extract, tincture, syrup, pills, medicinal wine.
Notes This plant is extensively used in liquor distilling because of its pleasant aroma and for its digestive qualities. Various delicious jams and jellies are made with the leaf petioles as a basis; these have a slight laxative quality. The petioles can also be eaten raw. The purgative effect is similar to that of senna and of the alder buckthorn.

258 RHODODENDRON FERRUGINEUM L.
Alpenrose

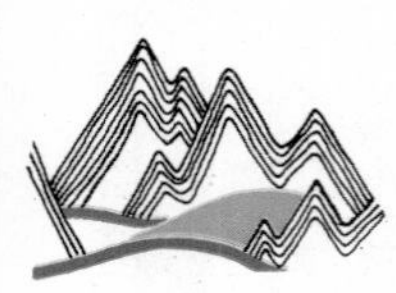

Family Ericaceae.
Description A bushy, evergreen shrub, with few branches, it may reach a height of 3-4 feet (90 cm-1.20 m). The leaves are leathery, dark green on the upper leaf surface and reddish on the lower. The pink or red flowers, borne in corymbs, are tubular, having a 5-petalled, bell-shaped corolla with 10 stamens and a 5-sectioned ovary. The fruit is an oblong capsule bearing a great many flattened seeds. This plant grows wild in the southern European mountains. The medicinally useful parts are gathered in autumn.
Parts used Leaves and galls.
Chemical compounds Arbutin, ericolin (an ill-defined glucoside), rhodoxanthin, resin, glucose.
Properties Diuretic, antirheumatic, antineuralgic.
Forms of use Infusion, oil solution.
Notes *Rhododendron ferrugineum* is much used, together with another variety, *R. hirsutum*, in homoeopathic medicine, dynamizations being prepared for a number of antiflatulence treatments. Although it is also still used jointly with *Erica* (heaths and heathers) in remedies for many complaints of the urinary tract, it is inadvisable as cases of poisoning have arisen as a result. Some of the substances obtained from this plant have a herbicidal effect but research still needs to be done in this area in order to make full use of these. The galls, which are excrescences produced as a result of the presence of the larvae of certain insects, are macerated in oil to give oil of marmot which has an antineuralgic and analgesic effect on all rheumatic manifestations. The flowers have the same properties as the leaves.

---

259 RIBES GROSSULARIA L.
(now known as **Ribes uva-crispa** L.).
Gooseberry

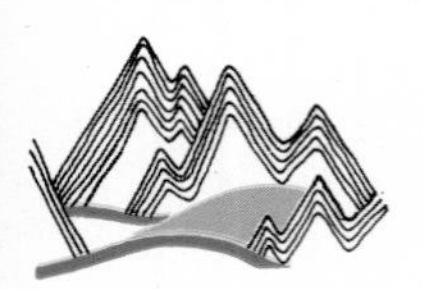

Family Grossulariaceae.
Description A very branched and spiny bush of up to 40 inches (1 m) in height, the leaves are in congested clusters, palmate-lobate with oval, serrate lobes and glabrous. There are several prickles at the base of each petiole. The flowers, borne on small peduncles, have a 5-sepalled, campanulate calyx; the white corolla has 5 small petals, 5 stamens and from 2-5 styles. The fruit consists of a globose, prickly, striate berry, varying in colour from green to greenish-orange or purplish-red, with the remains of the dry petals at the apex. The numerous small, albuminous seeds are contained in the fruit. Although this plant is quite extensively cultivated, it also grows wild in some parts of Europe, including Britain, where it can be found in hedgerows and by mountain sheep-tracks; it thrives on moist, calcareous ground. The fruit is gathered in summer.
Parts used Fruit.
Chemical compounds Tannin, citric acid, malic acid, tartaric acid, pectin, gum.
Properties Laxative, slimming.
Forms of use Juice, syrup.
Notes Delicious, slightly sharp jams and jellies, which are easy to digest, can be made with gooseberries. A type of slightly acid but very pleasant light wine can be made with the juice. The tannin-rich leaves are used in astringent decoctions to treat dysentery and to apply to dressings on wounds. The pulp of the berries is used cosmetically in face-masks for its cleansing effect on greasy skin.

260 RIBES RUBRUM L.

Redcurrant

Family Grossulariaceae.

Description A bush that may grow to a height of 40 inches (1 m) or more, it is very branched, glabrous and has a greyish bark. The leaves are borne on a long, pubescent petiole and are palmate-lobate and cordiform at the base with heavily dentate oval and obtuse lobes; the upper surface is glabrous and the lower pubescent. The greenish flowers are carried on pendulous racemes and have small pedicels; the calyx is 5-sepalled and the corolla 5-petalled with 5 stamens. The ruby-red fruit is a globose, shiny berry containing many spheroidal seeds. In some areas of Europe the redcurrant grows wild in damp, shady hedgerows. It is also cultivated in the British Isles and particularly on the lower mountain slopes of central Europe. It is gathered in June.

Parts used Fruit.

Chemical compounds Citric acid, malic acid, succinic acid, mucilage, pectin, salts, vitamins A, B_1, B_2 and C.

Properties Diuretic, laxative, vitamin-rich, depurative.

Forms of use Juice, syrup.

Notes Delicious jams and jellies can be made from the berries as well as a light wine which is much used in some areas. The leaves, in the form of a concoction or fluid extract, can be used (as can those of the blackcurrant (*Ribes nigrum*) to relieve rheumatic symptoms. They can also be used externally in poultices to treat sprains or relieve the pain of dislocations. The fruit is used cosmetically in face-masks for firming up tired, lifeless skin. When eaten as dessert they aid digestion and act as a mild laxative.

---

261 ROBINIA PSEUDACACIA L.

False acacia

Family Leguminosae.

Description A tree about 26-33 feet (8-10 m) in height, it has a thick, creeping, stolon-producing root. The well-branched trunk has a dark brown, ridged bark. The leaves carried on the spiny branches are imparipinnate with pale green, elliptical leaflets. The flowers, which hang in heavily scented racemes from the leaf axils, have a triangular-toothed calyx and a white corolla. The fruit is a flattened, leathery pod containing oblong, blackish seeds. Originally from North America, it is now widely distributed throughout much of Europe, including Britain, in fields, by roadsides, on river banks and gently sloping hills. The medicinal parts are gathered in summer.

Parts used Bark, leaves and flowers.

Chemical compounds Bark: Robin, emulsin, urease, phytosterol, colouring substance. Leaves: Robinin, quercitrin, salts. Flowers: essence, robinin, inositol, asparagine.

Properties Bark: emetic. Leaves: cholagogic, emetic. Flowers: laxative, antispasmodic.

Forms of use Powder, infusion, tincture, medicinal wine.

Notes Because of its robin content it is inadvisable to use the bark. The flowers can be employed to make jams and pancakes. The wood is used for posts, fencing and wooden pins in timbered ships as it is very hard and continues to harden as it weathers. The essence obtained from the flowers is highly valued and is employed in the perfume industry; it contains linalool, piperonal, terpinol and nerol. The flowers are very attractive to bees. A drying oil can be obtained from the seeds.

262 RICINUS COMMUNIS L.
Castor oil plant

Family Euphorbiaceae.
Description A shrub-like tree that is indigenous to tropical areas, where is reaches a height of up to about 33 feet (10 m), it has now become naturalized in almost every region of the world. It is taprooted with an erect, dark red stem that may remain herbaceous or become woody, hollow and branched, according to its habitat. The alternate leaves, which are furnished with stipules at the base of their long, glandular petioles, are palmate-parted in 7-9 lanceolate, dentate lobes, the middle one being the largest. The male and female flowers are on the same plant and form clusters in terminal panicles. The upper clusters bear the male flowers and the lower ones the females; the tubular perianth is 5-lobed. The fruit is a 3-lobed, dehiscent, 3-sectioned capsule, each section containing a single seed; this is smooth, glossy, elliptical, convex on one side and flat on the other and may be reddish or brown with one end covered by a fleshy protuberance. The integument and cotyledons are flat and slender. The plant is gathered in November.
Parts used Seeds.
Chemical compounds Ricin, ricinine (or ricidine), lipase, triricinoleine, proteins, stearin, tripalmitin, ricinoleic acid, isoricinoleic acid, toxistearic acid, chymase.
Properties Purgative, emollient.
Forms of use Oil, capsules, enema, ointment, suppositories.
Notes The seeds must never be swallowed: 5-6 will kill a child, 10 will kill an adult – there is no specific antidote. The best way of extracting castor oil by expression is the 'cold drawn' or 'Italian' method whereby the seeds are winnowed before pressing to remove all the hard seed coats, which fall off when dry. This leaves behind a cake of solid material containing a large proportion of the highly phytotoxic albumin ricin which is as poisonous as strychnine. The oil is completely atoxic and can be used as a mild purgative, although it has a nauseous taste and smell. The cake of waste material can be used as manure; it can also be used as cattle fodder, after removal of the ricin.

Castor oil has no congestive effect; it stimulates the enteric mucus and the peristaltic action of the stomach and bowels, with simultaneous lubrication of the intestinal walls. It is recommended for constipation in children and pregnant women. The oil is included in fuel mixtures for precision engines and used as a lubricating oil; it is also used as a drying oil in painting and as a basic ingredient in emollient soaps. Pharmacological compounds to combat hair-loss usually contain castor oil and it has a remarkable antidandruff effect.

The plant is often grown for its handsome bearing and fine leaves although, even in a warm Mediterranean climate, it seldom grows to a height of more than about 16 feet (5 m). It is said that flies are repelled by the castor oil plant and that one in the home will keep it free of these pests. The fibrous steles have been used in the making of ropes.

Castor oil is often adulterated with the oils of other members of the spurge *(Euphorbiaceae)* family, which can provoke intestinal irritation; a common adulteration is to mix castor oil with croton oil, which is much more active but also much more drastic.

263 ROSA CANINA L.

Rosa glauca Schott.
Dog rose

Family Rosaceae.
Description This bushy shrub has a long, fibrous root and ascendant, straight or drooping thorny stems with a great many branchlets. The plant may reach a height of over 6½ feet (2 m). The leaves are imparipinnate, the leaflets being oval or elliptical with an acute apex. The whole petiole is stipulate. The flowers are borne either in corymbs or singly; they have triangular sepals and 5 white, pinkish-white or pink petals with numerous stamens. The fruit are achenes, several of which are enclosed in an ellipsoidal, fleshy receptacle with a flattened apex. This false fruit, which turns scarlet as it ripens, is known as a hip. Dog rose is commonly found in Europe, including Britain, growing wild in hedgerows and on the outskirts of woods at levels ranging from low-lying to hilly areas. The various parts are gathered in May and October.
Parts used Petals, hips and galls.
Chemical compounds Tannin, essence, citric acid, vitamin C.
Properties Laxative, ophthalmic, diuretic, lithontriptic.
Forms of use Infusion, fluid extract, syrup, jam, tincture, distilled water, essence, powder.
Notes A yield of 0.2% of essence, yellow in colour, is obtained; it contains geraniol, citral, nerol, eugenol and citronellol. The distilled water is well known as a slightly astringent lotion for delicate skin. The leaves can be used as a substitute for coffee or, after curing, as an ingredient in a type of pipe-tobacco mixture. Delicious jams and preserves can be made from the hips, after removal of the skin and fruits. The seeds, which are oil-bearing, have a vermifuge effect. The petals are used to make an unusual, scented jam.

---

264 ROSMARINUS OFFICINALIS L.

Rosemary

Family Labiatae.

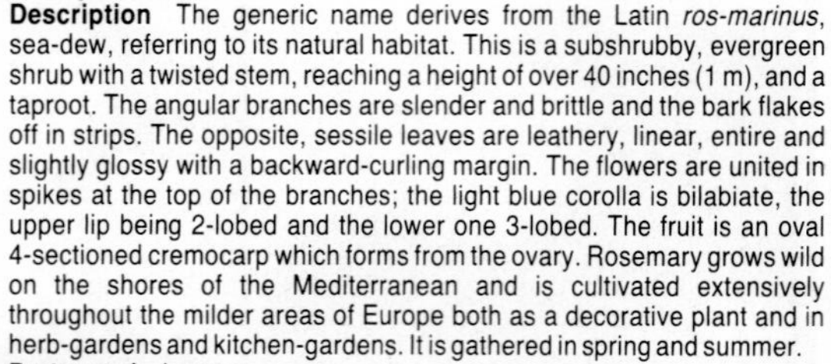

Description The generic name derives from the Latin *ros-marinus*, sea-dew, referring to its natural habitat. This is a subshrubby, evergreen shrub with a twisted stem, reaching a height of over 40 inches (1 m), and a taproot. The angular branches are slender and brittle and the bark flakes off in strips. The opposite, sessile leaves are leathery, linear, entire and slightly glossy with a backward-curling margin. The flowers are united in spikes at the top of the branches; the light blue corolla is bilabiate, the upper lip being 2-lobed and the lower one 3-lobed. The fruit is an oval 4-sectioned cremocarp which forms from the ovary. Rosemary grows wild on the shores of the Mediterranean and is cultivated extensively throughout the milder areas of Europe both as a decorative plant and in herb-gardens and kitchen-gardens. It is gathered in spring and summer.
Parts used Leaves.
Chemical compounds Essence, tannin, bitter principle, resin, saponin.
Properties Stomachic, carminative, cholagogic, emmenagogic, anti-spasmodic.

Forms of use Infusion, essence, tincture, fluid extract, dry extract, distilled water, syrup, medicinal wine.
Notes A yield of 1.5% of almost colourless, aromatic essence, with a density of 0.9, is obtained from the plant; this contains pinene, camphene, borneol and camphor. The well-known Hungary water, used a great deal in the perfumery industry, is made from the leaves. The flowers are generous producers of pollen and are, therefore, much favoured by bees. A distilled water is obtained from the flowers which is used as an eyewash. The essence is antiparasitical as well as relieving rheumatic pains. It is also employed in various slimming compounds.

265 RUBIA TINCTORUM L.
Madder

Family Rubiaceae.
Description The generic name derives from the Latin *ruber*, red, referring to the colour that can be extracted from this plant. It has a rhizomatose root with square, nodose, spiny stems arising from the root reaching a height of 40 inches (1 m) or more. The opposite leaves are lanceolate and dentate with a small petiole; they have 2 stipules with which they form nodal whorls. The flowers are united at the top of the branches; they have a 5-lobed, tubular corolla. The fruit is a berry that is red at first, maturing to black, and contains 2 sub-spherical, yellow seeds. Although this plant was once cultivated, it now grows wild in southern Europe, including southern Britain, especially on neglected ground, in hedgerows and among rubble. It is gathered in autumn.
Parts used Root.
Chemical compounds Rubiadin, erythrosin, ruberythric acid, resin, calcium, oil.
Properties Cholagogic, lithontriptic, aperient, diuretic, emmenagogic.
Forms of use Decoction, powder, fluid extract, tincture.
Notes Madder was extensively grown, until recent years, for its red colouring substances. It is still grown in some gardens in order to make a decoction for dyeing the hair or fabrics red. Should this plant become mixed in with animal fodder, the bones of the animals will take on a reddish hue. Sufferers from albuminaria (albumen in the urine) should not be treated with any medicinal preparation based on madder.

---

266 RUBUS FRUTICOSUS L.
Blackberry

Family Rosaceae.
Description A wild shrub with a scrambling, sprawling habit and a woody root which puts up numerous suckers. The reddish-brown, very prickly stems are woody and several yards long, being erect when young but soon becoming procumbent if there is no nearby means of support. The branches produce many stolons. The alternate, petiolate leaves are palmate, composed of 3-5 oval leaves with a dentate margin and a pubescent lower surface. The flowers may be white or pink and united in apical groups; they have 5 sepals and 5 petals. The fruit, consisting of clusters of small drupes united around the receptacle, is red at first and black when ripe. A very common plant, it may be found wild throughout Europe, including Britain, almost anywhere; it self-propagates very easily. The medicinally useful parts can be gathered throughout the year in a warm climate but from summer-autumn in temperate or cold climates.
Parts used Leaves.
Chemical compounds Tannin, sugar, pectin, inositol, lactic acid, oxalic acid.
Properties Astringent, depurative, vulnerary, antidiarrhoeic.
Forms of use Infusion, juice, tincture, poultice.
Notes Some delicious jams, jellies and refreshing drinks can be made with blackberries. The young shoots, exposed to the sun, produce a fluid which is very effective in healing wounds; it also has a mildly disinfectant effect. A type of tea prepared with the leaves and flowers, mixed with those of raspberries, makes a delightful, scented drink. The roots, if neither very large nor very old, can be eaten after being boiled for a long time. A decoction of the leaves is useful as a gargle in treating thrush and makes a good general mouthwash.

267 RUBUS IDAEUS L.
Raspberry

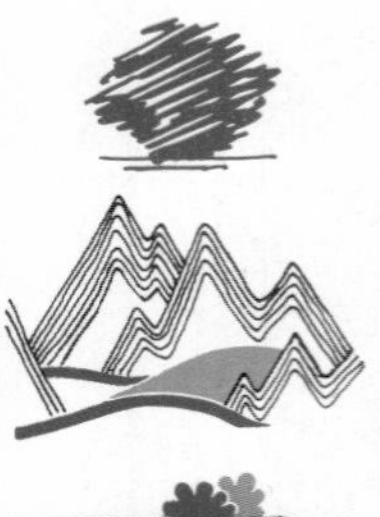

Family Rosaceae.
Description This shrub has a creeping rhizome and erect, branched, thorny stems, which are whitish in colour and may reach 6½ feet (2 m) or more in length. The branches have a wavy form. The alternate leaves are imparipinnate with ovate-lanceolate leaflets; these have a serrate margin, a wooly-haired lower leaf surface and a channelled petiole. The flowers are borne in the leaf axils or at the apex of the branches; the calyx is 5-sepalled and the white corolla 5-petalled. The fruit consists of small, fragrant, globose drupes. The plant can often be seen in Europe, including Britain, growing wild on moist, neglected land and on the outskirts of woods and is widely cultivated in many varieties. It is gathered in summer.
Parts used Leaves and fruit.

Chemical compounds Leaves: tannin, oxalic acid, pectin. Fruit: malic, oxalic, tartaric and salicylic acids, sugars, vitamins.
Properties Leaves: astringent, decongestant, ophthalmic. Fruit: diuretic, thirst-quencher, antiscorbutic.
Forms of use Infusion, pulp, distilled water, juice, tincture, electuary.

Notes The fruit is used to make jams and jellies, and corrective juice for pharmaceutical use is extractred from it. Some delicious syrups and distilled liquors are obtained from the fruit, as well as a very delicate essence. The seeds are oil-bearing. The roots, if well cooked, can be eaten like those of the blackberry. A type of tea made from raspberry and blackberry leaves is an excellent alternative to coffee. Cosmetically, decongestant face-masks are made with the fruit to soothe reddened skin.

---

268 RUMEX ACETOSA L.
Sheeps' sorrel

Family Polygonaceae.
Description This herbaceous plant has a large, deep, rhizomatose root. The erect, branched stem can reach a height of 40 inches (1 m). The basal, petiolate leaves, in rosette form, are lanceolate or arrow-shaped and pointed at the apex; the stem leaves are sheathing. The flowers, male and female, usually on different plants, are borne in a terminal panicle with rust-red tepals. The fruit consists of a 3-sided nut. The plant grows freely throughout most of Europe, including Britain, in meadows and uncultivated fields, on the banks of streams and on waste ground. It is gathered in May.

Parts used Whole plant.
Chemical compounds Acid oxalate of potash, anthraquinons, fat, sugar.
Properties Antiscorbutic, laxative, diuretic.
Forms of use Decoction, syrup.

Notes A plant that is often used in salads because of the pleasantly acidulous tang it lends to them. Due to its high oxalate content, it should never be used by anyone suffering, or prone to suffer, from concretions (stones in the bladder, calculi in the salivary gland ducts, etc.). For external use, a face-mask of finely chopped or pounded leaves is an excellent decongestant. The root can be used as an easily obtainable but innocuous laxative because of its anthraquinon content. The syrup is much used to treat vitamin deficiencies.

269 RUSCUS ACULEATUS L.
Butcher's broom

Family Liliaceae.
Description A subshrub which, in some instances, may grow to as high as 40 inches (1 m). It has a fibrous, oblique, whitish rhizome from which emerge green, striate stems. The branches take on a leaf-like form and are known as cladodes; they are green, leathery and ovate-lanceolate with a spine at the top. The true leaves are represented by scales. The greenish-white, 6-petalled flowers are borne on a lanceolate bract on the first half of the cladode. The fruit is an almost spherical, red berry with 1-2 seeds and viscous pulp. This unusual type of shrub can often be seen wild throughout Britain and Europe on the outskirts of woods and in moist, uncultivated ground. It is collected in September but as it is a protected plant, special permission is needed.
Parts used Rhizome.
Chemical compounds Resins, essence, bitter substance, potassium salts.
Properties Diuretic, depurative, anti-arthritic, vasoconstrictive.
Forms of use Decoction, fluid extract, tincture, syrup, medicinal wine.
Notes The young shoots are sometimes eaten like asparagus. In times of hardship, the seeds have been roasted and used as a substitute for coffee. The rhizome is one of the ingredients from which '5-root syrup' is made.

---

270 RUTA GRAVEOLENS L.
Rue

Family Rutaceae.
Description A wild or cultivated plant that can reach a height of about 40 inches (1 m), it has a woody, fasciculate root and an erect, cylindrical, branched stem. The whole plant is glandular and has a distinctive odour. The alternate, petiolate leaves are fleshy, 3-lobed and clothed with oily glands. The greenish-yellow flowers are united in an apical corymb; they have a 4-5 sepalled calyx and a 5-petalled corolla. The fruit is a globose capsule containing black, kidney-shaped seeds. Although found in the wild in southern Europe, it is more frequently found under cultivation or naturalized from gardens; its preference is for an open, sunny position near the sea. It is gathered in summer.
Parts used Whole plant.
Chemical compounds Rutin, essential oil with methyl salicylate, valerianic ether, acetic ether, limonene, pinene, tannin.
Properties Antihysteric, emmenagogic, ophthalmic, vermifuge, carminative, anti-epileptic, revulsive, anthelminthic, abortive.
Forms of use Infusion, powder, tincture, fluid extract, essence, distilled water, oily solution, ointment.
Notes Because of its uterine congestant effect and its abortive action, well known in forensic medicine, rue must not be taken during pregnancy. It can have a poisonous effect, if taken in large amounts, but a few leaves may be used in salads for their aromatic quality. The essence and the whole plant are also used to give an aromatic tang to Italian *grappa* and other types of spirituous liquors. Rue can cause 'contact dermatitis' when exposed to light because of its xanthotoxin content. The use of rue in ophthalmology was advocated centuries ago and its usefulness is still acknowledged today.

271 SALIX ALBA L.
White willow

Family Salicaceae.
Description The generic name of this tree derives from the Celtic *sal-lis*, near water. It has a robust trunk with a deeply fissured, ash-grey bark and small but sturdy, slightly pubescent branches. It grows to a height of up to 66 feet (20 m). The alternate leaves, borne on a short petiole, are oblong-lanceolate with an acute apex; the upper leaf surface is glabrous, the lower pubescent, and the margin toothed. The male flowers are grouped together in catkins at the apex of the branches, together with small leaves; the females, carried on a separate tree, are in smaller catkins and have a nectar-producing gland. The fruit is a bivalve capsule with very small seeds. The tree can be seen quite frequently throughout Britain and Europe, either growing wild or cultivated, on both low-lying and hilly ground, on river banks, by almost any stretch of water and even overhanging ditches. The medicinally useful parts are gathered in September.
Parts used Bark of the branches.
Chemical compounds Salicin, tannin, colouring substance, resin, gum.
Properties Antipyretic, sedative, hypnotic, antirheumatic.
Forms of use Powder, infusion, fluid extract, syrup, medicinal wine.
Notes The bark, after acetic maceration, is used to remove corns and hard skin. An infusion of the leaves has a calming effect and, with its mildly soporific action, is helpful in cases of nervous insomnia. A preparation made from the leaves, when used in the bath, is of real benefit in relieving widespread rheumatism. It is thought that the white willow contains oestrogens. Wood- or soft-charcoal is made from the wood and used effectively as an absorbent element in treating waterbrash. The young branches can be cut into thin, flexible strips for plaiting into baskets.

---

272 SALVIA OFFICINALIS L.
Common sage

Family Labiatae.
Description This evergreen subshrub reaches an average height of about 40 inches (1 m). Its taproot is branched and woody from which develop square stems with a number of whitish, wooly-haired small branches. The opposite leaves are elliptical, the lower ones being petiolate and the apical sessile; they have a round or acute base, a denticulate margin, are covered with an obvious network of veins, and are soft and whitish underneath. The flowers are in whorls with a 3-lobed, tubular calyx; the purple or blue-violet, tubular corolla has a 3-lobed lower lip. The fruit is an ovoid, 4-sectioned nutlet. Though occasionally found in the wild, this is a popular herb grown throughout Europe, including Britain, in kitchen- or herb-gardens. The useful parts are gathered in spring and summer.
Parts used Leaves and flowering tops.
Chemical compounds Essence, saponin, tannin, resin, acids, mucilage, salts, vitamins, oestrogens, asparagine.
Properties Digestive, hypoglycaemic, antisudoriferous, cholagogic, emmenagogic, anti-asthmatic, carminative, antiseptic.
Forms of use Infusion, powder, syrup, fluid extract, tincture, essence, distilled water, dry extract, inhalations, anti-asthma cigarettes, medicinal wine, ointment.
Notes The essence consists of pinene, salvene, thujone, eucalyptol, borneol and camphene. It is a very effective 'fixer' in the making of perfumes. The leaves are used as a culinary herb. The essence is included in many bio-activating cosmetic products and in toothpastes. The tincture, in the form of a scalp friction, is effective in treating dandruff. Dried sage leaves can be smoked to give relief in asthmatic attacks.

273 SAMBUCUS EBULUS L.

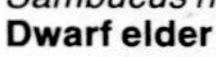

Sambucus humilis Mill., *Ebulum humile* Gorke
Dwarf elder

Family Caprifoliaceae.
Description This herbaceous plant, with a creeping rhizome, can grow to a height of 40 inches (1 m). The herbaceous stems are grooved and the opposite leaves pinnate with lanceolate, acute, serrate leaflets. The flowers are gathered in densely branched pyramidal clusters; they have a tubular calyx with a 5-toothed margin, a white, 5-lobed corolla and purple anthers. The fruits are black, globose berries with many seeds. The plant can often be seen in Europe growing wild on waste ground, by the roadside in clumps and on the calcareous soil of the plains. It has become naturalized in Britain following centuries of cultivation. The medicinally useful parts are gathered in summer.
Parts used Leaves and rhizome.
Chemical compounds Leaves: Glycoside sambunigrine, essence, tannin, malic acid, valeric acid, tartaric acid. Rhizome: acetic acid, malic acid, saponin, resins.
Properties Leaves: laxative, antiphlogistic. Rhizome: purgative, diuretic.
Forms of use Infusion, powder, fluid extract.
Notes This plant exudes a foetid smell. A colouring substance, with a dark blue base, is extracted from the berries. These are never used internally as they can produce symptoms of toxicity. The dwarf elder is often used to adulterate the common elder (*Sambucus nigra*).

---

274 SAMBUCUS NIGRA L.
Elder

Family Caprifoliaceae.
Description A sprawling shrub that may become a small tree, it easily reaches a height of 20-23 feet (6-7 m). Its light brown branches are covered with lenticels and they have soft, spongy pith. The opposite leaves are imparipinnate with ovate, serrate, delicate leaflets which have an acute apex. The flowers, in flat-topped flower clusters at the apex of the branches, have a tubular, 5-toothed calyx and a yellowish-white, scented, 5-lobed corolla. The fruits are purple-black, globose berries. This plant may be found wild throughout Europe, including Britain, by the roadside, near houses and in hedges, from low-lying to hilly areas. It is gathered in summer.
Parts used Leaves, liber (phloem), berries, flowers.
Chemical compounds Leaves: glycoside sambunigrine, essence, malic and valeric acids, carotene, vitamin C. Phloem: sambucin, resin, sambucigrine, potassium nitrate. Berries: glycoside sambunigrine, isoquercitrin, vitamin C, sugar, acetic acid, malic acid, tartaric acid. Flowers: sambucin, sambucigrine, essence, rutin, choline, tannin, resin.
Properties Leaves: laxative, haemostatic. Phloem: diuretic, purgative. Berries: depurative, laxative, antineuralgic. Flowers: diaphoretic, antitussive, galactagogic, diuretic.
Forms of use Infusion, decoction, syrup, juice, tincture, fluid extract, poultice, powder, ointment, distilled water, oily solution.
Notes This plant is used extensively in industry for the essence that is extracted from it; this is particularly suitable for adding fragrance to food and wine products. It is also used in the making of delicious jams, jellies and liquors. Decoctions made from the leaves have an insecticidal effect. The wood of the adult plant is highly-prized by carpenters.

275 SAMBUCUS RACEMOSA L.

Red-berried elder

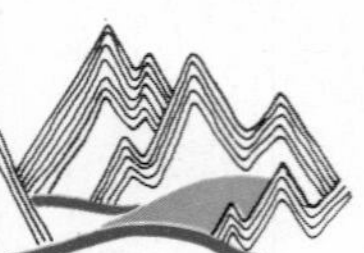

Family Caprifoliaceae.
Description This shrub can grow to a height of 10-13 feet (3-4 m). It has a grey-brown bark with yellowish pith. The opposite leaves are pinnate and slightly petiolate with oval, acuminate, slightly dentate margined leaflets. The greenish flowers are clustered in pyramidal panicles; they have a 5-toothed, tubular calyx and a 5-lobed corolla. The fruit is a scarlet, sharp-tasting berry which contains a great many seeds. Its natural habitat is among the moist, rocky terrain of the lower to middle mountain slopes of Europe. In Britain it has become naturalized. It is gathered in summer.
Parts used Fruits and leaves.
Chemical compounds Fruits: malic, acetic and tartaric acids, sugar, tannin, colouring substance, vitamin C. Leaves: glycoside sambunigrine, essence, valerianic and malic acids.
Properties Fruits: laxative, depurative. Leaves: sudorific, diuretic, resolvent.
Forms of use Infusion, juice, powder.
Notes This is the most edible and tasty of the elders and some fine jams and jellies can be made from its berries. The wood is often used to manufacture various domestic items. The bark is a purgative, as is that of the other varieties of elder. The leaves can be used externally as resolvents to soothe abscesses and boils. The seeds contain a fatty oil which it is hoped may be used in some way, but have not yet been researched.

---

276 SANGUISORBA OFFICINALIS L.

Poterium officinale A. Gray, *Sanguisorba major* Gilib.
Great burnet

Family Rosaceae.
Description The generic name derives from the Latin *sanguis* and *sorbere*, to absorb blood. It is a herbaceous plant with an oblique, dark brown root and many fibrous rootlets. The stem, which may exceed 40 inches (1 m) in height, is erect and striate with imparipinnate leaves that have ovate, cordiform leaflets with a serrate margin. The dark red flowers, which have 4-sectioned calices, are borne in densely packed, oblong heads. The fruit is a rough, ribbed achene. This plant is frequently found growing wild at most altitudes throughout Europe, including Britain, especially in moist, shady sites on siliceous soils. It is gathered in summer.
Parts used Whole plant.
Chemical compounds Sanguisorbin, tannin, gum, salts.
Properties Astringent, vulnerary, tonic.
Forms of use Powder, decoction, tincture, juice, poultice.
Notes This plant tastes like cucumber and is often included in salads to improve their flavour. It is also one of the ingredients in some digestive tisanes. The root can be used in the tanning of leather because of its high tannin content. It is sometimes referred to as *Pimpinella major* (great pimpinel) to distinguish it from *Pimpinella saxifraga* (burnet [or lesser] saxifrage or pimpinel), which has the same properties.

277 SANICULA EUROPAEA L.

Sanicula officinarum Neck.
Sanicle

Family Umbelliferae.
Description A rhizomatose, herbaceous plant with many rootlets and an erect, simple stem, it reaches an average height of 12-16 inches (30-40 cm). The basal leaves are in rosette form with long petioles; they are palmate-lobate with a dentate margin. The upper leaf surface is dark green and shiny. The flowers are united in umbels on long peduncles; the calyx on each flower is 5-lobed and 5-toothed while the white corolla has 5 oval petals with an acute apex. The fruit consists of a diachenium with a spiny, hooked surface. The plant grows wild in woodlands, on damp, shady sites and in some mountainous areas of Britain and Europe. It is gathered in summer.
Parts used Roots.
Chemical compounds Saponin, tannin, mucilage, salts.
Properties Astringent, antitussive.
Forms of use Powder, infusion, tincture, medicinal wine.
Notes The leaves and, in particular, the roots are used to make an ointment to relieve the pain of haemorrhoids. Good results are obtained by making compresses from a decoction of the roots and putting them on chilblains and inflammations in general. In the past, sanicle was much more extensively used than today.

---

278 SANTOLINA CHAMAECYPARISSUS L.

Santolina incana Lam.
Lavender cotton

Family Compositae.
Description A hardy, evergreen, dwarf subshrub, it has a woody root and numerous rootlets. It has a very branched stem, of up to 20 inches (50 cm), with straight branchlets. The leaves are linear, pinnately lobed and slightly fleshy. The flowering heads, surrounded by bracts, are borne at the apex of a simple peduncle; the little yellow flowers are hermaphrodite at the centre of each head but may occasionally be just female on the periphery. The fruit is a compressed, ellipsoidal achene. A native of southern France and the northern Mediterranean area, where it can be seen growing in neglected fields and on calcareous ground, lavender cotton is widely cultivated throughout Europe, including the British Isles. It is gathered in summer.
Parts used Flowering tops.
Chemical compounds Essence, tannin, resin, bitter substance.
Properties Anthelminthic, antispasmodic, emmenagogic.
Forms of use Infusion, essence, powder.
Notes When finely ground and applied to insect stings or bites, this plant will immediately ease the pain. If applied to surface wounds, it will hasten the healing process by encouraging scar formation.

279 SAPONARIA OFFICINALIS L.
Soapwort

Family Caryophyllaceae.
Description An upright, herbaceous plant with a contorted, stoloniferous rhizome, its reddish-green stems are erect, rotund and may reach a height of 40 inches (1 m). The pale green leaves are opposite, oval and acute, with veins running the whole length of the leaf blade. The clustered apical flowers have a cylindrical, 5-toothed calyx and 5 white or pink petals. The fruit is an ovoid, dehiscent capsule with kidney-shaped, flattened seeds. The plant can commonly be seen growing wild in Britain and Europe, in fields, by country roadsides and along the banks of streams. It is gathered in spring.
Parts used Rhizome.
Chemical compounds Saponin, bassorin, galactan, fat, essence, resin.
Properties Depurative, diaphoretic, expectorant, antirheumatic.
Forms of use Decoction, syrup, fluid extract.
Notes This plant used to be extensively grown in order to make the lye which was used for washing clothes and fabrics. As an internal medicine, it should be treated with the greatest caution as it can cause paralysis of the vasomotor centre because of its high saponin content. The frothy liquid obtained by boiling the root in water is a very effective cleaning medium for furniture and pictures. If powdered, the root is an irritant to the nasal mucous membranes and it has, therefore, sometimes been used to treat cases of anosmia (loss of the sense of smell). It can be used externally, in local compresses, on scaly skin eruptions, such as cold sores, and eczema.

---

280 SATUREJA HORTENSIS L.
Summer savory

Family Labiatae.
Description The generic name derives from the Latin *satyrus*, a satyr, because of the aphrodisiac effect with which the plant was credited. A hardy annual with a small, fibrous, spindle-shaped root and branched, striate stem, it has a bushy habit, and grows to a height of 8-12 inches (20-30 cm). The mid-green, glandular leaves are opposite, entire and lanceolate-linear with a short petiole. The flowers, carried in clusters arising from the leaf axils, have a campanulate, veined calyx and a white, 2-lipped, 5-lobed corolla. The fruit is a brownish, oval, 4-sectioned nutlet. Although a native of the Mediterranean area, this plant is widely cultivated in moderately moist kitchen- and herb-gardens throughout Europe. It is gathered from summer-autumn.
Parts used Flowering tops.
Chemical compounds Essence, tannin, sugar, pyrocatechol.
Properties Carminative, digestive, antiseptic, eupeptic, stomachic, possibly aphrodisiac.
Forms of use Infusion, essence, fluid extract, tincture, medicinal wine.
Notes The light green essential oil that is obtained from this plant gives an average yield of 0.5% and has a density of 0.9; it consists of cymene, dipentene, carvacrol, thymol, phenols, alcohols and esters. It is used extensively in the making of perfumes to give a particular quality to a fragrance. Similar use is made of it in the distillation of spirits and in wine-making to introduce an especially subtle flavour. Suitably diluted, it forms an ingredient in lotions for the scalp in cases of incipient baldness. The ointment, when rubbed well into the affected areas, helps to relieve rheumatism. It is a very attractive plant to bees and is well worth cultivating in or near an apiary.

281 SCABIOSA SUCCISA L.

Succisa pratensis Moench.
Devil's bit scabious

Family Dipsacaceae.
Description An erect herbaceous plant with blackish, fasciculate roots and a delicate, branched stem, it grows to an average height of 16 inches (40 cm). The leaves are entire, oblong-oval and arranged in a basal rosette. The flowers, which are grouped in globose, pedunculate heads, have a calyx which is divided into 4 lobes and a light blue or pink corolla. The fruit is a ridged achene. This dainty plant is commonly seen in meadows and pastures, by country roads and on almost any open ground throughout Europe, from low-lying to hilly areas. It is gathered in summer.
Parts used Whole plant.
Chemical compounds Tannin, scabiosin, gum, saponin, sucrose.
Properties Depurative, emmenagogic, diuretic, vulnerary, slightly diaphoretic.
Forms of use Infusion, fluid extract, tincture, syrup.
Notes A compress of freshly chopped devils's bit scabious is still a popular remedy, in some rural areas, for outbreaks of eczema and other skin complaints. Good results have been achieved by using the distilled water as an eye-wash to treat conjunctivitis. In spring, the tender young leaflets are sometimes used as a salad ingredient. A green colouring material, extracted from the leaves, is used in dyeing wool and other fabrics. At one time it was believed that scabious could get rid of scabies, hence its name. The tincture has a gentle but reliable effect on bruises, aiding quick re-absorption of the blood pigment.

282 SCOLOPENDRIUM OFFICINALE Sm.

Scolopendrium vulgare Sm., *Phyllitis scolopendrium* (L.) Newm., *Asplenium scolopendrium* L., *Scolopendrium officinarum* Sw.
Hart's tongue

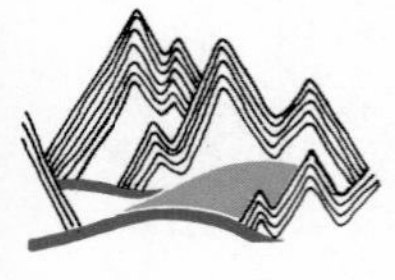

Family Polypodiaceae.
Description This fern has a small, reddish, scaly rhizome with a number of little rootlets. The erect, glossy green, undulate fronds, which can be as tall as 20 inches (50 cm), are cordiform at the base and lanceolate at the apex. The distinctive marking on the surface of the fronds consists of veins running parallel to each other, branching out from the well-defined median rib. Rust-coloured sporangia are arranged in parallel lines on the lower leaf surface from which the spores emerge on ripening. This attractive fern is frequently seen throughout western Europe, including Britain, growing out from between the stones of old wells or grottoes where water is constantly dripping, amongst the undergrowth of wet woodlands and near waterfalls and fountains. The medicinally useful parts are gathered from June-September.
Parts used Leaves.
Chemical compounds Mucilage, tannin, gallic acid, aromatic bitter substance.
Properties Expectorant, cholagogic, vulnerary.
Forms of use Infusion, tincture, poultice.
Notes Because of its attractive appearance this fern is cultivated and sold as an indoor plant. It is used cosmetically, in decoction, to counteract greasy hair and as a face-pack for delicate skin. At one time it was regarded as one of the 5 important capillary herbs.

283 SEDUM ACRE L.
Biting stonecrop

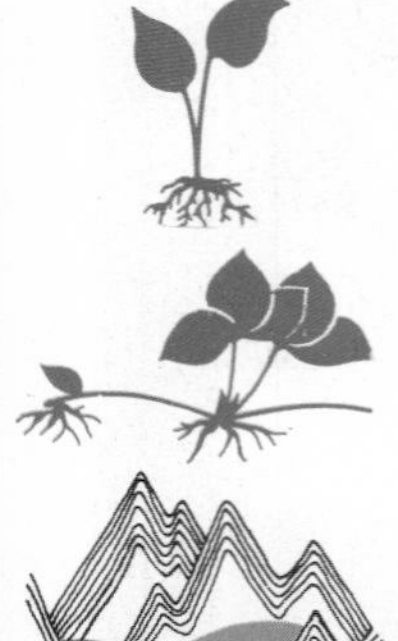

Family Crassulaceae.
Description The generic name derives from the Latin *sedare*, to calm, because of its emollient properties. It is a succulent plant with a great many closely growing, creeping and erect stems, reaching an average height of about 2 inches (5 cm). The alternate, fleshy, sessile leaves are close together or overlapping and oval-cylindrical in shape; at the point at which they emerge from the stem they are slightly amplexicaul. The yellow flowers, arranged in clusters of 2-4, have a 5-sepalled calyx and a corolla with 5 lanceolate-acute petals. The fruit is a capsule containing oval seeds. The plant is frequently to be found in Britain and Europe, growing wild on old walls, rocks and cottage roofs, from low-lying to hilly areas. It is gathered in spring and summer.
Parts used Whole plant, fresh rather than dried.
Chemical compounds Rutin, sedidrin, mucilage, gum, resin.
Properties Hypotensive, vulnerary, corn-remover, antiwart, rubifacient.
Forms of use Juice, infusion, ointment, medicinal wine.
Notes Despite its undoubted hypotensive effect (that is, reduction of arterial pressure), it is not unusual for this plant to produce an intolerant reaction when taken internally. It also has a dintinctly acrid taste. It is nearly always employed externally, one of its main uses being as an effective and harmless natural corn-remover. It can also be used to bring boils to a head, although this may cause some local irritation. An invasive plant, once gathered it cannot be kept for any length of time as it is difficult to dry.

---

284 SEMPERVIVUM ARACHNOIDEUM L.
Cobweb houseleek

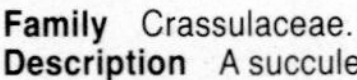

Family Crassulaceae.
Description A succulent plant with erect stems, it may grow to a height of 4 inches (10 cm) or more. The leaves are obovate, oblong and glandular with a subacute apex; the leaf-tips are entwined into a mat of white hairs resembling a cobweb. The flowers, which are united in corymbs, have 12 lanceolate, pinkish-red petals. It flourishes in continental Europe among rocks and stones in a temperate to cold climate and is not found wild in Britain. The medicinally useful parts are gathered in summer.

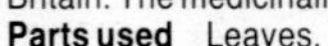

Parts used Leaves.
Chemical compounds Mucilage, tannin, malates, formic acid.
Properties Emollient, corn-remover, sedative, haemostatic, ophthalmic.
Forms of use Juice, tincture, maceration, ointment.

Notes Boils can be brought to a head by applying local applications of the crushed plant. Nose-bleeding can be stopped by inhaling some of the plant juice; it will also stop loss of blood from minor wounds. Slightly warmed, a few drops of juice in the ear will also relieve inflammation of the ear. Toothache can be eased by chewing a few leaves. Corns and warts can be cured by macerating some of the leaves in vinegar and applying the liquid to the affected parts 2-3 times a day. The pulp can be used to make a cooling face-mask for reddened or sunburnt skin.

285 SENECIO VULGARIS L.

Common groundsel

Family Compositae.
Description The generic name derives from the Latin *senex*, an old man, referring to the white pappus hairs. It is a herbaceous plant with a taproot and many rootlets. The fragile, little-branched stem can exceed a height of 12 inches (30 cm). The leaves are alternate, the upper ones being spoon-shaped and lobed with obtuse, sometimes dentate, segments; the lower ones are elongate and spoon-shaped. The flowers are united in an inflorescence consisting of erect or pendulous heads; the bracts form an involucre inside which are the yellow flowers with a 5-toothed corolla. The fruit is an almost cylindrical, pubescent, whitish achene with a pappus. It is frequently found throughout Europe, including Britain, growing wild by the roadside and on waste and cultivated ground where it is regarded as one of the commonest weeds. It is gathered in May.
Parts used Whole plant.
Chemical compounds Senecin, seniocin, resin, inulin, glucose, potassium salts.
Properties Emmenagogic, vasoconstrictive, cardiac sedative.
Forms of use Infusion, tincture, fluid extract, powder, syrup.
Notes Groundsel is used in some areas as a salad ingredient, although the presence of several alkaloids in it make this inadvisable. It should certainly never be used by pregnant women because of its congestant effect on the uterus. Although it has been used in folk medicine as a laxative and to increase the flow of bile, it should on no account be employed for these purposes. It may, however, be used successfully as an ointment in the treatment of haemorrhoids.

---

286 SISYMBRIUM OFFICINALE (L.) Scop.

Erysimum officinale L.
Common hedge mustard

Family Cruciferae.
Description A taprooted plant with a very branched, erect stem, it averages about 20 inches (50 cm) in height. The lower leaves, which are petiolate and arranged in rosette form, are pinnately-lobed with oval lobes; the upper leaves are almost sessile and hastate in shape. The flowers, gathered in terminal racemes on very short pedicels, have 4 sepals and 4 sulphur-yellow petals. The fruit is a pod-like structure with a stalk appressed to the stem; it contains dark brown seeds. Commonly found in most of Europe, including Britain, growing almost anywhere from low-lying to hilly areas, the plant has a preference for uncultivated ground and the sites of ruined buildings. It is gathered in June.
Parts used Whole plant.
Chemical compounds Essence, myrosin, mucilage, dextrin, pectin, glucoside.
Properties Anti-aphonic, decongestant, diuretic, expectorant.
Forms of use Syrup, infusion, fluid extract, powder, juice.
Notes This was, at one time, known as the 'singer's plant' due to its use in the treatment of aphonia (loss of voice). It is often used in association with the juices of watercress and horseradish as a decongestant to relieve irritation of the larynx. Its action is thought to be due to the sulphuretted volatile oil which it contains. As hedge mustard is almost inactive when dry, only freshly picked plants can be used effectively to make any of the above preparations.

287 SMILAX ASPERA L.
Italian smilax

Family Liliaceae.
Description This climbing subshrub has a short rhizome and whitish roots. The stem, which can be as long as 6½ feet (2 m), is scrambling and has very spiny branchlets. The dark green, persistent leaves are leathery, spiny, cordiform and networked with veins. The flowers may be white or greenish and are united in clusters arising from the leaf axils. The fruit is a red berry which contains almost spherical seeds. Indigenous to the Mediterranean area, Italian smilax usually grows near the sea and in the immediate hinterland where urbanization has not yet taken place. It is gathered in spring.
Parts used Root.
Chemical compounds Starch, choline, mannose, glucose, phenol, potassium nitrate, ethereal compound.
Properties Depurative, diuretic, diaphoretic.
Forms of use Decoction, fluid extract, powder, syrup.
Notes This climbing shrub is used in many places as a protective hedge around fields as it soon becomes impenetrable. It has all the qualities of sarsaparilla, although to a rather lesser degree, and is used to adulterate the tropical American smilax. As a depurative plant (that is, one which eliminates toxins), it is without equal and is, therefore, nearly always used with woody nightshade (*Solanum dulcamara*) in springtime depurative preparations. In dairy-farming areas, it is sometimes crushed and used on the crust of fresh milk as a poultice.

---

288 SOLANUM DULCAMARA L.
Bittersweet

Family Solanaceae.
Description The generic name derives from the Latin *solamen*, a consolation or comfort. A scrambling, shrubby plant with a light brown, cylindrical, branched stem several feet long. The root is cylindrical and fibrous. The alternate, petiolate leaves are oval, acuminate, cordate and 3-lobed with 2 lateral leaflets that are smaller than the central one. The violet flowers, which are in cymes, have a 5-lobed calyx. The fruit is an ovoidal, juicy berry containing a number of seeds; it is green at first, ripening to red. This plant is frequently to be seen in the wild, in Europe, including most of Britain, excluding the extreme north; it grows in hedgerows, by walls and on the banks of streams and rivers, almost anywhere from low-lying to hilly areas. It is gathered in April.
Parts used Shoots.
Chemical compounds Dulcamarine, solania, dulcamarinic acid, tannin, bitter substance, pectin.
Properties Depurative, diaphoretic, sedative.
Forms of use Powder, decoction, fluid extract, tincture.
Notes Although small quantities of this plant can be taken, it is poisonous and acts directly on the blood. Poisoning may cause vomiting, acute diarrhoea and cramp but if immediate steps are taken the prognosis is invariably favourable. In the modern phytocosmetic field, good results are currently being achieved in treating cellulite with compresses of finely chopped leaves. The green twigs, if chewed, have a nauseous, bitter taste at first which then becomes sweet, hence the synonym bittersweet. It can be used successfully in place of sarsaparilla, as its effect is similar.

289 SOLANUM MELONGENA L.

Egg plant or **Aubergine**

Family Solanaceae.
Description An erect, herbaceous plant with branched stems, it can grow to a height of 28 inches (70 cm) or more. The alternate, petiolate leaves are ovate-elliptic with an acute apex; they are entire or lobate-dentate and slightly wooly-haired. The flowers, which are carried on pedicels and arise from the leaf axils, have a many-lobed calyx and a many-lobed tubular, violet corolla. The fruit is a large, ellipsoid or globose berry containing firm, fleshy material and a great many brown seeds. Originally from India, this plant was introduced into Europe many years ago and is cultivated outdoors in the warmer areas and under glass elsewhere. It is seldom found growing in the wild. It is gathered from summer-autumn.
Parts used Fruit.
Chemical compounds Protein, carbohydrates, vitamins A, B_1, B_2 and C, cinerin-like substances.
Properties Hypotensive, antihaemorrhoidal.
Forms of use Decoction, tincture, medicinal wine, ointment.
Notes This plant is an excellent cholesterol regulator. It is very effective, too, when used externally in a fat- or oil-based preparation to relieve haemorrhoidal discomfort. Aubergines are preserved in various ways for use both as a food and a medicine. They are very nutritious and are sometimes referred to as 'poor man's meat'.

---

290 SOLANUM NIGRUM L.

Black nightshade

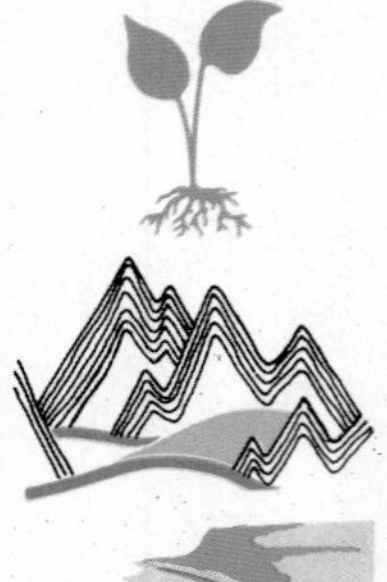

Family Solanaceae.
Description An annual herbaceous plant with a whitish taproot, its herbaceous, branched stem can grow to a height of 40 inches (1 m). The mid-green, alternate leaves are ovate, rhomboidal or ovate-rhomboidal, pointed, slender and slightly pubescent. The white flowers are 5-lobed and borne in apical corymbs. The berries are green at first but become juicy and black as they ripen; they contain many small, kidney-shaped seeds. The plant flourishes in Britain and Europe on uncultivated and waste land, and on any ground that is rich in salts, from low-lying to hilly areas. It is gathered in autumn.
Parts used Whole plant.
Chemical compounds Solanin, asparagine, rutin, tannin, linoleic and palmitic acids, solangustin.
Properties Sedative, narcotic, emollient.
Forms of use Juice, tincture, fluid and semi-fluid extracts, oily solution.
Notes This plant has been used since antiquity for its sedative and paralyzing effect on the nerve ends. It was one of the ingredients, together with other members of the Solanaceae family, used in the manufacture of locally analgesic ointments. The juice of the berries also has an analgesic effect on toothache, a drop or two being allowed to evaporate on the affected tooth. Although inadvisable for internal use because of its poisonous qualities, it can be used externally to relieve periarteritis.

291 SOLANUM TUBEROSUM L.

Solanum esculentum Neck.
Potato

Family Solanaceae.
Description A herbaceous plant with a stolon-bearing tuberous root and branched, angular stems which may grow to more than 40 inches (1 m) high. The alternate, petiolate leaves are imparipinnate with pilose segments. The flowers, which are united in a scorpioid cyme, have a cup-shaped calyx and a white or purple corolla. The fruit is a greenish, globose berry which contains the seeds. Originally from South America, the plant is now cultivated extensively throughout Europe. The medicinally useful parts are gathered in spring.
Parts used Leaves.
Chemical compounds Solanine, starch, tropeine, acids.
Properties Antispasmodic, antiphlogistic.
Forms of use Decoction, fluid extract, ointment.
Notes The leaves, green tubers and fruits are dangerously toxic because of their high solanine content. Apart from its culinary value, the white tuber has various medicinal qualities. It has a soothing effect on eye irritations and can be used as a paste on skin irritations, sores and haemorrhoids. The water in which potatoes have been boiled can be used to clean silver and restore a shine to furniture and leather objects. The juice of the plant is used, by some people, to relieve heartburn and waterbrash, but this is inadvisable. Emollient and cleansing face-masks are also made from it to treat greasy or wrinkled skin.

---

292 SOLDANELLA ALPINA L.

Alpine snowbell

Family Primulaceae.
Description A herbaceous plant which averages about 4 inches (10 cm) in height, it has an oblique rhizome and numerous rootlets from which the leaves emerge; these have a kidney-shaped leaf blade with long, leathery and slightly succulent, cylindrical petioles. The flowers are either solitary or in clusters of 2-4 and are borne on long peduncles with a group of bracts at the apex; the calyx is 5-parted and the lilac or violet corolla is bell-shaped, the upper part of the bell being deeply fringed; there are 5 stamens and a button-like stigma. The fruit is a ridged capsule containing kidney-shaped seeds. This plant is characteristic of the mountain pasturelands of continental Europe, and is found near to the snow- and glacier-line. It is gathered in summer.
Parts used Rhizome.
Chemical compounds Tannin, salts, glucoside.
Properties Purgative.
Forms of use Decoction.
Notes The soldanella rhizome has been and is still used in mountain regions for its laxative qualities, and it is perhaps for this reason that the plant has now become extremely rare.

293 SOLIDAGO VIRGAUREA L.

Solidago reticulata Lapeyr.
Golden rod

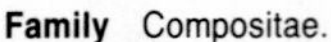

Family Compositae.
Description This is an erect plant with a taprooted rhizome from which branched stems arise to an average height of 20 inches (50cm). The alternate leaves are petiolate, the basal ones being oval or elliptical, acute and dentate, while the upper ones are entire and sessile. The flowers and leaves are in branched racemes with heads which have a number of overlapping bracts; the ligulate flowers are golden yellow, as are the central disc flowers, the corolla of which is tubular. The fruit is an angular achene furnished with a bristly pappus. This plant is widely distributed throughout Europe, including the British Isles, as well as central Asia and North America; it thrives almost anywhere, from the plains to the hills, in uncultivated fields and especially where the ground is silica-rich. It is gathered in summer.
Parts used Flowering tops.
Chemical compounds Inulin, saponin, resin, essence, mucilage, tannin.
Properties Diuretic, antiseptic, urocolitic, diaphoretic.
Forms of use Infusion, tincture, fluid extract, syrup.
Notes This plant is very well known for its apparent lithontriptic effect on renal calculi. It is also used as a mild medicine, because of its antiseptic qualities, in cases of enteritis in children; Purple loosestrife (*Lythrum salicaria*) is often used in conjunction with it. It makes an excellent mouthwash in the treatment of thrush and it can also be used externally as a cold compress on fresh wounds. A vinous or slightly alcoholic preparation seems to be more active than the infusion.

---

294 SORBUS AUCUPARIA L.

Pyrus aucuparia (L.) Gaert.
Mountain ash

Family Rosaceae.
Description A tree which has a straight bole and a reddish bark, it grows to a height of 40 feet (12m) or more. The alternate leaves, borne on a small petiole, are stipulate, imparipinnate, oblong, acute, serrate and asymmetrical; the upper leaf surface is greener than the lower. The numerous white flowers are grouped in apical corymbs; the calyx is 5-sepalled and the corolla 5-petalled. The fruits are composed of seeds enclosed by the fleshy part of the receptacle. The false fruit is ovoid and orange-red or carmine. This tree grows wild throughout Europe, including Britain. The medicinally useful parts are gathered in September.
Parts used Fruits.
Chemical compounds Tannin, sorbitol, sorbic acid, sucrose, malic acid, sorbin, vitamin C.
Properties Astringent, antidiarrhoeic.
Forms of use Syrup, juice, fluid extract, electuary.
Notes The false fruits can be made into delicious, if slightly acidulous, jams and jellies; they can also be macerated to obtain alcohol. The seeds contain hydrocyanic acid as well as oil and must not, therefore, be used to make home-made preparations. Decoctions of the bark and infusions of the leaves, which contain the same astringent properties as the fruits, can be used as a mouthwash to treat thrush and heartburn. For external use, the false fruits may be used to make astringent face-masks to combat wrinkled skin. Mountain ash wood is highly esteemed by wood-turners because of its compactness, and, because of its elasticity, is used to make hoops for barrels.

295 SORGHUM BICOLOR (L.) Moench

Sorghum vulgare Pers.
Broom-corn

Family Gramineae.
Description A cereal grass with fibrous, spreading roots and an erect, nodose culm, reaching a height of 6½ feet (2m) or more. The leaves are broad, dentate, rough-textured, ligulate and ribbed. The apical panicle is formed by several reddish spikelets. The fruit consists of an oblong caryopsis. Originally native to India, broom-corn is now cultivated extensively in southern Europe, the Mediterranean region and North America. It is harvested in summer and autumn.
Parts used Inflorescence.
Chemical compounds Starch, sugar, durrine, acids, pyrogallic acid, pectin.
Properties Astringent, haemostatic, antidiarrhoeic.
Forms of use Infusion, tincture, medicinal wine.
Notes This plant is extensively grown for its grain which, apart from giving a very white flour when ground, is a particularly nutritive cattle fodder due to its content of sugars. Special mashes are made from concentrated decoctions of the roots and culms for fattening geese and hens. There have been attempts to extract the sugar from the culms as an alternative to using sugar beet, but the substances which form the waste materials were found to be difficult to eliminate. In North America broom-corn is also grown for the manufacture of besom-type brooms, hence its common name.

---

296 SPARTIUM JUNCEUM L.

Genista juncea Scop., *Genista odorata* Moench
Spanish broom

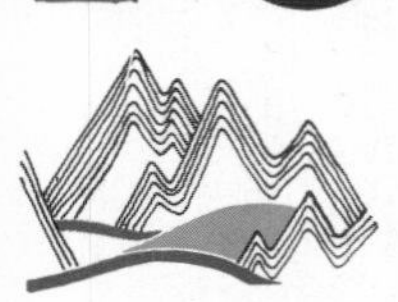

Family Leguminosae.
Description The generic name derives from the Greek *sparton*, a strand, alluding to the textile fibres which may be obtained from the stems of this plant. It is a spiny shrub with a taproot and many rootlets. The erect, very branched stems reach a height of 10 feet (3m) or more and the branches are cylindrical, striate, flexible and pithy. The alternate leaves are linear-lanceolate and caducous. The flowers are in dense almost rounded clusters with a 5-toothed calyx and a carina of 2 separate petals. The fruit is a blackish, flat pod containing dark-coloured, ovoidal seeds. A native of the Mediterranean area, Spanish broom grows wild and under cultivation near the sea, on sloping ground, railway embankments and steep, rocky sites, having a preference for calcareous soil. It is gathered in summer.
Parts used Flowering tops.
Chemical compounds Cytisine, colouring substance, essence, tannin.
Properties Diuretic, purgative.
Forms of use Infusion, tincture, medicinal wine.
Notes Only limited amounts should be taken of any preparation made from this plant, as the cytisine content can provoke a toxic condition. It is thought that cytisine may have a slight antidotal effect on the venom of vipers but this has still to be proved. Spanish broom has an efficacious and potent diuretic action. It can be used commercially as a source of fibrous material for rope-making and canvas-weaving. The smaller branches are used to make baskets, rather like osiers in wickerwork. A yellow colouring substance can be extracted from the flowers. The branches are often made into brooms.

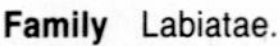

297 STACHYS OFFICINALIS (L.) Trev.

Betonica officinalis L.
Betony

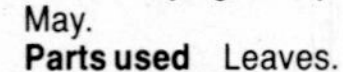

Family Labiatae.
Description A perennial plant with a small rhizome from which emerges a slender, square, pilose stem, sometimes over 1 foot (30cm) high. The basal leaves are borne on long petioles but these become shorter in the stem leaves until, towards the apex of the plant, the leaves become sessile; they are cordate, elliptical, opposite, dentate and pilose. The flowers, united in whorls in loose spikes, have a tubular, campanulate calyx; the pink corolla has an obtuse upper lip and the lower one is trilobate. The fruit is an ovoid, 4-sectioned nutlet. Betony is quite commonly seen in Europe, including Britain, growing wild in moist fields from low-lying to hilly areas. The medicinally useful parts are gathered in May.
Parts used Leaves.
Chemical compounds Tannin, stachydrine, choline, betaine, essence.
Properties Cholagogic, carminative, digestive, vulnerary, anti-headache.
Forms of use Infusion, powder, fluid extract, medicinal wine.
Notes Betony powder is a sternutatory (that is, it causes sneezing) and helps, therefore, to relieve head colds. It has a specific internal action in cases of severe headache and, externally, on wounds where its scar-forming properties act very quickly with a collateral cleansing effect. Great care must be taken if internal use is made of the root in any form, as it can cause vomiting and violent diarrhoea.

298 STELLARIA MEDIA (L.) Vill.

Alsine media L.
Common chickweed

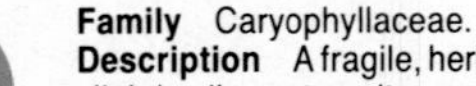

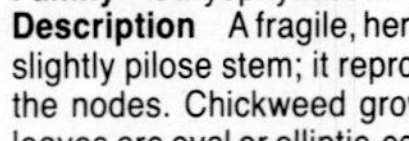

Family Caryophyllaceae.
Description A fragile, herbaceous, often sprawling plant with branched, slightly pilose stem; it reproduces itself by throwing out new shoots from the nodes. Chickweed grows to a height of 4-5 inches (10-15cm). The leaves are oval or elliptic-cordate with an entire margin; they are borne on a short petiole while those nearest the top may be sessile. The white flowers, carried at the apex of the stalks, have 5 sepals and 5 deeply notched petals and are present for most of the year. The fruit is an oval capsule containing flat, brownish seeds. Regarded by most people as a troublesome weed, chickweed will grow almost anywhere in Europe from cultivated land to the cracks between paving stones. It is gathered in summer.

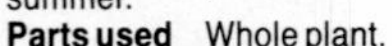

Parts used Whole plant.
Chemical compounds Saponin, salts, tannin.
Properties Diuretic, vulnerary, astringent.
Forms of use Infusion, juice, distilled water, tincture.
Notes Chickweed is treated as a salad ingredient, in some areas, the apical part only being used; this practice is inadvisable, however, because of the presence of saponin. It is a favourite food of geese. Applied externally, as a poultice, it relieves any kind of roseola and is effective wherever there are fragile superficial veins. The juice was, at one time, used in the preparation of eyewashes but has now been replaced by much more active plants.

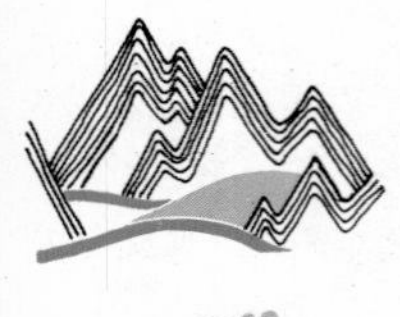

299 TAMARINDUS INDICA L.

Tamarind

Family Leguminosae
Description The generic name derives from the Arabic *tamar-hindi*, the date-palm of India. This is an evergreen tree which can vary in height from 33-82 feet (10-25 m); the trunk is branched from the base and the bark is fissured and scaly. The alternate, pinnate leaves are divided into petiolate, oblong, entire, glabrous leaflets with a round apex. The orange-yellow flowers, grouped in apical racemes, are 4-sepalled and 5-petalled. The fruit is an indehiscent pod with fibrous pulp containing round seeds. Originally from Madagascar, the tamarind can now be found naturalized in many tropical and subtropical countries, where it is also cultivated. The fruit is gathered when ripe.
Parts used Pulp of the fruit.
Chemical compounds Tartaric acid, citric acid, malic acid, pectin, invert sugar.
Properties Laxative, choleretic.
Forms of use Pulp, electuary, syrup.
Notes The pulp is used to make delightful and refreshing summer drinks as well as in the preparation of a number of traditional Indian, West Indian and tropical African dishes. It is also used quite frequently in the pharmacy as a corrective in many otherwise unpleasant-tasting preparations.

---

300 TAMARIX GALLICA L.

Tamariscus narbonensis Garsault
Tamarisk

Family Tamaricaceae.
Description The generic and English names possibly derive from the River Tamaris in the Pyrenees. A shrub with a bushy habit growing to a height of 16½ feet (5 m) or more, it has brownish bark and numerous slender branches which bear erect, caducous branchlets. The leaves, carried on the branchlets, are alternate, overlapping, linear, glabrous and sessile. The white or pink flowers, borne in small spikes, have a basal bract that is toothed; they are 5-sepalled and 5-petalled with 5 stamens, 3 stigmas and anthers with 2 compartments. The fruit is a single, compartmented capsule containing seeds with an apical thread. Tamarisk grows in the wild in many coastal areas that enjoy a Mediterranean climate; it is also propagated by cuttings and cultivated as hedges in the temperate areas of Europe, including Britain; to act as a windbreak near the sea. The medicinally useful parts are gathered in autumn.
Parts used Branchlets, with leaves.
Chemical compounds Tannin, gallic acid, colouring substance, sodium sulphate, methylquercitol.
Properties Astringent, antidiarrhoeic, diuretic.
Forms of use Decoction, tincture, medicinal wine.
Notes This plant has been used in the tanning industry because of its high tannin content. It also provides a colouring substance suitable for dyeing fabrics. A popular remedy, practised in some parts of southern Europe, is to apply compresses of tamarisk to wounds to stop bleeding.

301 TAMUS COMMUNIS L.
Black bryony

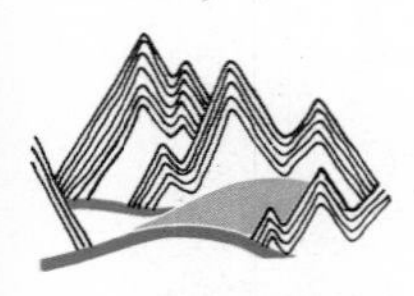

Family Dioscoreaceae.
Description A climbing plant with a long, black, tuberous root from which the cylindrical, reddish stems arise; these grow to considerable length, twisting and turning in all directions. The brilliant green, petiolate leaves are cordate-ovate and acuminate. The petiole has 2 basal glands. The greenish-yellow flowers, arranged in axillary racemes, are grouped into male and female inflorescences. The fruits are red, globose berries containing large, albuminous seeds; these clusters remain during autumn, looking very colourful and decorative, festooned in the bare hedgerows and undergrowth. The black byrony is quite frequently to be seen growing wild in woods and coppices throughout Europe, the British Isles, Asia and North Africa. It is gathered in October.
Parts used Root.
Chemical compounds Saponin, calcium oxalate, tannin, starch, potassium oxalate.
Properties Emetic, haemolytic, drastic, anti-ecchymotic.
Forms of use Fluid extract, tincture, pulp.
Notes Serious irritations can be caused by the consumption of massive doses of any preparation containing this drug, due to its high saponin content. It is mainly used externally in treating alopecia (baldness), ecchymosis and rheumatism. The young shoots are sometimes gathered and then cooked and eaten, as can be done with hop shoots, although they have a decidedly bitter flavour. The root pulp can be used to make local compresses to ease many types of pain where heat needs to be generated, such as in the treatment of gout, rheumatism and paralysis.

---

302 TANACETUM VULGARE L.
Pyrethrum vulgare (L.) Boiss., *Chrysanthemum vulgare* (L.) Bernh.
Tansy

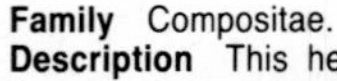

Family Compositae.
Description This herbaceous plant has an oblique rhizome which throws out a great many rootlets. The erect, sparsely branched, ridged stem, may reach a height of 40 inches (1 m). The alternate leaves are pinnate-parted with incised segments; some are petiolate and others are sessile, according to their height of attachment on the plant. The flowers, grouped in heads which cluster to form a yellow apical corymb, have tubular corollas. The fruits are ribbed achenes with a rim-like pappus. This plant is sometimes cultivated in kitchen-gardens but is mainly found throughout Europe, including Britain, growing wild in waste ground, by the roadside and among rubble. It is gathered in summer.
Parts used Flowering tops.
Chemical compounds Tanacetin, tanacetotannic acid, resin and an essence consisting of terpenes, ketone, and esters.
Properties Bitter, carminative, emmenagogic, anthelminthic, taenifuge.
Forms of use Powder, syrup, infusion, essence, tincture, fluid extract.
Notes An aromatic, greenish essential oil, with a density of 0.92, can be extracted from this plant by distillation to give an average yield of 0.15%. If large amounts of any preparation containing tansy are taken, toxicosis with epileptic convulsions may result. The essence is an insecticide. In some areas, the leaflets are used as aromatic herbs in home-made pancakes and salads. As this is an emmenagogic plant (one which restores the menstrual flow) it should on no account be taken in any form by pregnant women.

303 TARAXACUM OFFICINALE Web.

Taraxacum dens-leonis Desf., *Taraxacum officinarum* Rupr., *Leontodon officinale* Gmel., *Leontodon taraxacum* L.

Dandelion

Family Compositae.
Description A wild plant, it has a fleshy taproot which is white on the inside and dark brown on the outside, with filamentous latex. The stems are simple, hollow and leafless, reaching a height of 4 inches (10 cm) or more. The sessile leaves, which rise directly from the root to form a rosette at the base of the plant, are lanceolate and pinnatifid or pinnate-parted, with a dentate margin and curved lobes. The yellow, ligulate flowers are borne in heads with a double involucre of bracts, the inner ones being erect and the outer curved backwards. The fruits consist of oval achenes with 2 rows of small teeth surmounted by a white pappus. This is a very common weed in Britain and Europe, found in fields and waste ground, by the roadside and even between paving stones. It is gathered in autumn.
Parts used Root.
Chemical compounds Taraxacin, choline, inulin, phytosterol, tannin, mucilage.
Properties Cholagogic, laxative, depurative, tonic.
Forms of use Juice, fluid extract, tincture, infusion, homoeopathic dynamizations.
Notes This plant is often used as an addition to salads. The latex contained in the whole plant is very efficacious in removing corns and in treating warts and verrucae. An excellent distilled water, obtained from the ligules, clears the skin and is particularly effective in fading freckles. The flower-buds can be preserved in vinegar, like capers. The latex has a specific action on cholecystitis (inflammation of the gall bladder) and is thought also to have a lithontriptic action on hepatic calculi. The crushed root is a very good, and widely used, coffee substitute.

---

304 TAXUS BACCATA L.

Yew

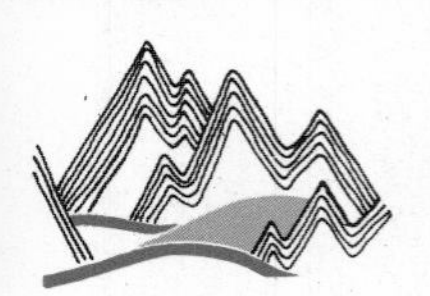

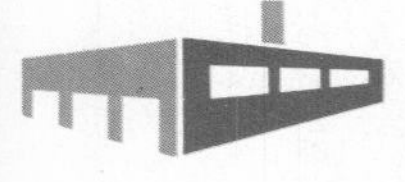

Family Taxaceae.
Description This tree can grow to a height of 33 feet (10 m) or more; the trunk is erect and has a thin, rust-red bark, but unlike other coniferous trees, it has no resin canals. The evergreen leaves, which are arranged spirally, are like flattened needles, the lower surface being a lighter green than the upper. The yew is a dioecious tree, male and female flowers usually being borne on separate trees; the male inflorescence consists of a small catkin with bracts while the female takes the form of a fleshy apical disc with a few scales at its base. The fruit is composed of a red, fleshy, cuplike casing surrounding a single seed. A tree that has been cultivated in Europe and Britain for centuries, it is rarely found in the wild. The medicinally useful parts are gathered in spring.
Parts used Leaves.
Chemical compounds Taxine, milossin, taxicotine, resin, tannin, essence.
Properties Emmenagogic, paralyzing, cardiotonic, narcotic.
Forms of use Powder, infusion, tincture.
Notes A very long-lived tree, it is said to be able to survive for over 1,000 years. It is very poisonous, having a paralyzing action on the heart. It can also provoke abortion. The leaves are the most poisonous part while the aril can, in fact, be eaten provided the seed is not swallowed. It was believed in the past that anyone who slept under the branches of a yew-tree would drift off into eternal sleep, hence its folk-name, in some areas, of the 'tree of death'. The wood, which used to be employed in the manufacture of bows due to its springiness, is now greatly esteemed by cabinet-makers.

305 TEUCRIUM CHAMAEDRYS L.
Wall germander

Family Labiatae.
Description This perennial plant has a slender rhizome and many rootlets. The stem, up to about 1 foot (30 cm) high, is woody at the base but becomes herbaceous towards the apex. The opposite leaves, borne on a short petiole, are oval and leathery with a crenate margin; the upper ones are sessile and entire. The flowers appear in leafy spikes; they have a tubular, 5-toothed calyx and a pink, bilabiate, tubular corolla with a 3-lobed lower lip. The fruit consists of 4 ovoid nutlets. Wall germander is frequently seen wild in central and southern Europe in sunny, rather dry places, on waste ground and on rocky outcrops. It is gathered in summer.
Parts used Whole plant.
Chemical compounds Teucrioresin, scutellarin, choline, tannin, essence.
Properties Digestive, aromatic, carminative, stomachic.
Forms of use Infusion, tincture, fluid extract, powder.
Notes This plant is extensively used in the making of alcoholic drinks with a bitter base, which have digestive- or appetite-promoting qualities. A yellow essence, with a distinctive odour, is obtained from the plant, giving an average yield of 0.06%; it contains pinene, camphene, borneol, bornyl acetate, caryophyllene and isovaleraldehyde. It is used externally as an astringent infusion in the treatment of gums for pyorrhoea and gingivitis. In the past it was used for healing wounds because of its tannin content.

---

306 THEOBROMA CACAO L.
Cacao

Family Sterculiaceae.
Description A native of Central America where it is now extensively cultivated, this tree can reach a height of 23-26 feet (7-8 m). Its much branched trunk is of a light, porous wood with pale chestnut-brown bark. The bright green, petiolate leaves are glossy and oval-oblong with an acute apex. The flowers are united in clusters at the leaf axil. The fruit, which is ovoid, almost pear-shaped, and acute, is reddish-yellow when fresh and brown when dried; the outer casing is woody, ribbed, having 5 indehiscent compartments with seeds arranged in a row. The ripe fruits are gathered twice a year.
Parts used Seeds, roasted.
Chemical compounds Fatty substances, colouring material (cacao red), starch, cellulose, sugar, salts, theobromine, caffeine.
Properties Stimulant, nervine, anti-angina pectoris, nutrient.
Forms of use Powder.
Notes There is a great demand for cacao, both in its powdered form as cocoa and made into chocolate. A red colouring material is also extracted from it as well as a fatty substance known as cocoa butter, the latter having a protective effect on the skin. Theobromine has an even milder nervine effect than caffeine and also has a good effect on the progress of angina pectoris.

307 THUJA OCCIDENTALIS L.
White cedar

Family Cupressaceae.
Description An evergreen tree, which seldom grows to a height of more than about 30 feet (9 m), it has an erect, branched trunk. Its vast number of overlapping leaflets completely cover the bearing branches; they are opposite and decussate, scale-like, slighly succulent and greenish-yellow, with resin-bearing glands. The bark is reddish-brown. The flowers are unisexual, the males being ovate and globose while the females have subsidiary bracts which are fatter at the base. The fruit is a small ovoid pine-cone consisting of elongated scales covering the seeds. Originally from Virginia and Canada, the white cedar was introduced into Europe in 1500. It has since been widely cultivated in cemeteries, in gardens and used to line roads. The medicinally useful parts are gathered in June.
Parts used Leaves.
Chemical compounds Essence with terpenic ketones, tannin, wax, sugars, bitter substance, thujic acid, thujin.
Properties Diuretic, insecticidal, anthelminthic, revulsive.
Forms of use Fluid extract, tincture, syrup.
Notes Preparations based on the white cedar are much used in homoeopathy for treating warts, verrucae and swellings of the mucous membrane, both in dynamization and mother tincture forms. On no account should amounts larger than those prescribed by a qualified person be taken, or serious poisoning may result.

---

308 THYMUS SERPYLLUM L.
Wild Thyme

Family Labiatae.
Description A small, shrubby, perennial plant, it has a woody, fibrous root and a great many rootlets. From its long, creeping stem rise a number of branchlets; these are square in cross-section, pilosect and light reddish-brown. The opposite, almost sessile leaves, which are subrotund or linear, are positioned close together on the sterile branches and further apart on the fertile ones. The mauve flowers are borne on a short stalk in a short, dense, rounded spike; they have a campanulate calyx and a bilabiate tubular corolla, the lower lip being 3-lobed. The fruit consists of a dark-brown, ovoid, 4-sectioned nutlet which may be found at the base of the persistent calyx. Wild thyme grows beside mountain sheep-tracks and on dry, stony ground, from coastal areas inland to the lower mountain slopes of central and northern Europe, including Britain. It is gathered from May-August.
Parts used Flowering tops.
Chemical compounds Essence: thymol, carvacrol, cymene, pinene; tannin, resin, saponin.
Properties Antiseptic, antispasmodic, carminative, diuretic, expectorant.
Forms of use Powder, essence, infusion, tincture.
Notes It is used in a similar way to garden thyme – although its thymol content is lower – not only in the kitchen but also in the liquor-distilling and perfume industries. The essence is odontalgic and antiseptic. The tincture can be used externally, with complete confidence, as a disinfectant. The plant is a great favourite of bees. The dried leaves are used as an ingredient of many aromatic infusions.

309 THYMUS VULGARIS L.

Garden thyme

Family Labiatae.
Description This evergreen dwarf subshrub grows up to 12 inches (30 cm) in height. Its roots are fairly robust and its stem very branched. The sessile leaves can vary in shape from elliptic to linear or diamond-shaped towards the apex; the young leaves are slightly wooly. The flowers, united in spikes at the top of the branches, have a bilobate, tube-like calyx and a bilabiate, tubular corolla with a 3-lobed lower lip. The fruit consists of a smooth, dark-coloured 4-sectioned nutlet found in the remains of the calyx. The whole plant has an aromatic fragrance. It grows wild in the Mediterranean area with a preference for a sunny position in dry, gravelly soil. In the rest of Europe, including Britain, it is gathered in spring and summer.
Parts used Flowering tops.
Chemical compounds Essence: thymol, carvacrol, borneol, eucalyptol, menthene, thymene; tannin, resin.
Properties Antiseptic, balsamic, antispasmodic, carminative, antibiotic.
Forms of use Infusion, fluid extract, tincture, syrup, essence, powder, medicinal wine.
Notes This plant is extensively used in the kitchen, perfumery and liquor distillery. In aromatherapy, garden thyme is regarded as one of the most important elements because of its antiseptic properties. The essence is effective in treating whooping cough as well as the parasitic infestation known as ancylostomiasis. It is used for its mouthwash value in appropriate preparations such as liquid dentifrices. Garden thyme is a great favourite with bees and the honey obtained from it has the same properties as the plant itself.

---

310 TILIA PLATYPHYLLOS Scop.

Tilia grandiflora Ehrh.
Large-leaved lime

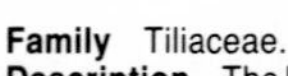

Family Tiliaceae.
Description The large-leaved European lime is widely cultivated. It may grow up to nearly 100 feet (30 m) and is very long-lived. The bark on its straight, tall trunk and branches is smooth. The leaves are subrotund, asymmetrical at the base or cordiform with an acute apex; the margin is slightly toothed. The upper surface of the leaves is glabrous and the lower greyish-white, downy, with little hairs at the insertion of the main and secondary veins. The flowers are in drooping clusters, each cluster half joined to a large oblong bract; every flower has a 5-sepalled calyx and a yellow, 5-petalled corolla. The leathery fruit is almost spherical with protruding longitudinal ribbing. Although this species is sometimes found growing wild in central and southern Europe, it is seen more frequently under cultivation. It is gathered in summer.
Parts used Flowers with their bract.
Chemical compounds Essence containing farnesol; mucilage, tannin, sugar, acids, vitamin C, carotene.
Properties Diaphoretic, diuretic, sedative, antispasmodic.
Forms of use Infusion, fluid extract, dry extract, tincture, syrup, distilled water.
Notes Vegetable charcoal, used for smoking and preserving certain foodstuffs, is made with lime-wood. The charcoal is used as well, to make artists' charcoal. It is also quite an effective vasodilator. The inner bark or 'bast' may be treated in such a way as to produce fibres which can be woven into sacks. Lime flowers are great favourites with bees. They are also the basic ingredient in certain soothing drinks for over-wrought or over-excited children.

311 TRAGOPOGON PRATENSIS L.
Goat's beard

Family Compositae.
Description This herbaceous, biennial plant has an oblique taproot. The stem is herbaceous and hollow, with an average height of 20 inches (50 cm). The leaves are amplexicaul, linear and grass-like with a well-defined central vein and an entire margin. Each head of flowers is borne on a long peduncle; the flowers are ligulate with a yellow corolla. The fruit is a greyish achene with a pappus of white hairs. This plant is quite commonly seen throughout Europe, including Britain, growing in meadowland and by the side of country roads. It is gathered in autumn.
Parts used Root.
Chemical compounds Inulin, inositol, mannitol, phytosterol.
Properties Nutritive, depurative, expectorant, astringent.
Forms of use Decoction, syrup, fluid extract.
Notes The roots of this plant have great culinary value due to their inulin content which gives them a very sweet flavour. The leaves, too, can be used in various soups. An infusion made from goat's beard petals helps to clear the skin and is particularly effective in lightening freckles. The syrup gives great relief in cases of obstinate coughs and bronchitis. The distilled water is used in cleansing lotions for dry skin. Although fairly common in the wild, it is also frequently grown in kitchen-gardens in some areas of Europe.

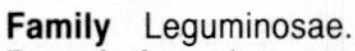

312 TRIFOLIUM ARVENSE L.
Hare's-foot clover

Family Leguminosae.
Description A taprooted plant, it has an erect, branched stem that grows up to 16 inches (40 cm) high. The leaves, borne on a short petiole, are composed of 3 oval, very finely toothed leaflets. The dense, rounded cluster of flowers are white, pink or mauve and have a calyx of very narrow sepals. The plant is much appreciated by cattle. It grows wild throughout Europe, including Britain, on waste ground and in cultivated fields, from low-lying to hilly areas. It is gathered in summer.
Parts used Flowers.
Chemical compounds Tannin, resin, salts, essence, glycerides, colouring substance.
Properties Antidiarrhoeic, vulnerary, antileucorrhoeic.
Forms of use Infusion, lavage.
Notes An infusion used as a mouthwash helps to strengthen weak, bleeding gums and has a somewhat restraining effect on pyorrhoea; it can also be used to make wet compresses for varicose ulcers which tend to heal if the compresses are applied with great regularity. Hare's-foot clover can also be used externally to stop bleeding if crushed and applied to recently made surface wounds.

313 TRIGONELLA FOENUM-GRAECUM L.

Foenum-graecum officinale Moench
Fenugreek

Family Leguminosae.
Description A herbaceous plant with a taproot, its stems are erect and hollow, with a few branches, reaching a height of up to 20 inches (50 cm). The alternate, trifoliate leaves are borne on a short petiole with 2 small stipules at the base; the leaflets are oval, their margins finely denticulate and their upper leaf surface is pilose. The flowers are sessile with a campanulate, 5-lobed calyx; the yellow-white corolla is 5-petalled with a protruding standard. The fruit is a compressed pod containing yellow seeds. Seldom found growing wild, fenugreek is widely cultivated in southern and central Europe as cattle fodder. It is gathered in August.
Parts used Seeds.
Chemical compounds Trigonelline, choline, enzymes, proteins, mucilage, oil, resin, mineral salts, essence with a yield of 0.01%.
Properties Emollient, anticholesterolemic, antiglycaemic, analeptic, galactagogic.
Forms of use Powder, fluid extract, infusion, poultice.
Notes Fenugreek flour has the same qualities as linseed when used as a poultice. It is also used cosmetically in skin-nourishing face-masks as well as to firm the bust, achieved through its galactogogic action (increasing the flow of milk). Taken internally, it serves to drain off the sweat ducts. It is one of the most efficacious tonics in cases of physical debilitation, where a nervous factor is involved. It is often used as a culinary herb for its distinctive flavour.

---

314 TROLLIUS EUROPAEUS L.

Globeflower

Family Ranunculaceae.
Description A herbaceous plant, it has a fasciculate root and an erect, ridged, glabrous stem of up to 40 inches (50 cm) in height. The leaves, which are dark green on the upper surface, are palmate-parted with incised and dentate lobes. The large, golden-yellow flowers, in the form of a floral button, have up to 10 petal-like sepals curving at the top and a great many stamens; the seeds in the follicles are ovate. Characteristic of the mountain pastures of northern and central Europe, including the northern areas of the British Isles, it thrives particularly well in moist ground and by streams. It is gathered in August.
Parts used Root.
Chemical compounds Anemonin, proto-anemonin, essence, tannin.
Properties Purgative, rubefacient.
Forms of use Decoction, poultice.
Notes This plant, like all the buttercup family, is poisonous but much of its toxic principle is lost if it is dried. It must, therefore, be used absolutely fresh to take advantage of its rubefacient (bringing the blood to the surface) action, in poultice form, on rheumatism and periarthritis. At one time, distilled water made from the globeflower, which had a milder action than the decoction, was used to treat neuralgia.

315 TROPAEOLUM MAJUS L.
Nasturtium

Family Tropaeolaceae.
Description This climbing herbaceous annual has a tuberous root and a very branched stem which can exceed 13 feet (4 m) in length. The petiolate leaves, which are both opposite and alternate, are peltate and have an undulating, slightly lobed margin. The reddish-orange, 5-petalled flowers are borne singly on a long pedicel which rises from the leaf axils. The fruit consists of 3 fleshy cocci. Originally from South America, this plant has now become acclimatized to European conditions and has been enthusiastically cultivated because of its attractive climbing habit. The medicinally useful parts are gathered in summer.
Parts used Leaves.
Chemical compounds Isobutyl isothiocyanate, glycotropeoline, spilanthol, oxalic acid, vitamin C.
Properties Expectorant, diuretic, aperient.
Forms of use Juice, infusion.
Notes The whole plant has a sharp, pungent flavour but, used sparingly, it adds a delicious tang to salads. A high percentage yield of oil is obtained from the seeds which, like linseed, is used as a drying oil. The fruits are powdered, in some areas, for use as a mild home-made laxative. The juice, apart from its use as a cough remedy, has a strengthening effect on the capillary bulbs and is often used as an ingredient inombat alopecia (baldness). Nasturtium juice also has a remarkable effect, when drunk with milk, on cases of pulmonary emphysema.

---

316 TUSSILAGO FARFARA L.
Coltsfoot

Family Compositae.
Description The generic name derives from the Latin *tussis* and *agere*, to take away the cough. Coltsfoot has a creeping, stolon-producing rhizome and stems which are clothed in oval scales closely pressed against the stem and which are slightly decussate; these stems can reach a height of about 8 inches (20 cm). The petiolate leaves, arranged in rosette form, are cordate with a dentate margin, the upper leaf surface being mid-green and the lower downy-white. Each head, borne singly at the apex of the stem, has flowers consisting of numeous yellow ligules. The fruit is an almost cylindrical achene with a pappus. Coltsfoot is frequently seen wild in most of Europe, including Britain, by streams and cart-tracks, on railway embankments and almost anywhere that offers root-hold, from low-lying to hilly areas. It is gathered in July.
Parts used Leaves.
Chemical compounds Mucilage, tussillaginine, peptin, gallic acid, acetic acid, essence.
Properties Antitussive, bronchial sedative, anti-eczematous, antineuraligic, emollient.
Forms of use Infusion, syrup, juice, poultice.
Notes Coltsfoot has always been regarded as a particularly effective drug in all types of bronchial inflammation. The flowers are used externally, in poultice form, for their soothing effect on various skin disorders. They are also effective in relieving neuralgia. Because of their liquorice-like fragrance the flowers are used, too, in the curing of pipe-tobacco. Bitter, tonic and a diaphoretic preparation (to induce perspiration) can be obtained from the root.

317 ULMUS PROCERA Salis.

Ulmus campestris Mill.
English elm

Family Ulmaceae.
Description A very branched tree of between 65-100 feet (20-30 m) in height, it has a rough, fissured bark. The branches are pilose when young but become glabrous with age. The petiolate, alternate leaves are elliptical, asymmetrical, acute, doubly toothed, pinnately veined, pilose and with some downy patches below. The 5-sepalled flowers are united in axillary clusters. The fruit is an obovate, yellowish samara with a winged seed. This is a tree that has been extensively cultivated as well as growing wild throughout western Europe, including Britain; it is often to be seen as a large bush in field hedges. Unfortunately, it is subject to disease in Europe and much of the elm population has recently been decimated in this way. The parts used are gathered in autumn.
Parts used Liber (phloem).
Chemical compounds Ulmin, resin, mucilage, phytosterol, tannin, stigmasterin.
Properties Antiherpetic, vulnerary, diuretic, resolvent.
Forms of use Decoction, syrup, juice, powder, ointment.
Notes In vine-growing countries, a technique is sometimes used in which the vines are trained up into and between carefully pruned elms, giving the appearance of a high, solid wall. Tannin is extracted from the inner bark and a colouring substance is also obtained from it. The sap, obtained by tapping the young branches, has been used as a lotion to combat alopecia (baldness). The powdered leaves, mixed with a suitable excipient, make an effective antihaemorrhoidal ointment. The decoction can be used on reddened and inflamed skin as well as to relieve various skin disorders. The timber is used in carpentry; it is a very hard wood but will not take a high polish.

---

318 UMBILICUS RUPESTRIS (Salisb.) Dandy

Umbilicus pendulinus DC., *Cotyledon tuberosa* Halacsy
Kidneywort

Family Crassulaceae.
Description A succulent plant with a small rhizome and slightly tuberous stem, it can reach a height of 16 inches (40 cm). The leaves are fleshy, drooping, shield-shaped and crenate. The flowers are in racemes with a whitish or reddish-green cylindrical corolla, which is divided into acute teeth for about a quarter of its length. The fruit is formed of 5 free follicles. A tenacious plant, it clings to cracks in walls and craggy rocks, grows on roofs and, in the warmer climates, likes the vicinity of olive-groves. A native of southern and western Europe, including Britain, it is gathered in summer.

Parts used Leaves.
Chemical compounds Trimethylamine, waxes, chlorophyll, phytosterol.

Properties Lenitive, diuretic.
Forms of use Juice, pulp, infusion.
Notes The crushed leaves, which have a healing effect, will bring boils to a head. The leaves are also used in ointments to relieve painful haemorrhoids. The juice from the crushed leaves can be used in the form of drops in the auditory canal to relieve otitis externa. This attractive little plant is often grown in small country gardens where the ground is rocky, as it thrives on very little soil.

319 URTICA URENS L.
Annual nettle

Family Urticaceae.
Description A herbaceous plant with a creeping rhizome and numerous rootlets, it has an erect, woody stem of up to about 40 inches (1 m) in height, clothed with stinging hairs. The small, light green leaves are oval, deeply toothed and are also clad in stinging hairs. The flowers are grouped in simple hanging clusters, the male and female flowers being in separate clusters on the same plant with each ovoid ovary having a tufted stigma. The fruit is an ellipsoid nutlet enclosing a single seed. Generally regarded as a troublesome weed, this plant will grow almost anywhere throughout the temperate regions of the world; it thrives particularly well on nitrogenous, neglected ground, by the roadside and near buildings. The leaves are gathered in spring and the rhizome in autumn.
Parts used Leaves and rhizome.
Chemical compounds Gallic acid, formic acid, carotene, vitamin A, tannin, potassium, iron, calcium, silicon.
Properties Diuretic, urticant revulsive, depurative, haemostatic, remineralizing, lithontriptic.
Forms of use Infusion, tincture, juice.
Notes The young tops, parboiled, make a delicious salad ingredient. A high percentage of chlorophyll was at one time obtained from this plant. Fibres from the stems have been used to make a cotton-like fabric as well as very strong ropes. If cut and made into hay, nettles make an excellent addition to the diet of cattle and rabbits; dried and powdered, they can be mixed in with chicken and duck food, while pigs thrive on the boiled plant. The roots help to eliminate small stones from the bladder. In some parts of the world, rheumatic pains are still treated by beating the body with stinging nettles – an effective, though painful, remedy.

---

320 UTRICULARIA VULGARIS L.
Common bladderwort

Family Lentibulariaceae.
Description An aquatic, floating plant, it has submerged root-like capillary branches which may be as long as 6-7 feet (2 m). The leaves, which are 2-lobed from the base, the lobes being pinnately divided, have small, air-filled vesicles (bladders) at irregular intervals. The 5-10 flowers, borne in racemes, have a striate, yellowish corolla; their upper lip is entire with slightly undulate margins while the lower one is deflexed. The fruit is a capsule containing several rough-textured seeds. This plant is commonly found throughout most of Europe, including Britain, in marsh- and swamplands, wet ditches, ponds and rice-fields. It is gathered in summer.
Parts used Whole plant.
Chemical compounds Organic salts, tannin, ethereal oil.
Properties Diuretic, vulnerary.
Forms of use Juice, infusion, poultice.
Notes Bladderwort vesicles enable the strands of its stem to remain afloat and thus to perform their vegetative function. It is really a tropical plant although at least 6 species thrive in Europe. Ducks eat it in quantity and this fact has induced people locally to collect it and drink the juice made from it, for its evident remineralization qualities. In the days when rice was harvested by hand, bladderwort was often used by workers in the form of local poultices on wounds because of its mildly astringent effect.

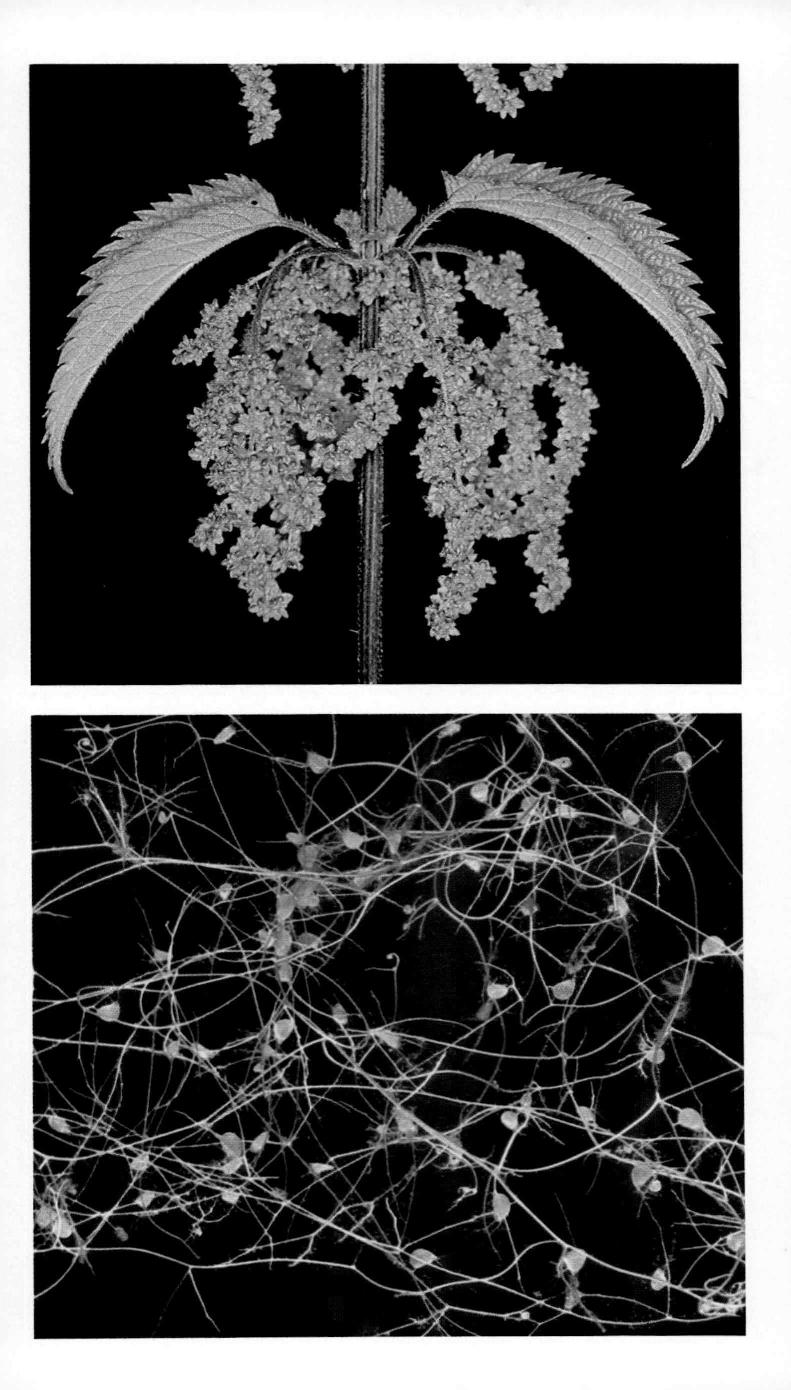

321 VACCINIUM MYRTILLUS L.
Bilberry

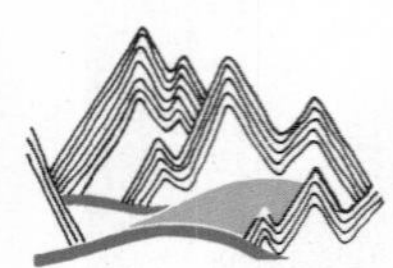

Family Ericaceae.
Description A subshrub of between 12-16 inches (30-40 cm) high, it has a long root and erect, branched, flowering stems. The branchlets are angular. The alternate, light green leaves, carried on a short petiole, are flat, oval and pointed with a toothed margin; the upper leaf surface is smooth and the lower one paler in colour with prominent venation. The flowers emerge from the leaf axils on a short pedicel; they have a 4-5-lobed calyx and a tube-shaped corolla, widening from the narrow apex to the base, with 4-5 white or pink petals. The fruit is a deep violet, fleshy spherical berry with a surface bloom, enclosing crescent-shaped seeds. This is a fairly common plant which grows wild throughout Europe, including Britain, in moist undergrowth. It is gathered in summer.
Parts used Fruits and leaves.
Chemical compounds Fruits: tannin, sugars, inositol, pectin, carotene, myrtilline. Leaves: tannin, arbutin, ericolin, myrtilline, resin, mucilage.
Properties Astringent, antidiarrhoeic, hypoglycaemic, ophthalmic.
Forms of use Juice, decoction, fluid extract, dry extract, tincture, powder.
Notes Delicious jams and juices can be made from the fruits. In terms of their styptic quality (arresting bleeding), the fruits are most effective when dry. The leaves and berries contain a green colouring substance which can be used to dye fabrics. The skin of the fruits is specific in treating hemeralopia (day-blindness) because of its anthocyanin content. Distilled water obtained from the leaves is an excellent eyewash for soothing inflamed eyes.

---

322 VACCINIUM VITIS-IDAEA L.
Cowberry

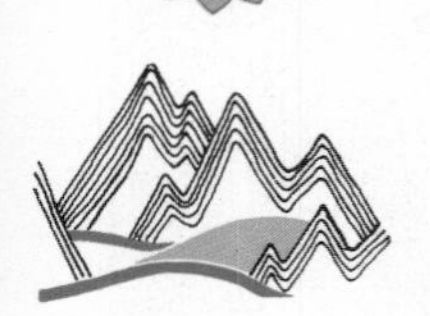

Family Ericaceae.
Description A very branched, evergreen shrublet, it can reach a height of about 14 inches (35 cm) and has a creeping rhizome. The perennial, alternate leaves have short petioles and are leathery, elliptical with an obtuse apex and a margin that is rolled under. The flowers, in drooping racemes at the apex of the branches, have a 5-lobed calyx and an open bell-shaped corolla which is greenish-white tinged with red and which ends in 5 lobes. The fruit is a sharp-tasting, spherical, red berry containing seeds with a high albumen content. The cowberry's natural environment is the sunny mountain meadowlands and peat moors of Europe and some northern areas of the British Isles. It is gathered in June.
Parts used Leaves.
Chemical compounds Ericolin, arbutin, vaccinine, tannin, gallic acid, citric acid, sugar, chatarine.
Properties Antiseptic, diuretic, astringent, lithontriptic.
Forms of use Decoction, fluid extract, tincture.
Notes A substitute for the bearberry, it is so similar that its leaves are often used to adulterate those of the latter plant. The fruits, which are edible and, in fact, quite pleasant to eat, can be made into rather unusual jellies and jams. The tanning industry makes use of the whole plant, especially for fine leathers, in Iceland, Sweden and the U.S.S.R. Because it produces a great deal of nectar, the cowberry is very attractive to bees.

323 VALERIANA OFFICINALIS L.
Valerian

Family Valerianaceae.
Description This herbaceous plant has a short rhizome and a great many fasciculate rootlets with hollow centres. The simple, grooved, hollow stem grows to a height of about 3¼ feet (1 m). The leaves are opposite, pinnate and mostly sessile, although the basal ones are petiolate; the leaflets are oblong with a dentate margin. The flowers are grouped in an apical corymb; they have a many-toothed calyx and a pink, 5-lobed corolla. The fruit is one-seeded with a feathery persistent calyx. A common plant that grows throughout Europe, including Britain, and northern Asia, both in the wild and under cultivation, it thrives best on the banks of streams, by ditches and in marshy thickets, its specific habitat being essentially moist. It is gathered from spring onwards.
Parts used Rhizome and rootlets.
Chemical compounds Valerian, chatarine, essence, glucose, tannin, valerianine, enzymes.
Properties Sedative, anti-epileptic, hypotensive, cardiotonic, anti-depressant.
Forms of use Powder, tincture, juice, fluid extract, infusion.
Notes A yellowish essential oil, with a density of 0.93, can be distilled from valerian, the components of which are: pinene, camphene, borneol and bornyl isovalerate. An average yield of 1% is obtained. Valerian is regarded as one of the most effective remedies in the treatment of neuroses, although the mechanism of its action is still not fully understood. For external use, compresses made from a decoction of the roots and applied to local areas of muscular pain have an analgesic action.

---

324 VANILLA PLANIFOLIA Andrews
Vanilla plant

Family Orchidaceae.
Description This plant establishes itself by throwing down rootlets from its dark violet-green, woody, cylindrical stem, which may be as long as 50 feet (15 m). The alternate leaves are elliptical or ovate-oblong with an acute apex, and both the blade and margin are glabrous. The 6-sepalled, greenish-yellow or orange flowers are united in racemes that arise from the leaf axils on a long peduncle which emerges from an ovate bract. The fruit is an almost cylindrical, fleshy pod enclosing a number of small, shiny, almost black seeds. Originally from Central America, it is now being grown in Australia and Africa. The medicinally useful parts are gathered when they are ripe.
Parts used Fruits.
Chemical compounds Vanilla, vanillic acid, resins, mucilage, tannin, anisaldehyde, anisic acid, piperonal.
Properties Stimulant, digestive, choleretic, aromatic.
Forms of use Syrup, tincture.
Notes Vanilla is one of the ingredients of a great many products of the pastry-cook and perfumier. When taking any preparation with a vanilla content internally, it is important not to exceed the prescribed amount in order to avoid such unpleasant results as inflammation or irritation. The familiar fragrance only develops in the vanilla-pod when this has been allowed to ferment for a certain length of time; the pod has no odour at all when fresh.

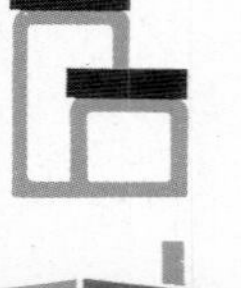

325 VERATRUM ALBUM L.
White false helleborine

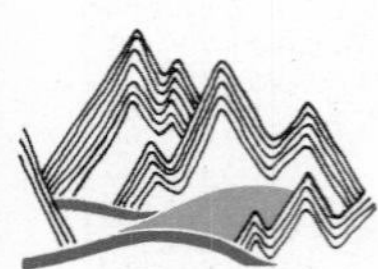

Family Liliaceae.
Description A perennial plant, its dark-coloured, fibrous, creeping rhizome, on which old leaves have left deep scars, has an abundance of rootlets. The alternate leaves form a sheath around the erect, hollow stem which may reach a height of 5 feet (1.5 m). They are somewhat leathery in texture and are oval-elliptic with an acute apex, having pleated, lengthways venation, an entire margin and a glabrous upper leaf surface. The flowers are borne in a panicle, each flower having a greenish-yellow stalk and 6 lanceolate tepals. The fruit is a 3-sectioned capsule containing flat seeds. The plant is commonly found in the mountain pastures of continental Europe. It is gathered in early autumn.
Parts used Rhizome.
Chemical compounds Protoveratrine, germerine, jervine, veratramine, veratrosine, veratralbine, chelidonic acid, gum, sugar, starch.
Properties Analgesic, emetic-cathartic, antirheumatic, sternutatory.
Forms of use Powder, tincture, ointment.
Notes A very poisonous plant which should never be used in home-made remedies as it can have a paralyzing action on the nervous system. Even preparations for external use as local analgesics should only be used on unbroken skin. A decoction made from this plant will kill most insects because of its pyrethrum content and it is, therefore, highly regarded as a natural insecticide. Diluted with starch or some other mild powder, it can be inhaled as a sternutatory (that is, to cause sneezing). Great care should always be taken when collecting gentian roots not to dig up the roots of this plant, which are poisonous, in error. Such a mistake is easy to make as the leaves of both plants are almost identical.

---

326 VERBASCUM THAPSUS L.
Aaron's Rod

Family Scrophulariaceae.
Description A grey or white, mealy, herbaceous plant with a white taproot, the simple stem can be up to 6½ feet (2 m) high. The alternate leaves are oval-lanceolate and wooly with a small petiole; the basal leaves are in rosette form and the stem leaves sessile. The flowers are in racemes which often form a panicle; each one has a 5-lobed calyx and a yellow corolla which is tubular at the base and becomes lobed at the top. The fruit is an ellipsoidal capsule with rugose seeds. A common plant throughout Europe, including Britain, found in sunny positions in uncultivated fields, by the roadside and on waste ground. It is gathered in summer.
Parts use Flowers.
Chemical compounds Thapsic acid, mucilage, verbascosaponin, inositol, sugar, resin.
Properties Antispasmodic, antitussive, emollient, antineuralgic, antihaemorrhoidal.
Forms of use Infusion, tincture, ointment.
Notes The dried leaves of this plant can be made into cigarettes and smoked to give relief from asthmatic attacks and spasmodic coughs in general. The leaves can also be finely chopped or ground and made into compresses for local application to ease neuralgic pains. Ointment made with the leaves and flowers has an antihaemorrhoidal action. The seeds contain oil and can be made into a decoction which helps to soothe chilblains and chapped skin. Any preparation made with Aaron's rod should always be strained or sieved carefully in order to prevent any of its small hairs from remaining as they could cause very disagreeable irritation.

327 VERBENA OFFICINALIS L.
Vervain

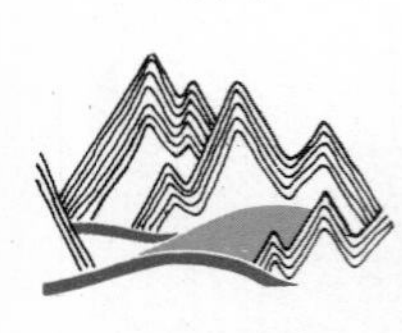

Family Verbenaceae.
Description An erect plant, up to 20 inches (50 cm) high, it has a spindle-shaped root. The square stem is branched and channelled on opposite sides. The opposite leaves are pinnately lobed, the upper ones being crenate. The mauvy-pink flowers, borne in long, terminal spikes forming apical panicles, have a 5-toothed calyx and a tubular, 5-lobed corolla. The fruits are nutlets. Widely distributed throughout the world, vervain can be seen in Europe, including Britain, by the roadside, on waste ground and among ruined buildings. It is gathered in summer.
Parts used Whole plant.
Chemical compounds Verbenaline, mucilage, tannin, essence, bitter substance.
Properties Stomachic, biliary deobstruent, resolvent, antineuralgic.
Forms of use Infusion, tincture, fluid extract, poultice.
Notes Vervain is also known as *Herba sacra* (holy plant) as, in ancient Rome, it was always carried by the *verbenarius*, as an auspice during peace negotiations. It has, in the past, been credited with aphrodisiac qualities but these have not been confirmed by modern analyses. Some remarkable results have been obtained from its use in the treatment of certain tumours, but further research and clinical tests have to be done before definite claims can be made. Vervain is used as a bitter in the making of spirituous liquors and as a substitute for tea. An aromatic oil can be extracted from the plant but the yield is too low to justify its commercial use. The essence called verbena oil derives from a different plant that has nothing to do with *Verbena officinalis*.

---

328 VICIA FABA L.
Broadbean

Family Leguminosae.
Description An erect, glabrous, herbaceous plant with a taproot, the stem is 4-angled, reaching a height of up to about 32 inches (80 cm). The alternate, pinnate leaves with stipules at the base are composed of 2-5 oval, entire leaflets, each ending abruptly in a tiny point. The flowers, united in small axilliary clusters, are white with deep purple wings; the calyx has triangular upper teeth while the lower ones are lanceolate. The oblong pods, which are fleshy when young and become leathery as they mature, contain flattened or angular seeds. This plant, of which the origin is unknown, is seldom to be found wild in Europe but is widely cultivated in temperate climates. It is gathered in summer.
Parts used Pods.
Chemical compounds Legumin, vitamins C, PP, B_1, A, K and E.
Properties Diuretic, lithontriptic.
Forms of use Decoction, powder.
Notes Excessive consumption of raw broadbeans can induce the disease known as favism which produces such symptoms as pallor, fever, shivering and delirium. The pollen, if inhaled, can also bring on an attack. Broadbean flour is very rich in proteins and vitamins and these nourishing qualities mean that it can be used either on its own, or mixed with other flours.

329 VINCA MINOR L.
Lesser periwinkle

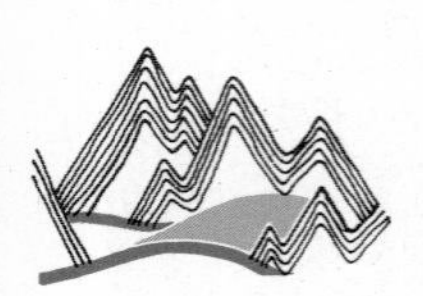

Family Apocynaceae.
Description The generic name derives from the Latin *vincire*, to bind or tie round, referring to the tendency of the branches. The plant has a great many creeping, prostrate stems and a very branched root. The stems can be as long as 6½ feet (1.8 m). The glossy, dark green, perennial leaves, borne on a small petiole, are opposite, elliptical or lanceolate and leathery with a prominent central venation. The blue-purple flowers rise from the leaf axils, each on a long pedicel; they have 5 truncate propeller-shaped petals fused into a tube-shape and 5 stamens. In many parts of Europe, including Britain, it can often been seen growing wild in fields and on the outskirts of woods; it is also widely cultivated as a garden plant. The leaves are gathered in spring and the roots in autumn.
Parts used Leaves and root.
Chemical compounds Leaves: vincine, vincoside, saponin, carotene, tannin. Root: vincamine, vincamirine, isovincamine.
Properties Leaves: bitter, stomachic, detergent. Root: hypotensive, antispasmodic.
Forms of use Leaves: decoction, powder, tincture. Root: fluid extract, tincture, medicinal wine.
Notes In some areas, the trailing stems are used for basket-making. The lesser periwinkle is often used as an edging plant for flower-beds. The crushed leaves, when applied to surface wounds, have astringent and healing properties.

---

330 VIOLA ODORATA L.
Sweet violet

Family Violaceae.
Description This herbaceous perennial plant has a short rhizome and creeping stolons which put out roots. The petiolate basal leaves are in rosette form; mid-green in colour, they are kidney-shaped with a corrugate surface, well-defined venation and a crenate margin. The flowers are borne on a long, reddish-brown pedicel with 2 bracteoles about midway between the apex and base; each flower has 5 oval sepals and a violet 5-petalled corolla, the lower petal projecting backwards to form a spur. The fruit is a subspherical capsule containing dark seeds which have an outgrowth at one side. The sweet violet is found in most of Europe, including Britain, growing wild in fields, meadows and woodlands, from low-lying to hilly areas. The flowers are gathered in spring and the rhizomes in autumn.
Parts used Flowers and rhizome.
Chemical compounds Flowers: essence, ethereal compound, mucilage, saponin, gum. Root: haematin violet or violine.
Properties Emollient, expectorant, laxative.
Forms of use Infusion, fluid extract, tincture, syrup.
Notes Essence of violets, which is extremely costly, is obtained by means of the *enfleurage* process, giving a yield of about 2 oz (50 g) of essence from over 220 lb (100 kg) of flowers. An essence is also obtained from the leaves which adds a herbaceous note to the perfume. Tincture of violets, like that of capers, is an acid and alkali reactive.

331 VIOLA TRICOLOR L.
Heartsease

Family Violaceae.
Description A herbaceous plant with a rhizomatous root and slender rootlets, its stem may be simple or slightly branched and remains close to the ground at first, then becoming erect to a maximum height of 20 inches (50 cm). The lower leaves are oval and petiolate, the medians are ovate-lanceolate and the upper ones are elliptical, lanceolate and sessile. There are 2 stipules at the base of each petiole. The flower is borne singly, at the apex of a long pedicel emerging from the axil of the upper leaves; the calyx is 5-sepalled and pointed while the corolla is 5-petalled, violet-blue and yellow, the petals being arranged in slightly overlapping pairs; the lower petal is equipped with a spur. The fruit is an oval capsule containing numerous dark seeds. A fairly common wild plant throughout Europe, including Britain, it will grow almost anywhere from coastal to mountainous areas. It is gathered from April-August.
Parts use Whole plant.
Chemical compounds Viola-quercetin, methyl salicylate, saponin, tannin, sugar, albumin, resin, colouring substance.
Properties Depurative, diaphoretic, laxative, emollient, antirheumatic.
Forms of use Infusion, fluid extract, tincture, syrup.
Notes Bathing in waters containing a concentrated decoction of the leaves has proved beneficial to sufferers from rheumatic diseases. The root is an emetic (causing vomiting).

---

332 VISCUM ALBUM L.
Mistletoe

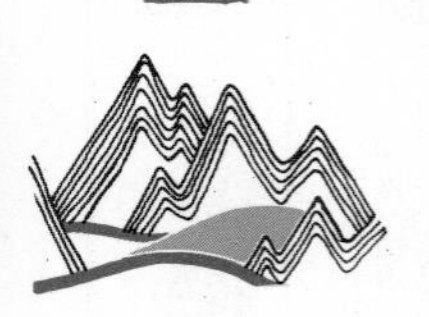

Family Loranthaceae.
Description A parasitic shrub, it grows on many trees by means of haustorii (a type of penetrant sucker). The yellowish-green stems are forked and glabrous. The opposite leaves are oblong, parallel veined, leathery and persistent. The flowers are arranged in axillary clusters; the male flowers have a 4-lobed perianth, with no calyx, while the female ones have a 4-sepalled and 4-petalled perianth. The fruit is a whitish berry with a viscous pulp containing a single seed. Mistletoe is quite frequently found on poplar, chestnut, elm, birch and, most commonly, apple trees. Some of its branches can be more than 24 inches (60 cm) long. Mistletoe is gathered in autumn.
Parts used Leaves and branchlets.
Chemical compounds Choline, viscalbine, viscoflavin, acetylcholine, viscotoxin, inositol, mannitol, saponin, acids, salts, vitamin C, resin.
Properties Hypotensive, vasodilatory, anti-epileptic, diuretic.
Forms of use Infusion, tincture, syrup, fluid extract, medicinal wine, aqueous extract.
Notes Bird-catchers used to make birdlime from the berries by means of maceration and fermentation. The leaves mixed with hay have, in the past, been used in some rural areas to increased lactation in cows. For external use, a decoction of the branchlets is quite effective in treating chilblains. It should be borne in mind that preparations in which mistletoe is used may provoke an intolerant reaction to certain substances.

333 VITIS VINIFERA L.
Vine

Family Vitaceae.
Description A climbing shrub that has an erect, somewhat contorted stem with dark brown bark that peels off in strips. The branches have a number of tendrils which enable the plant to cling on to supports. The alternate leaves which are opposite the tendrils and carried on a sturdy petiole, are palmate and 3-5 lobed with a glabrous surface. The flowers are grouped in panicles, each flower having a 5-lobed calyx and a pale green, 5-petalled corolla. The fruit is a berry which varies in colour; in the juicy pulp a few pear-shaped seeds (pips) are immersed. Although it is not uncommon to find vines growing in the wild, they are extensively cultivated in many varieties throughout Europe. The medicinally useful parts are gathered in autumn.
Parts used Leaves.
Chemical compounds Tannin, quercetin, quercitrin, tartrates, sugars, inositol, acids, choline, carotene.
Properties Astringent, anti-inflammatory.
Forms of use Decoction, ointment.
Notes Grapes have always been widely used as a means of obtaining wine and alcohol. A liquid which can be obtained in drops by breaking the branches, is an excellent diuretic and eyewash. A constrictive decoction, for use in attacks of diarrhoea, can be made from the tendrils. The seeds contain an edible oil similar to sunflower oil and, when roasted, they can be used as a coffee substitute. The laxative action of cream of tartar, obtained from marc (the refuse from pressed grapes) and the sediment in wine-making barrels, is particularly suitable for relieving constipation in sufferers who cannot tolerate other purgatives. People with a torpid liver or sluggish biliary function are sometimes advised to undergo a special cure based on eating grapes.

---

334 ZEA MAYS L.
Maize

Family Gramineae.
Description An annual plant with many fasciculate roots, the culm is erect and the leaves that emerge from its nodes are alternate, lanceolate, acuminate and parallel-veined with small ligules. This plant can reach a height of about 10 feet (3 m). The male and female flowers are present on the same plant: the male flowers are united in an apical panicle while the female are in spikes or 'ears' with an enlarged axis and enveloped in papery bracts. The orange caryopses are prismatic with a rounded surface. Originating in South America, maize has now become well established as a cereal crop in Europe and North America, as well as other parts of the world. It is only to be found growing wild near fields where it has been cultivated, as the result of a few seeds having escaped or been carried by birds. It is harvested in September.
Parts used Styles and stigmas of the female inflorescences known as corn silk.
Chemical compounds Oil, resin, tannin, glucose, potassium, sodium, phosphorus, sulphur and the following acids: salicyclic, lauric, palmitic, oleic and stearic.
Properties Diuretic, lithontriptic.
Forms of use Infusion, fluid extract.
Notes Attempts have been made, but with difficulty, to extract sugar from the culms. The caryopses are sometimes roasted and used as a coffee substitute. Cellulose and furfurol are obtained from the corn-cobs by means of distillation. A dietetic edible oil is obtained from the germ. The bracts are used to make 'straw' hats and mats. The young culms can be lightly boiled and eaten.

GLOSSARY

Note: this glossary includes the botanical and medical terms most frequently used in the introduction and the entries

acaulescent having no stem or almost none.
achene a small, dry fruit that does not open spontaneously.
acicular shape of a narrow, cylindrical leaf; needle-like.
acorn an achene that grows in a cup.
aculeate bearing prickles.
acuminate tapering to a sharp point.
adpressed pressed flat to the axis.
agglomerate collected or gathered in a mass.
air-layering a method of vegetative reproduction.
albumin a nutritive substance of the embryo of a seed.
alburnum the lightest coloured wood immediately beneath the bark; sapwood.
alcoholate the product obtained from the alcoholic distillation of medicinal herbs.
amenorrhoea the absence of menstruation during the time of life when it should occur.
amplexicaul a sessile leaf with its base clasping the stem or scape.
anaesthetic produces insensibility to external sensations.
analgesic relieves or diminishes pain.
anodyne relieves or soothes pain.
anorexia loss of appetite.
anthelmintic expels parasitic worms from the intestine.
anther the part of the stamen which contains the pollen.
anti-aphonic restores the voice.
anti-atonic soothes tired muscles.
anticholesterolemic prevents the build up of abnormal cholesterol levels in the blood.
antidermatosic acts to prevent or cure skin complaints.
antidiarrhoeic controls diarrhoea.
antidropsical prevents water retention (dropsy).
anti-ecchymotic prevents bruising.
anti-enuretic prevents bed-wetting and incontinence.
anti-glycosuric reduces level of sugar in the urine; used to treat diabetes.
anti-icteric combats jaundice.
antileucorrhoeic reduces vaginal discharge sometimes known as 'whites'.
antineuralgic relieves aches and pains.
anti-oedematous reduces swelling.
antiphlogistic reduces inflammation.
antiplethoric acts against high blood pressure and circulatory disturbances.

antipruritic relieves itching.
antipyretic prevents or reduces high temperatures.
antisaturnismic an antidepressant.
antisclerotic softens unnaturally hard skin.
antiscorbutic prevents or cures scurvy by providing vitamin C.
antiseptic destroys germs and microorganisms that produce disease.
antispasmodic relieves or prevents involuntary muscular spasms.
antitussive relieves coughing.
anti-uricaemic prevents build up of abnormal levels of uric acid in the blood (gout).
aperient a mild laxative.
aperitif encourages the appetite.
apex tip, point, vertex.
apical forming a point.
apiculate ending in a short, sharp point.
aril a secondary covering over the seeds of some plants.
aristate tipped with a beard or awn (e.g. barley).
aromatherapy a method of treatment using essential oils.
aromatic/distilled water a secondary product of the distillation of medicinal herb essences.
aseptic free from germs and microorganisms.
astringent a medicine that reduces the flow of secretions and discharges.
awn the apical bristle on the bracts that envelop the inflorescences of the Gramineae (grasses). Also called arista or beard.
axil angle between upper side of leaf and supporting branch or stem.

balsamic heals or soothes inflammation.
bearded equipped with an awn, beard or arista.
berry a fruit with an inner layer to the fruit wall, a fleshy central tissue area and a number of seeds (e.g. tomato).
bilabiate formed into two lips.
biliary deobstruent promotes the flow of bile.
biternate (of leaves) formed into two sets of three.
bitter a bitter principle which acts on the mucous membranes of the mouth and stomach to increase appetite and promote digestion.
blepharitis inflammation of the eyelids.
bradycardia abnormally slow heartbeat.
bud a protruberance on a plant, from which a leaf, shoot or flower develops.
bulb an ovoid, underground stem consisting of overlapping layers of fleshy leaves.

bulbil a small bulb replacing flower buds (e.g. common onion).

caducous dropping off very early; deciduous.
calamus the hollow stem of a plant with few articulations (e.g. reed).
calyptra the apical part of a root. Also known as the pileorhiza, root-cap.
calyx a collective name for the outer whorl of the flower formed by leaf-like parts known as sepals and which are usually green.
capitulum, head an inflorescence consisting of a head of densely-packed stalkless flowers.
capsule dry, many-sectioned fruit which generally splits open to release its numerous seeds.
cardiokinetic strengthens the heart.
cardiotonic has a tonic effect on the heart.
carina a longitudinal ridge; part of the flowers of legumes.
carminative expels gas from the intestines.
carpel one of the modified fertile leaves, a component of the gynaecium that encloses the ovules and bears the stigma.
caryopsis a small achene in which the pericarp is fused to the seed (e.g. wheat).
cataplasm or poultice – a hot or warm application of specially prepared medicinal herbs.
cathartic having a gentle purgative action.
catkin a pendulous, slender spike of unisexual flowers.
cauline, caulinary growing from the stem.
caustic corrosive or burning.
cholagogue, cholagogic a medicament that increases the flow of bile.
choleretic stimulates the secretion of bile.
cicatrizer a medicament which accelerates the formation of scar tissue.
cladode a modified stem resembling a leaf.
collodion a yellowish fluid used for sealing wounds or burns.
collutory a mouthwash or gargle.
collyrium a lotion for eye disorders, an eyewash.
compound (of leaves) composed of two or more leaflets.
condenser, cooler that part of the distilling apparatus where the vapour condenses.
cones, strobilus bracts forming an inflorescence in a cylindrical-conical shape; characteristic of conifers.
connate joined or attached to; used with similar parts fused during formation (e.g. petals).
cordate (of leaves) heart-shaped.
coriaceous leather-like.
corolla collective term for all the petals of a flower.

cortex the covering of the trunk or main stem and branches of a bush, shrub or tree (bark).
corymb, corymbose flat-topped inflorescence where the flower stalks on the outside are longer so that the flowers are at the same level.
coryzide relieves the symptoms of the common cold.
cotyledon(s) the first seedling leaf or leaves which precede the new plant.
cremocarp a type of fruit which breaks up into two individual seeds which hang from the plant (diachaenium).
crenate (of leaves) edged with shallow, rounded indentations.
cryptogamic without true flowers and seeds (e.g. ferns and mosses).
culm a tough, hollow, jointed stalk (e.g. grasses and sedge).
cuneate (of leaves) wedge-shaped, tapering towards the stalk.
cutting a method of vegetative reproduction.
cyme an inflorescence in which the primary axis bears a single terminal flower which develops first, the inflorescence being continued by secondary, tertiary and other axes.
cytostatic slows down the growth process of tumours.

dechlorurant removes excess salt from the system.
deciduous shedding leaves seasonally.
decoction a preparation made by boiling a medicinal herb.
decongestant relieves congestion.
decorticated bark or husk that has been removed.
decurrent a leaf that narrows down into the petiole and main stem.
decussate said of pairs of opposite leaves when they are at a 90° angle to those above and below.
dehiscent (of fruits) that open spontaneously on ripening to release the seeds.
density the relationship between the mass of a body and the mass of water occupying an equal volume at 39.2°F. (4°C).
dentate (of leaves) with a sharply toothed margin.
depurative eliminates toxins and purifies the system.
derm(at)opathic pertaining to diseases of the skin.
detergent a cleansing agent that can be used directly on wounds.
diachaenium cremocarp.
diaphoretic induces perspiration.
digitate (of leaves) having leaflets which are arranged like the fingers of a hand (palmate).
dioecious (species) in which the male and female sex organs (flowers) are on separate plants.
distichous (of leaves) having the organs arranged in two vertical rows.

diuretic promotes the flow of urine.
double-locular having two chambers or compartments.
drastic has a violent purgative action.
drupe a fruit with a thin outer layer, a fleshy inner layer and a stone consisting of a hard casing and a seed.
dynamis, dynamization a process in the preparation of homoeopathic medicines.

ecchymosis, ecchymotic causes bruising.
écuelle process a process for extracting the essential oil from citrus fruit.
electuary a preparation made from powdered medicinal herbs mixed to a soft paste with honey or sugar.
elixir a liquid preparation consisting of the extract of a potent or unpleasant-tasting medicinal plant made palatable by adding aromatic substances and honey or sugar.
ellipsoidal having the nature or shape of an ellipse.
elliptical tapering at both ends with the broadest part across the middle.
embrocation a preparation for external application to a diseased part.
emetic induces vomiting.
emmenagogue, emmanagogic restores the menstrual flow.
emollient softens the skin.
endermic acting through the skin.
endocarp the interior of the fruit wall; it may be membranous or woody.
enfleurage a method of extracting essential oils.
ensiform (of leaves) sword-shaped.
epicarp the outermost layer of the fruit.
epispastic having a blistering action.
erythema inflammation of the skin in rose-coloured patches.
essential oil the result of the distillation of essence-producing plants.
ethereal compound an ether-based medicine.
eupeptic a digestive aid.
euphoric gives a general sense of well-being.
expectorant clears out phlegm from the chest by coughing.
extract a product resulting from a transformation of the simples; it can be dry, semi-fluid or fluid.

fasciculate growing in bundles.
febrifuge reduces high temperatures.
fistular, fistulose the hollow, cylindrical stem of a herbaceous plant (e.g. reed, grass).
flask a balloon-shaped glass vessel with a long, narrow neck and

usually, a flat bottom; it forms part of a distillation apparatus.

flexuous full of bends and curves.

Florentine flask a glass recipient with an outlet to one side, for the distillate.

galactofuge a medicine to reduce the flow of milk in nursing mothers.

galactogogue, galactagogic a medicine to increase the flow of milk in nursing mothers.

gall an excrescence on some part of a plant caused by an insect or disease organism.

gamopetalous having petals that are joined.

glabrous hairless.

glomerule a cluster of flowers.

glume one of a pair of dry bracts enclosing the base of each spikelet (of grasses).

green-manuring the planting of clover and other nitrogen-fixing plants to enrich the soil.

gynaecium the female part of the flower formed by the carpels.

haemolytic breaks down the red blood corpuscles to separate the haemoglobin.

haemopoietic promotes the formation of blood.

haemostatic controls haemorrhages.

hastate (of leaves) spear-shaped.

haustorium an organ of parasitical plants which penetrates the host plant and absorbs vital substances.

hepatoprotective protects the liver.

herbalism subject relating the the study of medicinal (officinal) plants.

herbalist a person who is knowledgeable about medicinal plants.

hesperidium a fruit of which the endocarp is divided into chambers (e.g. citrus fruits).

hispid covered with long stiff hairs.

homoeopathy therapy based on the concept of a close similarity between disease and remedy.

hydrofuge expels water (diuretic).

hypocholesterolic excessive cholesterol in the blood.

hypnotic (a remedy) to induce sleep.

hypoglycaemic reduces the level of sugar in the blood.

hypotensive reduces high blood-pressure.

imbricate overlapping, like tiles on a roof.

imparipinnate (of compound leaves) with a terminal leaflet.

indehiscent (a fruit) that does not drop its seeds spontaneously when they ripen.
indented (of leaves) with an indented margin.
inflorescence a group of flowers that grow on the same stem.
infusion a simple method of extracting the active principles of a plant.
inhalation a method of administering medicinal agents by means of steam inhalation.
involucre a collection or rosette of bracts subtending a flower cluster.

lacerate (of leaves) with a jagged, irregular margin.
laciniae deep, narrow incisions in the margin of a leaf or petal.
laciniate (of leaves) with a margin cut into deep, narrow and irregular strips.
lamina or blade, the flattened surface of a leaf.
lanceolate (of leaves) lance-shaped, tapering to a pointed apex.
lavage a cleansing of the stomach using emetics in large quantities of water.
laxative relaxes the bowels and has a gentle evacuant action.
layering a vegetative method of reproduction.
legume or pod, a fruit that opens into two on ripening.
lenitive has a mildly analgesic action.
lenticel a pore through young bark which allows for gaseous exchange.
ligule a thin appendage at the base of the blade of a leaf.
liniment a preparation for external application usually by rubbing.
lipid a preparation with a fatty excipient as a base, greasy to the touch and insoluble in water.
lithontriptic a preparation for the elimination of small stones from the body.
locule the chamber or cavity of an ovary.
lobate (of leaves) divided into lobes.
lyrate (of leaves) lyre-shaped, the terminal lobe being larger than the lateral ones.

maceration a simple method of extracting the active principles of a plant, where the ingredients are steeped in liquid.
medicinal wine a medicine with a wine base.
metrisis inflammation of the uterus.
metrorrhagia a uterine haemorrhage.
mucronate (of leaves) tipped with a short point.
multifid (of leaves) divided into several lobes for more than half its length.
mydriatic a preparation that dilates the pupil of the eyes.

narcotic a medicament that causes drowsiness.
nephritis inflammation of the kidneys especially in Bright's Disease.
nervine a preparation with a stimulatory effect.
nodose with knot-like protruberances.

obovate (of leaves), having an oval shape with the narrowest part at the base.
obtuse (of leaves) with the tip bluntly rounded.
odontalgic used for the treatment of toothache.
oleolite a medicine with an oily base.
ophthalmic relative to eye diseases.
orbicular (of leaves) more or less circular.
ovary the lower part of the pistil that contains the ovules.
ovoid egg-shaped; having the solid shape of an egg.
oxytocic a medicinal drug used to hasten parturition or stimulate uterine contractions.

pagina the surface of a leaf.
palmate (of leaves) shaped like the palm of a hand with deep, fingerlike lobes.
palmate-lobate applied to a palmate leaf with deep-cut lobes.
palmate-parted applied to a palmate leaf with lobes cut more than half-way.
palmatifid applied to a palmate leaf in which the incisions only reach half-way down the pagina.
palmatisect applied to a palmate leaf with deep divisions forming segments joined at the base.
panicle an inflorescence shaped like a pyramid.
pappus a ring of fine hairs on some types of seed which aid wind-dispersal.
parasympathetic has a tranquillizing effect.
paregoric a soothing remedy for coughs.
parenchyma a tissue of undifferentiated cells.
parted (of leaves) cleft almost to the mid-rib.
pectoral relieves respiratory problems.
pedicel the stalk of a flower.
peduncle the stalk of an inflorescence.
peltate almost circular and flat with a central pedicel (e.g. nasturtium).
perfoliate a leaf base which envelops its stem.
perianth a collective term for both the calyx and corolla.
pericarp the external layer of a fruit.
petiole a leaf-stalk.

phyllotaxis the system of leaf insertion on the stem.
phytotherapy therapy by means of medicinal (officinal) plants.
pileorhiza see calyptra.
pilose covered with downy hair.
pinnate applied to a compound leaf which has leaflets on both sides of its rachis (axis).
pinnate-parted (of leaves) cut almost to the mid-rib.
pinnatifid (of leaves) cut to about half-way between the margin and the mid-rib.
pinnatisect (of leaves) cut to the mid-rib.
pistil the female part of a flower.
plethoric a turgid condition due to an excess number of red blood cells.
powder a preparation obtained by the fine powdering of medicinal plants.
pubescent covered with soft, fine hairs.
purulent discharging pus.

raceme an inflorescence on a single axis where each flower is stalked.
rectinerved describes a leaf with reticulated venation.
resolvent a preparation to soothe inflammatory conditions.
revulsive a preparation that produces revulsion.
rhagades chaps of the skin.
rhizome an underground stem which acts as a storage organ.
root the part of a plant that anchors it in the soil and absorbs nutriment and moisture necessary for growth.
roseola rose-coloured rash.
rubefacient a counter-irritant.
runcinate applied to a pinnatifid leaf in which the sharply curved cuts between the lobes are directed towards the base.
runner a long slender stem with leaves springing from its nodes.

sacral fistula backache of the lower back.
sagittate (of leaves) arrow shaped.
samara an achene with a wing-like extension of the outer-casing.
scabrous with a rough surface.
scape a flower stalk which grows from the centre of a rosette of leaves.
sect (of leaves) a cut in the surface which reaches the mid-rib or the base.
seed the ripened ovule of a plant containing the embryo; the means by which a plant may propogate sexually.
sepal a leaf-like segment of the calyx, making up the outer whorl of the flower.

serous ulcer ulcer secreting serum.
serrate (of leaves) with a toothed margin, like a saw.
sessile without petiole, peduncle, or pedicel.
sialagogue encourages salivary secretion.
siliqua a fruit that opens on ripening to disclose a diaphragm with seeds.
sinuate (of leaf margins) with shallow indentations.
simple any plant with a medicinal use.
soporific induces sleep.
sorus a group of sporangia, which contain the reproductive cells of the plant, on the fronds of a fern.
spadix an inflorescence on a single axis surrounded by a type of bract known as a spathe.
spathe a large sheathing-leaf, which envelops the inflorescence.
spathulate (of leaves) spoon-shaped.
spine a needle-like modification of the epidermis.
spirit solution the product obtained from alcoholic maceration of medicinal herbs. Known also as tincture.
splenobiliary bile from the spleen.
stamen the masculine organ of a flower made up of a filament and anther.
stele the core of the stem (of plants).
stem or stalk, the bearing organ of the plant.
sternutatory causes sneezing.
stigma the terminal part of the gynaecium, which receives the pollen.
stipule a leaf-life appendage at the base of many leaves.
stolon a creeping root that puts out adventitious roots.
stomachic aids the stomach action.
stomatic a medicine for complaints of the mouth.
strobilus see cone.
stupefacient stupefying causing drowsiness.
style the narrow tube that runs between the ovary and the stigma.
sucker a shoot thrown up by an emergent root.
suffruticose, suffrutescent or subshrubby, applied to a small plant with woody branches but a herbaceous apex.
syconium, syconus a fleshy, false fruit that contains achenes.
synergic the combined effect of certain substances that exceeds the sum of their individual effects.

taenifuge combats tapeworms (taeniae).
taproot the main anchoring root which grows much larger than the secondary roots.

tincture a spirit solution.
tomentose covered with wooly hairs.
tonic a medicine to improve the general health of a person.
topical or local, any locally-applied, external remedy.
toxifuge dispels poisons.
trachoma an infection of the eyes or throat.
trigeminal pertaining to trigeminal nerve (deals with chewing, etc).
trigonal triangular in cross section.
trilocular having three chambers or cells.
tripinnatisect a leaf in which the pinnately divided leaflets are themselves pinnately divided.
triploid having a chromosome number that is three times the basic, or haploid, number.
trituration reduction to a fine powder by grinding.
tuber a swollen, underground stem containing a store of nutritive materials.
turion a fleshy, underground bud shooting up from the root.

umbel an inflorescence in which all the flowers are at the same height, their pedicels arising from the same level.
umbilicate having a navel-like depression.
urocolitic an inflammation of the urinary ducts.
urogenital pertaining to the urinary and genital organs.

vascular tissue plant tissue consisting of ducts or vessels that, in the higher plants, forms the tissue.
vascoconstrictive causes dilation of the blood vessels.
vasodilatory causing relaxation of the blood vessels.
venation the arrangement of the veins in a leaf.
vermifuge a medication to expel intestinal parasites.
vesicant blistering agent.
vesicatory causing blisters.
vexillum the large, upper petal of a papilionaceous.
vitamin supplement a preparation to combat vitamin deficiency (avitaminosis).
vulnerary a preparation for healing wounds.

whorl or verticel, an arrangement of leaves or flowers arising from the same level on the stem.

yield the percentage of the final product obtained after the transformation of the materials used.

INDEX

(Numbers in italic refer to entries)

The Publisher gratefully acknowledges the co-operation of the following: Piergiorgio Campodonico, The Hanbury Botanic Gardens (Ventimiglia); Simes Research Laboratories, Milan; Palynological Laboratory, Swedish Museum of Natural History, Stockholm; Garden Club, Monaco; Jardin Botanique Exotique, Menton-Garavan; Conservatoire et Jardin Botanique de la ville de Génève; Jean Giovannini and Gilbert Viethél, Division Jardins, Monaco; Marcel Kroenlein, Jardin Exotique de Monaco; Parfumerie Fragonard, Grasse; Société des Bains de Mer, Monaco.